David Rittenhouse

David Rittenhouse

BY BROOKE HINDLE

PRINCETON, NEW JERSEY

PRINCETON UNIVERSITY PRESS

1964

To

Carl Bridenbaugh

Acknowledgments

THIS study rests upon individual and institutional support of a magnitude that neither my footnote citations nor my bibliographical note begins to chronicle. New York University granted me sabbatical leave during the year 1957–1958 and released time for research in other years, arranged primarily through the efforts of Professor Bayrd Still, and on several occasions supported my research through the Graduate School Arts and Science Research Fund. A grant from the American Philosophical Society made possible research in Europe during the summer of 1961.

I have relied upon a few men more heavily than I can comfortably justify. Mr. Penrose R. Hoopes of Philadelphia has presented me with specific details and interpretive insights I would have attained in no other way. Dr. Whitfield J. Bell, Jr., of the American Philosophical Society Library, has supplied information and understanding. Dr. Howard C. Rice, Jr., of the Princeton University Library, made available knowledge gained from related research. Professor Carl Bridenbaugh, of Brown University, provided the initial stimulus for the investigation.

My colleagues at New York University have extended essential help in their own fields of specialization. Especially significant was the aid of Professors Vincent P. Carosso and Thomas P. Govan of the History Department, Dean Glen N. Cox of the School of Engineering and Science, Professor Ben Davidson of the Geophysical Sciences Laboratory, Professor Frederick A. Ficken of the Mathematics Department, and Professor Serge A. Korff of the Physics Department. Mr. Richard W. Lenk, Jr., was an effective research assistant and Mrs. Leon Lifton an excellent typist.

Descendents of the Rittenhouse family offered every assistance, especially Mr. C. Barton Brewster, Miss Elizabeth Sergeant Abbot, and Mrs. Thomas S. Gates.

A number of individuals, often spontaneously, supplied important help. Among them are: Mr. Lyman H. Butterfield of the Adams Papers, Dr. Eric T. Carlson of the New York Hospital, Mrs. Joseph Carson of Philadelphia, Professor Thomas D. Cope of the University of Pennsylvania, the late Mr. Hubertis Cummings, Mr. Samuel Y. Edgerton of Wheaton College, Mr. James T. Flexner of New York, Professor George F. Frick of the University of Delaware, Professor Roger Hahn of the University of California, Dr. C. Doris Hellman of Pratt Institute, Professor Forrest McDonald of Brown University, Mr. Charles E. Peterson of Philadelphia, Mrs. H. Spencer Roach of Philadelphia, Professor Caroline Robbins of Bryn Mawr College, and Professor Frederick B. Tolles of Swarthmore College.

Dr. George R. Bird of the Polaroid Corporation and Mr. Evans Kahn of the American Cyanamid Company kindly made available their own professional knowledge. Mr. Charles E. Smart of the W. & L. E. Gurley Company provided the insights of a manufacturer and a historian.

At libraries, museums, and other repositories, I was unfailingly accorded ready and informed guidance. A few of the many individuals responsible for this kindness must be mentioned by name: at the American Philosophical Society Library, Dr. Richard H. Shryock, Mrs. Gertrude D. Hess, and Mr. Murphy D. Smith; at the Drexel Institute of Technology, Mrs. Geraldine P. Staub; at the Franklin Papers, Dr. Leonard W. Labaree; at the Department of Records of the Friends Philadelphia Yearly Meeting, Miss Mary Ogilvie; at the Historical Society of Pennsylvania, Mr. R. N. Williams 2d and Miss Catharine Miller; at the Library Company of Philadelphia, Mr. Edwin Wolf 2d and Mr. Barney Chesnick; at the Library of Congress, Dr. David C. Mearns and Dr. Nathan Reingold; at the National Archives, Mr. W. Neil Franklin; at the National Park Service, Mr. John D. R. Platt and Mr. Denis Kurjack; at the New York Public Library, Mrs. Maud Cole and Mr. Lewis M. Stark; at the New York State Library, Mr. Donald C. Anthony; at the Pennsylvania Historical and Museum Commission, Mr. Henry Howard Eddy and Mr. Frank B. Evans; at the Presbyterian Historical Society in Philadelphia, Dr. Guy S. Klett; at the Smithsonian Institution, Dr. Robert P. Multhauf, Dr. Wilcomb E. Washburn, and Mr. Silvio A. Bedini; at the United States Mint, Miss Eva Adams and Mr. Michael Sura; and at the University of Pennsylvania, Professor Leonidas Dodson, and Professor Anthony N. B. Garvan.

Most helpful in the European repositories were: Mr. A. H. Westwood at the Birmingham Assay Office, Mr. V. K. Chew of the Science Museum in South Kensington, Mr. Francis Maddison of the Museum of the History of Science at Oxford, Dr. Olin J. Eggen then of the Royal Greenwich Observatory, Commander David Waters of the National Maritime Museum at Greenwich, and Dr. Maria Rooseboom of the National Museum for the History of Science in Leiden.

My final debts are to my wife, Helen Morris Hindle, who has contributed to every phase of the work, and to the Princeton University Press, especially to Mrs. Ross Filion and Mrs. James Holly Hanford, who guided the manuscript through to the book.

Table of Contents

List of Abbreviations

A few compressed abbreviations have been used throughout the footnotes for the purpose of brevity:

APS   American Philosophical Society
DR   David Rittenhouse
HSP   Historical Society of Pennsylvania
LC   Library of Congress
LCP   Library Company of Philadelphia
MHS   Massachusetts Historical Society
NYHS   New-York Historical Society
NYPL   New York Public Library
PMHB   *Pennsylvania Magazine of History and Biography*

List of Illustrations

David Rittenhouse

CHAPTER I

Eulogy to an Age

SOMBER excitement and a sense of occasion stirred the air in Philadelphia as the sun climbed toward its meridian on December 17, 1796. The day was crisp but comfortable, the temperature just above freezing. Ordinarily on a Saturday morning everyone would be at work, but on this day even the physicians limited their calls and the clergy chose some other time to write their sermons. Legislators arranged early adjournments, and other officials—federal, state, and city—freed themselves from their usual routine. In homes throughout the city, men and women bustled about, completing their preparations. Some few favored ones regarded a tall, exquisitely crafted clock that stood in a prominent place in their home with unusual poignancy and affection as they looked to see how much time remained.[1]

Before noon, individuals and quiet groups began to converge on the First Presbyterian Church in High Street—between Second and Third. Those who approached from the north had to walk around and past the market stalls in the street paralleling the building front. Even those who came from other directions could catch little more than a glimpse of the gleaming Corinthian columns until they were almost at the door. For many, this was an opportunity to see the interior of Dr. Ewing's new church, which was reputed to seat six hundred. Even so large a structure would be taxed to capacity today. Inside, the ushers awaited the flood that was almost upon them. They anticipated that the United States Senate and House, both houses of the

---

[1] DR, Notebook, 1792–96 (entry for Dec. 17, 1796, by unknown hand), APS; *Extracts from the Diary of Jacob Hiltzheimer* (Phila., 1893), 237; Mins. of the Select Council, Dec. 15, 1796, Phila. City Hall Annex.

Pennsylvania legislature, the city councils, the students, the faculty and trustees of the University, and the College of Physicians would attend in bodies. The sponsoring organization, the American Philosophical Society, met at its hall on Fifth Street at eleven o'clock so the members could walk in procession to the church. In addition, the diplomatic corps, the clergy of all the city's churches, and most other residents of distinction had been invited.[2]

The written acceptance of President Washington and his lady made it clear that none might regard the invitations lightly. The mayor made plans to attend, and the governor was kept away only by illness. The resulting assemblage shone with a luster that could have been duplicated nowhere else in America.[3]

The mood, however, was solemn. Six months after his death, David Rittenhouse was to be honored in a formal eulogy pronounced by the celebrated Dr. Benjamin Rush. Although the eulogist was distinguished by his quicksilver mind and a capacity for vitriolic remarks, everyone knew that today benevolence and love would dominate his performance. In a city of admirers of the late David Rittenhouse, Benjamin Rush was one of the most ardent.

Many in that audience had warm memories of the man to be honored, although few—perhaps none—could call themselves his close friends. William and Benjamin Smith Barton deeply admired their uncle, who had helped each of them along the road to success in different professions, but they had not enjoyed the equality of true friendship. Pennsylvania Chief Justice Thomas McKean and State Secretary Alexander James Dallas knew Rittenhouse as a close political associate, although, otherwise, they lived worlds apart. Congressman John Page of

[2] Floor Plan, Records of the First Presbyterian Church, 1810–17, Presbyterian Hist. Soc., Phila.; Edmund Hogan, *The Prospect of Philadelphia* (Phila., [1795]), 9; APS Mins., 1793–98, 107–9, 111; *Claypoole's Am. Daily Adver.*, Dec. 16, 1796.

[3] George W. Craik to S. Magaw and C. W. Peale, Dec. 12, 1796, Arch., APS; *Aurora*, Dec. 22, 1796; Kenneth and Anna M. Roberts, eds., *Moreau de St. Méry's American Journey* (Garden City, 1947), 336.

Virginia passionately admired Rittenhouse's scientific achievements,—but he could not really understand them. Charles Willson Peale had always felt honored by a close association dat-
ing from the darkest days of the Revolution. Yet even he
apprehended only intuitively the genius of the man whose distinction he celebrated. George Washington certainly never considered himself Rittenhouse's inferior, but their relationship of
mutual respect had always been bounded by austerity. Professor
Robert Patterson, who could indeed understand Rittenhouse's
scientific papers, never enjoyed more than an external acquaintance. Dozens had known one or another aspect of the man and
remained strangers still.

One, at least, sat long with his memories. The Reverend William Smith, onetime provost of the College of Philadelphia,
considered himself responsible for discovering Rittenhouse's
talents and introducing him to Philadelphia and to the world.
Smith had been a devoted advocate, and, under the most trying circumstances, Rittenhouse had gone out of his way to
reciprocate. Yet, an intimate friendship was prevented by personality factors and by Smith's equivocation when faced by a
Revolution which Rittenhouse accepted without restraint or
qualification.

Of Rittenhouse's closest friends, two had died before him
and one was absent. The Reverend Thomas Barton, his loyalist
brother-in-law, was the only man ever known to have called
him "Davy." [4] Judge Francis Hopkinson shared with Rittenhouse a multitude of relationships—undeterred by post-Revo-
lutionary political differences. Both Barton and Hopkinson had
been true friends.

The third friend was Thomas Jefferson—conspicuously but
unavoidably missing from this gathering. Long before, he had
retired to Monticello, where he now awaited the outcome of
the election of 1796, which, by December 17, was still unde-

[4] William Barton, *Memoirs of the Life of David Rittenhouse* (Phila.,
1813), 197.

5

cided. Had Rittenhouse lived just a little longer he would have served as a Jeffersonian elector, for he supported the Virginian's political leadership as warmly as the future President celebrated the scientific merit of David Rittenhouse. Indeed, no one would ever transcend the tributes Jefferson once paid his friend, whom he ranked "second to no astronomer living" and whom he regarded as one of nature's masterworks: "the world has but one Ryttenhouse, and . . . it never had one before." When Jefferson left Philadelphia some years earlier, Rittenhouse had written disconsolately, "I shall ever remember with pleasure whilst memory continues to perform its office, that I have counted the name of Mr. Jefferson in the very short list of my friends." [5]

The church was as crowded with memories of the men who were not there as it was with the visible audience when the little doctor finally rose. His address was a very model of what had been expected of him and captured the rapt attention of his distinguished listeners. The newspapers would later outdo themselves in praise: "Bold, original, liberal, and pathetic . . . abounding with ideas that were important; with sentiments that were noble and practical; with language glowing, energetic, and elegant." "A most masterly composition." With "the ability of an Orator" and the "feeling of a Friend," Rush made of the meeting the "solemn and affecting occasion" the entire city demanded.[6]

He was—and he knew it—dealing not only with a man recently deceased but with a symbol—with a myth. Even during his lifetime, David Rittenhouse had seemed the personification of aspirations seldom attained. In death, the image became yet a little clearer.

[5] *Claypoole's Am. Daily Adver.*, Nov. 25, 1796; *Aurora*, Dec. 17, 1796; Harry M. Tinkcom, *The Republicans and Federalists in Pennsylvania, 1790–1801* (Harrisburg, 1950), 167; [Thomas Jefferson], *Notes on the State of Virginia* (Paris, 1782 [1785]), 120; Julian P. Boyd, ed., *The Papers of Thomas Jefferson* (Princeton, 1950—), II, 203; DR to Jefferson, Jan. 11, 1793, Jefferson Papers, LC.

[6] *New World*, Dec. 19, 1796; *Phila. Gaz.*, Dec. 19, 1796; *Pa. Gaz.*, Dec. 21, 1796.

"Rittenhouse," Rush proclaimed, "the friend of God and man, is now no more!—For this, the temple of Science is hung in mourning,—for this, our eyes now drop a tributary tear. Nor do we weep alone.—The United States of America sympathize in our grief, for his name gave a splendor to the American character, and the friends of humanity in distant parts of the world, unite with us in lamenting our common loss,—for he belonged to the whole human race." Rush went on: Rittenhouse was a true philosopher, yet a bulwark of religion; a warm patriot, yet a citizen of the world and a friend of mankind; he was an honest democrat, a man of the people, yet a man of unquestioned nobility and exquisite capacity. These were the aspirations of the American Enlightenment, harmoniously combined, despite their apparent contradictions, in the person of David Rittenhouse. Rittenhouse was not merely a scientist, or a patriot, or a prominent citizen. He was one of the enlightened ones—"one of the luminaries of the eighteenth century." [7]

As Rush told it, Rittenhouse, though born to the plow, early demonstrated a remarkable genius in mathematics which permitted him to absorb all the advances of science by applying himself, unaided, to a small collection of books. When he turned to clockmaking, he produced the finest orrery, or mechanical planetarium, yet conceived. He displayed brilliance in his observations of the transit of Venus and in succeeding astronomical work. He applied his unusual depth of knowledge to the determination of several state boundaries and the establishment of the United States Mint. He was equally remarkable for the breadth of his interests, which included facility in French, German, and Dutch literature as well as in poetry, music, theology, and politics. He had been a republican before there was a republic. As a revolutionist, he had contributed heavily to American victory in the War for Independence. His honors multiplied with his accomplishments. Among the most significant,

[7] Benjamin Rush, *An Eulogium Intended to Perpetuate the Memory of David Rittenhouse* (Phila., [1796]), 5, 24.

Rush mentioned academic degrees, the presidency of the American Philosophical Society, and fellowship in the Royal Society. Pure morals and unaffected modesty further enhanced his greatness.

Thus was the image carved, and thus far it was accepted by most of the audience. Yet Rush's address contained a few allusions and certain overtones that were not equally acceptable to everyone. When the members of the American Philosophical Society retired from the church to their own hall, Judge Thomas McKean offered a *pro forma* resolution complimenting the doctor upon his eulogy. Surprisingly, the resolution ran into opposition. Indeed, the intensity of feeling rose to such a pitch that passage of the motion seemed improbable. Some of the members were determined not to place the stamp of society approval upon everything Rush had said. Dr. Charles Caldwell, who had no love for Dr. Rush but who held David Rittenhouse in the highest esteem, averted defeat by offering an amendment that emphasized "the thanks of the Society" rather than its approval of the contents of the address. He was moved by fear that failure to pass the resolution would reflect implicit criticism of Rittenhouse himself.[8]

Ostensibly, the cause of this unseemly crisis was the manner in which Rush had insisted that Rittenhouse lacked "what is called a liberal education." Far from viewing this as a disadvantage which Rittenhouse had managed to overcome, Rush defiantly proclaimed, "I am disposed to believe that his extensive knowledge, and splendid character are to be ascribed chiefly to his having escaped the pernicious influence of monkish learning upon his mind in early life."[9] In this pronouncement, Rush repeated that romantic strain of Enlightenment thought which pictured nature as an open book to be read by anyone with a pure heart and a mind unfettered by academic

[8] APS Mins., 1793–98, 111; Charles Caldwell, *Autobiography* (Phila., 1855), 265–68.
[9] Rush, *Eulogium*, 23.

8

artificialities. It had an additional patriotic appeal, for it made Rittenhouse's achievements appear the peculiar result of his American environment.

Some members of the society felt personally affronted. The Bartons were sure that their uncle was not self-taught to the extent Rush asserted; they knew that their father had helped him in his efforts to acquire the knowledge he wanted. William Smith and the University of Pennsylvania professors imagined that they were hidden targets of Rush's aggressiveness. Smith and Patterson realized that they understood Rittenhouse's scientific writings while Rush did not. They knew that however he had acquired his knowledge, Rittenhouse was an educated man whose insights came from an understanding of science rather than a neglect of its cumulative structure.

The dispute involved politics, too. McKean's resolution, supported most positively by Secretary Dallas, revealed that the Jeffersonian Republicans were well satisfied with Rush's performance. The doctor himself was moderate on this topic, but he suggested more than he actually stated when he emphasized Rittenhouse's republicanism and asserted his belief in the perfectability of political institutions. He confessed that, had he said less, he would have been accused by Rittenhouse's former political associates "of an act of treachery to his memory." To the extent that the Republicans were satisfied, the Federalists were almost equally dissatisfied, and Rush felt persecuted by their vengeance throughout the following year.[10] They were determined that Rittenhouse's memory should not be used to advance the political fortunes of their opponents. Indeed, this was one of the motives which led William Barton, years later, to attempt to redress the balance with a book about his uncle.

While Rush admitted his subject's political radicalism, he went out of his way to establish his religious conformity. This

---

[10] *Ibid.*, 37; Rush to William Barton, May 20, 1812, Rush MSS, xxxix, 96, LCP; L. H. Butterfield, ed., *Letters of Benjamin Rush* (Princeton, 1951), II, 793.

was something the doctor himself worried about. Apparently, he succeeded in satisfying the clergy, and any who recognized the distortion refrained from breaking the peace.

Clearly each group, in education, politics, or religion, would have tailored Rittenhouse's image to a somewhat different measure. He was a symbol of such great importance that no single segment of opinion could be permitted to appropriate him. Everyone admired the man and considered him an ornament to society, but, precisely because he was so universally acclaimed, it was essential that he not be misinterpreted.

The importance of the symbol became starkly clear during the afternoon following the eulogy, but this was not the beginning of the story. More than most men, Rittenhouse had spent his life trying to fulfill an ideal; an ideal continually influenced and altered by the expectations he encountered in his associates. He had gone further than men had any right to expect in attaining the destiny they claimed for him, but his achievement was the result of studied and continued effort. He was a product not of his heredity and his opportunities alone, but of his dreams and the dreams of some of the best men he knew. To his contemporaries, David Rittenhouse seemed the embodiment of virtues they wished they possessed themselves —the embodiment of the noblest virtues of the age.

CHAPTER II

Heritage of a Clockmaker

1732–1767

Thε idea that David Rittenhouse rose to distinction despite an inferior heredity could not have been further from the truth. His heritage was more rare and valuable than that possessed by all but a handful of men in his day or in any day. He inherited an unusual capacity for intellectual growth. By no standard can he be described as less than gifted.

Contemporaries were misled by the lack of distinction of Rittenhouse's parents. Neither in social and economic attainments nor in intellectual and cultural pursuits did they command attention. His father, Matthias, was a farmer, self-sustaining and respectable but no more remarkable than thousands of other small farmers throughout the colonies. Within the limits of his work, Matthias was not unsuccessful for he gave David a modest property and provided in some way for all his other children. He appeared industrious and reliable to everyone who knew him, but to his grandson, William Barton, the conclusion was inescapable that Matthias "had no claims to what is termed genius." [1]

On the other hand, Matthias Rittenhouse demonstrated much more adaptability and fortitude than a casual observer was likely to see. He had not been raised a farmer but was associated from boyhood with his father and brothers in the operation of the family paper mill near the Wissahickon. When his oldest brother, William, inherited the mill, Matthias bought a farm in nearby Norriton Township. That this relocation was not easy is suggested by scattered hints. None of his children bore

[1] Barton, *Memoirs*, 98.

the name of any of his relatives although several received names of members of the maternal family. Again, Matthias revealed a consistent antagonism toward craftsmanship and manufacturing in opposing David's early interests.

The education of David's mother, Elizabeth Williams Rittenhouse, was too limited to permit her to display any sort of intellectual capacity. Daughter of Evan and Dorothy Williams, Welsh Quakers, she had been raised from childhood by an elderly relative, Richard Jones. Her people had been farmers and she was able to aid her husband in many ways as he developed his new career. Quick and alert where Matthias was slow, she gave a very different impression to people. Convinced that they must find evidence of David's capacities in one of his parents, William Barton and Benjamin Rittenhouse concurred that his "genius was more derived from his mother than his father." [2] Limited by the prevalent concepts of heredity, they never thought of looking at the generations before Rittenhouse's parents for evidences of genius. Besides, they were inclined to value British above German ancestry.

However, Matthias' father Nicholas, or Claus, and still more impressively his grandfather William left unequivocal evidence of superior capacity. Born in the German Rhineland, Wilhelm Rittinghausen lived in the Netherlands as Willem Rittinghuysen for ten years before he took his family to Pennsylvania. There in 1690, drawing upon his European experience in paper making, he established a paper mill on the banks of the Monoshoe Creek near where it empties into the Wissahickon. This was a landmark in the development of the colonial economy, and its success brought William into contact with several prominent men in the province, including William Penn himself. William became a leader of the German community and was chosen first minister of the Mennonites who clustered in his vicinity.[3]

[2] *Ibid.*, 93, 109, 111.
[3] Daniel K. Cassel, *A Genea-Biographical History of the Rittenhouse*

Nicholas, also born in Germany, married a Dutch girl, Willemigntie de Wees, in New York shortly after his arrival in the colonies. As a result, Dutch as well as German was spoken in his home just as it had been in William's. The mill prospered under Nicholas' management and even justified expansion. Nicholas followed further in his father's footsteps by serving as a Mennonite minister.

Inexorably, the genetic portion of his inheritance had already been transmitted when David Rittenhouse was born, on April 8, 1732, in the solid stone house his great-grandfather had built. His ancestry contained enough evidences of capacity to make his own gifts believable. Their development and refinement began within the secure home provided by his parents —first at the family homestead along the Wissahickon and thereafter at the Norriton farm.[4]

The farm consisted of a hundred acres of gently rolling, high ground some three miles above the Schuylkill and twenty miles from Philadelphia. Initially, the household included Elizabeth's two younger brothers, and it soon embraced a considerable progeny. Matthias and Elizabeth had ten children of whom seven lived to maturity—five girls and two boys. Of these, David was the second child and the first son.

Only the broadest outline of David's familial life is known. In many respects, the family escaped from traditions which bound each parent to differing complexes of belief and behavior. Matthias broke free from his Germanic background into an Anglicized world more congenial with his wife's heritage. Yet, David's later facility with the German language suggests that German was either occasionally spoken or its study

Family (Phila., 1894), I, 78 [must be used with caution]; cf. Calvin I. Kephart, "Rittenhouse Genealogy Debunked," National Genealogical Soc. Quar., 26 (1938); Harold S. Bender, "William Rittenhouse," Mennonite Quar. Rev., 8 (1934), 58; Milton Rubincam, "William Rittenhouse," Pa. German Soc. Publications, xxxviii, 64.

[4] This birth date has been accepted but DR celebrated April 23 as his birthday (April 12 o.s.). See Catharine Van C. Mathews, Andrew Ellicott, His Life and Letters (N.Y., 1908), 57.

encouraged. The Mennonite religious affiliation was altogether abandoned; even with a strong will, it would have been difficult to maintain in that English community. For one period the parents attended a Baptist church. Elizabeth did not remain a steadfast Friend, but the Quaker influence was remarkably strong upon the entire family as the marriage of several of the children to Friends suggests. David himself, though never a member of the Society, chose both of his wives from that faith. Some of the Mennonite doctrines were complementary to those held by the Friends, so Matthias' background was not uncongenial. Nevertheless, circumstances conspired against any strong denominational loyalty.[5]

Records of David's boyhood do not exist, and many remembrances by his contemporaries were colored by the wish to discover every possible parallel with the life of Sir Isaac Newton. Some of them, however, ring true. David was credited with making a wooden model of a water mill at the age of eight—just as Newton was known to have made a model of a windmill when still a boy. David, of course, had been born beside a water mill and, however strained Matthias may have felt toward his family, it is likely that the boy did sometimes visit the Rittenhouses and their mill. David was also credited with building a wooden clock at sixteen and a brass clock shortly afterward—just as Newton had built a water clock and a sundial at an early age.[6]

Benjamin Rittenhouse recalled other incidents which linked his brother with Newton the mathematician. Specifically, he remembered finding chalked figures and calculations all over the plow handles and fences when he was commissioned to call in his older brother from his farm duties. Where David learned ciphering or reading and writing no one seemed to recall, and later students have erred in conjecturing ties with schoolmas-

[5] William W. Hinshaw and Thomas W. Marshall, comp., *Encyclopedia of American Quaker Genealogy* (Ann Arbor, 1938), II, 413, 650, 995; Barton, *Memoirs*, 98.
[6] *Ibid.*, 97–98.

ters of the area. Much of his early education was gained within the home—there especially he formed many of the attitudes and aspirations which never left him.[7]

Rittenhouse himself recalled one very tangible influence, important because it reinforced tendencies toward craftsmanship which his father might dislike but could not wholly repress. Elizabeth's brother, David Williams, in his work as an itinerant joiner, directly encouraged his nephew. During his lifetime, Uncle David frequently made his home at Norriton and, on his death, he left to his nephew a box of tools and books which young David always afterward recalled as a great "treasure." In addition to tools and implements used by carpenters, the box included a few elementary arithmetic and geometry books and sheets of calculations. The chest had real as well as symbolic importance; it fed David's already demonstrated interest in mechanical pursuits and it provided him an opportunity to develop his mathematical capacities.[8]

Clockmaking in eighteenth-century Pennsylvania was the most precise and stimulating craft open to boys with a bent for mechanics. It required a high degree of manual skill and some acquaintance with both arithmetic and elementary geometry. Norriton was not the most promising location to develop such a trade, but a wide market was accessible for the product of the clockmaker—in the homes of country people as well as in the capital city. Given David Rittenhouse's interests and capacities, clockmaking was the most suitable trade he could choose. Lacking a learned education and isolated on a farm, he could not have found a wider doorway to a variety of opportunities.

Moreover, clockmaking was sometimes allied with mathematical instrument making as, in time, it would be with Rittenhouse. From such a beginning, a group of men in England and in Scotland rose to deserved prominence in the world of sci-

[7] Rush, *Eulogium*, 7–8.
[8] Barton, *Memoirs*, 106.

ence. No American instrument maker succeeded so strikingly as Rittenhouse, but, in the mother country, James Short, John Dolland, Edward Nairne, and George Adams carved out careers which make Rittenhouse's seem less exceptional.

There is no record of the lucky or well-calculated stroke that led Rittenhouse to undertake the making of clocks, nor is there evidence that he was ever apprenticed to any one of several clockmakers from whom he might have learned the trade. There is eloquent circumstantial evidence in the clocks he constructed that he somehow became acquainted with the best techniques of English and American clockmaking. His clocks were not unusual either in design or in manner of construction but only in the fineness of their craftsmanship and in the individuality impressed upon each of them.[9]

Matthias Rittenhouse not only gave his reluctant consent that his son should give up farming but even provided the means for embarking upon a career in clockmaking. He offered to buy the basic tools, and he permitted his son to build a workshop on the Norriton farm alongside the road to town. David Rittenhouse made additional tools required in his work; he was continuously busy either in contriving and constructing or in studying. From 1750 or 1751 until the Revolution, he was a clockmaker by trade.

Norriton was not rich in intellectual resources. Rittenhouse's parents had little inclination in this direction, and the farmers round about had even less. The eager clockmaker met with hardly any opportunity for informed conversation or advice as he extended his studies of mathematics and the sciences. His scholarship was an even more lonely pursuit than, in some measure, scholarship must always be. Even his access to books was limited. In later years, his work continued to be marked by this individual, isolated character.

Thomas Barton's arrival as a schoolmaster in Norriton in-

[9] George H. Eckhardt, *Pennsylvania Clocks and Clockmakers* (N.Y., 1955), 35.

jected a dynamic, new element into Rittenhouse's environment in 1751. Barton at twenty-one was only two years his senior, but, freshly arrived from Ireland, he possessed learning and experience that made his friendship an important acquisition. An Anglican of English descent, he had studied at the University of Dublin. He had a wide range of intellectual interests in which the sciences were prominent although his taste and capacities were best suited for the study of natural history. Barton remained a neighbor for little more than a year, but his influence continued over a much longer period.[10]

Their friendship survived Barton's move to Philadelphia in 1752 to accept appointment as tutor in the Academy and Charitable School. From the city, he supplied his country friend with books and encouragement. Their earliest letters testify to a mutual warmth of feeling, which was guaranteed permanence by Barton's marriage to Rittenhouse's eldest sister, Esther. This event was celebrated on December 8, 1753, in Old Swedes' Church, Philadelphia—a distinct suggestion of the strength of Barton's dedication to the Church of England compared with Esther's relative freedom from church ties.[11]

Rittenhouse's ill health, of which he was to complain for the balance of his life, first assumed importance about this time. His illness was attributed to hard work and hard study without sufficient rest or relaxation. Seeking a cure, he spent some time at Yellow Springs, a chalybeate resort some fifteen miles from Norriton. The waters he took there and the rest seemed to improve the general state of his health, but his most specific complaint would not leave him then or ever again except for the briefest periods.

This disability he described as "a constant heat in the pit of the stomach, affecting a space not exceeding the size of a half

[10] Barton, *Memoirs*, 101–5, 118–22; Benjamin Smith Barton, *A Discourse on Some of the Principle Desiderata in Natural History* (Phila., 1807), 86; Charles W. Rutschky, Jr., "Thomas Barton's Collection of Minerals," *Pa. History*, 8 (1941), 148, 150.

[11] Edward Ford, *David Rittenhouse* (Phila., 1946), 17.

a guinea, attended at times with much pain." [12] His description coupled with his medical history and his personality strongly suggest that Rittenhouse suffered from a duodenal ulcer. His distress was intermittent, but no clear case history remains. The only relief he specifically recorded occurred when he left his usual routine of cares and annoyances to enjoy the beauties of the wilderness with the change of pace, the exercise, and the rougher life that attended his trips into the interior. Yet even this improvement did not last long, for in the woods, he soon became irked with the inconveniences and the physical discomfort.

Rittenhouse came to live with ill health and, in fact, to count upon it. Even common colds assumed importance to him; his friends thought of poor health as one of his most marked characteristics. He seldom felt well but apparently was never seriously sick until the final illness that claimed his life. Rush diagnosed the chronic discomfort as a constitutional ailment. He voiced the feeling of many that Rittenhouse's personality was influenced by the feebleness of his health—that his "habitual patience and resignation" were the result.[13]

There is no doubt that Rittenhouse's personality and health were linked, but it is likely that his illness owed as much to his personality as the reverse. Physically taller than average, Rittenhouse always remained slender and straight, quick in gait, and lively in his movements but complacent and benign in countenance. His quiet, greyish eyes hinted of suffering, while his handsome face conveyed both aloofness and restraint. He experienced warm emotions and strong reactions to both public and private affairs but his expression of these feelings he kept reined in with an iron discipline. He only relaxed this control in private company or when he spoke of his poor health, which he freely admitted, believing it beyond his volition. He was a realist, seldom able to rationalize away unpleasant facts or to

[12] Barton, *Memoirs*, 99.
[13] Rush, *Eulogium*, 42.

David Rittenhouse

By Charles Willson Peale, 1791

Princeton University Library

The Princeton Orrery

Drexel Institute of Technology

Rittenhouse's Finest Clock

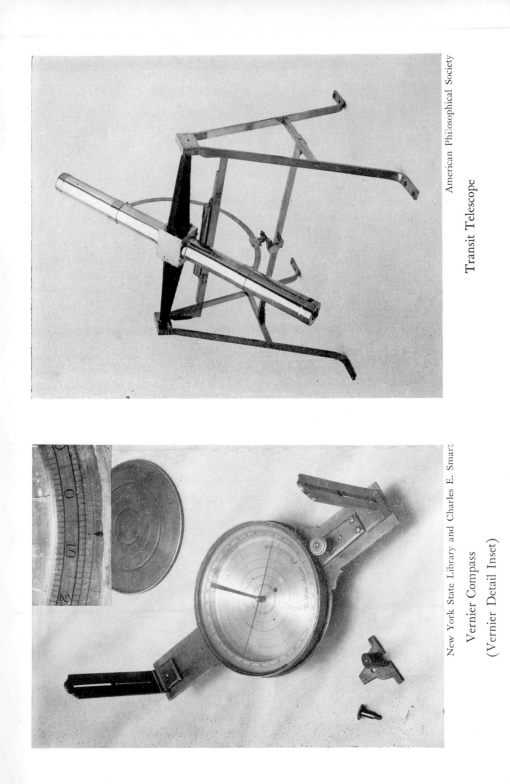

American Philosophical Society

Transit Telescope

New York State Library and Charles E. Smart

Vernier Compass
(Vernier Detail Inset)

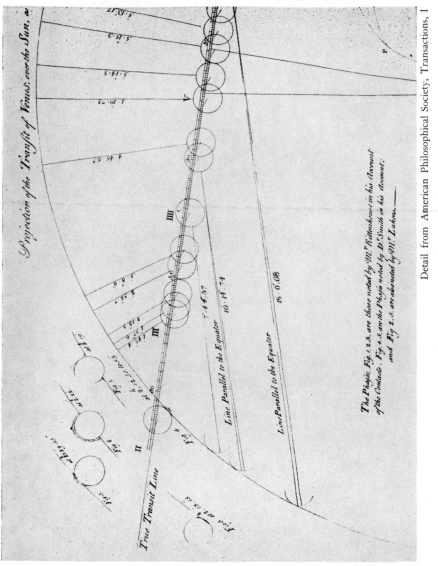

Detail from American Philosophical Society, Transactions, I

Rittenhouse's Transit of Venus Projection

permit the worlds of life and fantasy to merge. He lived with tension, repressed emotion, and unsatisfied aspiration from this early point of his life.

Thomas Barton was a sympathetic resource but not a relaxing one. He continued to encourage and to stimulate his friend. When he returned in 1755 from a trip to England to receive Episcopal ordination, he brought with him a parcel of books for Rittenhouse. For himself, he had obtained support from the Society for the Propagation of the Gospel in Foreign Parts and appointment to a mission at Sulphur Springs, near Carlisle, where he could look west toward the Pennsylvania frontier. During the Seven Years' War, he served for a time as military chaplain. Rittenhouse, of course, excused himself from war service on the grounds that he did not have the "health for a soldier."[14] Instead, he busied himself in the study of optics, self-consciously reflecting on Archimedes, who had been slain in wartime when similarly engaged in scientific investigations.

The Bartons' stay at Sulphur Springs provided Rittenhouse with the opportunity for his first recorded western excursion. With a fresh and alert mind, he viewed for the first time communities relatively close to his home. Reading, less than forty miles away, surprised him by its size; "the number and goodness of the buildings," he reported, "far exceeding my expectations."[15]

Less enthusiastic was his reaction to the Ephrata community of Seventh Day Baptists, which practiced an ascetic, monastic way of life. Such principles as pacifism and opposition to judicial oaths they shared with the Quakers and Mennonites, but neither this element of familiarity nor the extensive learning of Conrad Beissel, head of the order, reconciled Rittenhouse to the strange group. He commented, "I was there entertained with an epitome of all the whimsies mankind are capable of conceiving. Yet it seemed to me the most melancholy place in

[14] Barton, *Memoirs*, 105n.
[15] *Ibid.*, 115.

the world, and I believe would soon kill me were I to continue there." [16]

Returning to Norriton, Rittenhouse worked constantly to increase the skill of his hand and to broaden and deepen his knowledge of the principles of some of the sciences—still in isolation from competent guidance. His clocks were already as good as any produced in Pennsylvania in a day when the construction of tall clocks had become a fine art. Most of the forty odd examples of his work still surviving can be dated only very roughly, those with "Norriton" engraved on their face being, of course, the earlier. In addition to his name, the face sometimes carried a motto. In construction, he used the common anchor escapement except for his highly accurate astronomical clocks in which he introduced a dead-beat escapement and, in addition, some form of compensation pendulum. Even before he began adding devices for playing tunes and for the presentation of a great variety of information, the clocks he built for sale marked him as a master. These pendulum, weight-driven mechanisms command today the highest prices in the field of tall American clocks—basically because of their intrinsic merits rather than because of the fame of their maker.

Early in his career, he ventured upon the construction of a variety of other instruments. In 1756, he was at work on a telescope, an enterprise which accompanied his study of astronomy and optics. He also constructed the commonly used surveyors' instruments, especially compasses and levels. This activity must have begun before 1763 because in that year he was called upon to perform duties he could not have considered until he had mastered the skills of terrestrial and celestial surveying. To this knowledge, he moved through the craft of the instrument maker.

In 1763, the Reverend Richard Peters, secretary to the governor of Pennsylvania, called Rittenhouse to help with the pro-

[16] *Ibid.,* 113.

tracted effort to determine the boundary between Pennsylvania and Maryland. The basis of settlement had already been accepted by both parties, and joint commissioners had had surveyors at work for three years on the difficult geometrical problem of running the tangent line from the point that is now the southwest corner of the state of Delaware to the point where it intersects a twelve-mile circle about New Castle. This had been such a discouragingly slow affair that two English surveyors, Charles Mason and Jeremiah Dixon, were finally engaged to complete the boundary. Rittenhouse gave his "attendance" at New Castle at this juncture of the dispute.[17]

Whatever services he rendered were not extensive. When he received £6 for his efforts, he remarked that he had been paid "much more generously" than he expected. If he did verify latitudes, as has been asserted, it was the mathematical operation involved rather than the field observations that seemed most burdensome. He declared, "I found it a very laborious affair; being obliged, singly, to go through a number of intricate calculations." [18]

In any case, this episode brought Rittenhouse to the notice of intellectual and political leaders in Philadelphia. He was favorably introduced to the attention of Peters and his fellow Anglican clergyman, the Reverend William Smith. Both men were interested in the kind of intellectual attainment Rittenhouse represented and both were in positions to help. Peters immediately offered his assistance.

Through Barton's influence and through fortuitous circumstances, Rittenhouse was drawn into a friendly relationship with the Proprietary political faction, but his emotional attachment was not so readily engaged. The march of the Paxton Boys in

[17] *Message from the Governor of Maryland . . . in Relation to the Intersection of the Boundary Lines of the States of Maryland, Pennsylvania, and Delaware* (Washington, 1850), 24–26; Thomas D. Cope, "Charles Mason and Jeremiah Dixon," *Scientific Monthly*, 62 (1946), 543.
[18] Barton, *Memoirs*, 150.

early 1764 revealed a yawning gulf between the attitudes of this group and Rittenhouse's own feelings toward a complex of social and political attitudes.

Violence had erupted in Pennsylvania following the disasters of Pontiac's War in the summer of 1763. The ensuing winter saw the massacre of reservation Indians by irate frontiersmen who struck out against presumed Indian perfidy and demonstrable governmental inaction. The killings reflected a wrath which continued to rise in the West, culminating in an organized march on Philadelphia during the first few days of February. Before the marchers reached Philadelphia, however, a delegation of city leaders met and dissuaded them from violence. The crisis was marked by sympathy on the part of Anglicans and Presbyterians, who constituted the major elements of the Proprietary political faction, and by the strong antagonism of the Quakers and their supporters. The pamphlet war that followed further sharpened these differences along political, religious, and ethnic lines.[19]

Rittenhouse could not contain his fury at the rowdy behavior of the marchers: "About fifty of the scoundrels marched by my work-shop—I have seen hundreds of Indians travelling the country and can with truth affirm, that the behaviour of these fellows was ten times more savage and brutal than theirs. Frightening women, by running the muzzles of their guns through windows, swearing and hallooing; attacking men without the least provocation; dragging them by the hair to the ground, and pretending to scalp them; shooting a number of dogs and fowls—these are some of their exploits." [20]

His contempt was further confirmed by his sister Eleanor, who relayed the excitement into which Philadelphia was thrown by the threatened assault. She rejoiced that her Quaker husband, Daniel Evans, had mustered with the defense forces, "In less

[19] Brooke Hindle, "The March of the Paxton Boys," *William and Mary Quar.*, 3d ser., 3 (1946), 461–86.
[20] Barton, *Memoirs,* 148n.

than a quarter of an hour, they were all on their march,—it is supposed above a thousand of them." She further confided, "There were not ten [Presbyterians] among them . . . Instead of joining with the others, they would sneak into the corners, and applaud the 'Paxton-boys.' " [21]

Rittenhouse's personality, his family background, his experiences, and his reason led him to the attitude of the Quaker-Assembly faction even though that may not have been an expedient position from the viewpoint of his career. He found himself in the opposite camp from his brother-in-law. Barton was not only tied to the Anglican-Presbyterian-Proprietary faction but his time spent among the frontiersmen and his war experience gave him a sympathy Rittenhouse could not understand. Anonymously, Barton wrote a pamphlet entitled *The Conduct of the Paxton-Men, Impartially Represented* in which he tore at the hypocrisy of Quaker pacifism and the injustice of *"Quaker Government."* More specifically, his philippic was a party refutation of Benjamin Franklin's anti-Paxton *Narrative of the Late Massacres.*[22]

There was no way that Rittenhouse and Barton could have accommodated their viewpoints on this matter, but the difference did not strain their friendship. Indeed, that proved firm against still more serious stresses and each continued to react to the major political events in harmony with his own set of mind.

Later in 1764, Rittenhouse was assigned his patrimony by his father in the form of clear title to the Norriton farm. Matthias bought another farm in adjoining Worcester Township, where he moved his family, leaving David in possession of the old homestead and of his little workshop by the side of the road. At the time he received this remarkably large portion of all Matthias possessed, David agreed to assume large responsibilities for the rest of the family when his father should die. He

[21] *Ibid.*, 148n.–49n.
[22] Both works published anonymously, Phila., 1764.

would make specified monetary payments to his sisters and would share with his brother Benjamin care for the material welfare of their mother. Matthias intended to leave the Worcester farm to Benjamin under similar provisions. Benjamin remained with his parents at Worcester, where he developed a clockmaking business of his own. Each daughter was given a settlement upon her marriage, but the whole of Matthias' real property, much the larger part of his wealth, was to be divided between his two sons.[23]

On February 20, 1766, Rittenhouse married Eleanor Coulston, the Quaker daughter of a nearby Plymouth farmer. Now thirty-three, he owned his own home, followed a satisfying trade, and enjoyed a stability which would permit him to assume the responsibilities of married life without undue hazard. Indeed, his establishment cried out for a competent woman's hand. The marriage ceremony was conducted at Norriton by Thomas Barton, who now lived in Lancaster.[24]

The wedding, which followed Rittenhouse's wishes, posed a problem for the bride. As a birthright Friend, she was steadfastly dedicated to the Quaker way. Her marriage out of Meeting before a "hirling priest" was sufficient to cause her to be disowned by the Society. She was torn between her own religious sense and Rittenhouse's sympathetic but differing views. Finally, nearly a year and a half after the ceremony, the Meeting received Eleanor's written confession of error and expression of sorrow. She was reinstated on a probationary basis—"on trial of . . . future conduct." She never again strayed but remained a Friend until she died.[25]

Their first child was born on January 23, 1767, in a crisis that brought Rittenhouse to a high state of fear for the life of the mother, who, happily, did survive. Nelly, as Eleanor was

[23] Cassell, *History*, 169–71.
[24] Barton, *Memoirs*, 153.
[25] Gwynned Monthly Meeting, R.S., p. 10, Department of Records, Philadelphia Yearly Meeting (through the courtesy of Miss Mary Ogilvie).

known in the family, had intended naming the baby after Rittenhouse's closest friend, his brother-in-law, Thomas Barton. When it turned out to be a girl, the name of Rittenhouse's mother, Elizabeth, was used.[26]

By this time, Rittenhouse had begun to crowd the limits of his trade but was less and less able to satisfy his expanding ambitions. Increasingly, he pushed beyond the conventional bounds of clockmaking and even in instrument making found more joy in contriving new devices than in merely reproducing familiar and saleable items.

One invention of this period was distinctly remarkable. Before anyone in Europe is known to have made one, Rittenhouse produced a pocket, metallic thermometer. Metallic thermometers, indeed, were not new, but those that have survived or of which there is any record were cumbersome laboratory instruments. Rittenhouse devised one in which a needle, actuated by the expansion of metal with heat, moved against a semicircular scale to register the degree of temperature. The instrument was small and flat and the face was protected by glass. Even the first instruments made by Bréguet in the nineteenth century were inferior to this in compactness and portability. According to William Barton, its temperatures corresponded well with those registered by a mercury thermometer.[27]

Also in 1767, he produced the most complicated clock he ever made, a mechanism that was wondrous even in its conception. When placed in a magnificent Chinese Chippendale case, it measured a full nine feet in height and two in width. Its elaborately engraved face carried no less than six dials plus the usual semicircular device to portray the phases of the moon. Despite the complexity of hands, pointers, arms, scales, and indexes, the whole was combined in a balanced composition of great beauty in which the deep blue background subtly quieted the brilliant golds, silvers, and blacks. Seconds, min-

[26] Barton, *Memoirs*, 195–96.
[27] *Ibid.*, 155n., 450n.

utes, hours, days, and months could all be read on the face with
an accuracy that extended to the correction for leap year. One
dial even presented the equation of time—or the varying difference between local time and sidereal time. A little mechanical
planetarium depicted the relative position of the planets while
a lunarium showed the positions of the earth and the moon.
The clock struck quarter-hours and could be set to play any of
ten tunes on its chimes. It was greatly admired and immediately
drew attention to Rittenhouse's interest in the astronomy related to the measurement of time.[28]

Even this was not enough. No clock to compare with it had
ever been made in America and it is unlikely that any similarly
elaborate European clock or automaton preserved the simplicity
and beauty of Rittenhouse's. Yet Rittenhouse knew that his
friends and advocates anticipated something more. Both as a
mechanic and as a scholar he was expected to exceed and to
excel some of the best efforts of man. Barton continuously urged
him toward concrete accomplishment. Finally, they hit upon a
demonstration that would justify these anticipations. It would
perfectly reflect the image of the exquisite mechanic combined
in the same person with the learned scientist. Rittenhouse would
build an orrery, or mechanical planetarium, of hitherto unapproached precision.

[28] Now owned by the Drexel Institute of Technology.

CHAPTER III

Through the Orrery to the Stars
1767–1769

MECHANICAL planetaria emerged in the Age of Enlightenment as a major demonstration of skill by better clock and instrument makers. They were a form of clockwork but more intricate than clocks and more meaningful than the elaborate European automata that excited admiration by the variety of motions and operations they performed. The planetaria celebrated the Copernican cosmology, or, more accurately, gave a visual representation to Newton's "system of the world." They depicted the planets and satellites of the solar system moving through their orbits in mechanically precise paths. They served as monuments to man's new knowledge of the movements of the great heavenly bodies and to his hope that a similar precision of knowledge would be discovered in other areas of study. For an unusually skilled clockmaker who thought of himself as a Newtonian philosopher they presented an ideal exercise.

Many planetaria were constructed before Rittenhouse thought of turning his talents in that direction. Working cosmological models had been made in antiquity, and, since the late middle ages, the armillary sphere had served generally to give three-dimensional representation to concepts of the universe. In the seventeenth century, Christian Huygens designed a more refined clockwork model which exhibited the planetary motions. In Holland too, about 1700, Steven Thrasi built the larger and much more ambitious planetarium known as the "Leiden sphere." [1] In England, the prototype for a whole generation

[1] Both are in the National Museum for the History of Science in Leiden.

of planetaria was built early in the eighteenth century by John Rowley for Charles Boyle, fourth Earl of Orrery. Although it was a copy of a machine constructed earlier by the well-known instrument maker, George Graham, Rowley's device gave to all others of that class their name. The eighteenth-century planetarium was usually referred to as an "orrery"—after the owner of Rowley's planetarium.[2]

Orreries came into great demand. Although examples of fine craftsmanship, the machines of Graham and Rowley were simple and limited in the precision with which they portrayed the motions of moon and earth. Later orreries were more complicated, exhibited the motions of more bodies, and were more accurate in their actions. In Rittenhouse's day, Benjamin Martin offered large, finely constructed orreries at prices from £40 to £150. To satisfy those of smaller means, he sold a little hand orrery at only £2..12..6.[3]

Rittenhouse's thoughts, however, revolved about the challenge rather than the market. Here at last was a project demanding his best skill as a craftsman but equally worthy of the philosopher's attention. Benjamin Martin, George Adams, and James Ferguson not only made fine orreries but were still better known as expositors of Newtonian science. Surely recognition would come to anyone who could exceed the best work of the craftsmen-scientists of Europe.

Thomas Barton helped Rittenhouse to see his opportunity more clearly. He urged him to make his plan as perfect and as elaborate as possible, "pursue your Orrery in your own way, without any regard to an ignorant or prevailing taste. All you have to study is truth." Specifically he counseled, "I beg you will not limit yourself in the price." He was convinced that the orrery would find a buyer however expensive it became.[4]

[2] Graham's machine is in the Museum of the History of Science at Oxford and Rowley's in the Science Museum, London.

[3] Benjamin Martin, *The Description and Use of Both the Globes, the Armillary Sphere, and Orrery* (London, n.d.), Appendix, p. 3.

[4] Barton, *Memoirs*, 196.

Barton found several references but it is improbable that most of them would have helped much even if Rittenhouse had been able to obtain copies. For purchase, he commended Edmund Stone's translation of the valuable *Construction and Principal Uses of Mathematical Instruments* by a French instrument maker, Nicholas Bion. Of more general studies, he called attention to Roger Cotes, who had written a preface to the second English edition of Newton's *Principia*, to Richard Helsham's *Course of Lectures in Natural Philosophy*, and to Henry Power's outdated *Experimental Philosophy*. He also alluded to Christian Huygens, who had described his planetarium in writing. The most pertinent English works on orreries he failed to mention at all, and his selections cast doubt upon his acquaintance with the books he noted.[5]

Fortunately, Barton did have access to other works of greater relevance from some of which he transcribed passages for his brother-in-law's use. He sent, for example, Benjamin Martin's statement supporting the adaptation of the orrery to the form of an armillary sphere.

Rittenhouse responded sharply, "what has a Sphere, consisting of a great number of metaline Circles, to do with the true System of the World? Is there one real, or so much as apparent Circle in it? (the bodies of the Sun and Planets excepted.) Are they not all merely imaginary lines, contrived for the purpose of calculation? I did not intend to let one of them have a place in my Orrery, except the Zodiac, on which I would have the true latitude and longitude of each planet pointed out by its proper Index." [6]

Barton also located an orrery design in John Rowning's *Compendious System of Natural Philosophy*, which turned out to be much more to Rittenhouse's taste. Rowning also complained of orreries that made use of a series of metallic circles which were purely imaginary, as, for example, the circle representing

[5] *Ibid.*, 197–98.
[6] *Ibid.*, 194.

the ecliptic. Instead of this mixed system, Rowning suggested a machine which would reproduce apparent motions, "the Phænomena," rather than real motions. The observer would be placed *inside* this orrery and would see balls representing the sun and planets moving on a hemisphere surrounding him.[7]

For a moment, Rittenhouse was entranced, "Rowning's opinion of Orreries pleases me more than anything I had met with before." Yet both he and Rowning knew that such a scheme was mechanically impracticable. This exciting proposal would have to await the development of the optical planetarium. The American clockmaker concluded, "The idea of his *imaginary* machine naturally presents itself to persons conversant in Astronomy; but, if actually made, it could not answer the purpose, unless prodigiously large,—which I presume is the reason it has never been done." [8]

As his orrery took shape in his mind, Rittenhouse let his imagination loose and dreamed of a machine that would, beyond dispute, surpass any that had previously been constructed. He would aim not to "give the ignorant in astronomy a just view of the Solar System: but would rather astonish the skillful and curious examiner, by a most accurate correspondence between the situations and motions of those bodies, themselves." Existing orreries reflected only in the grossest way the relative distances and motions of the solar system. Rittenhouse would construct a scientific instrument rather than a display piece. He envisaged a mechanical table "capable of informing us, truly, of the astronomical phænomena for any particular point of time." He was perfectly right in observing that no orrery then made could perform such a service.[9]

As early as January 1767, he was at work on a specimen part of the orrery, and, in March, he hoped soon to have the elements depicting the motion of the moon completed. He was

[7] See John Rowning, *Compendious System of Natural Philosophy* (London, 1758), II, 150–57.

[8] Barton, *Memoirs*, 198.

[9] *Ibid.*, 194, 199–202; later version in APS, *Trans.*, 1 (1771), 1–3.

sufficiently clear in his plans to write out a detailed description of the entire machine for Barton. At almost every point, his design broke free from the conventions that had governed earlier orrery construction. His device would be like nothing ever built before.

The most obvious innovation was the vertical aspect of the machine; the planets would be made to revolve about the sun in a vertical plane rather than in a horizontal plane as had become customary despite Huygens' original vertical machine. Clocks, of course, were constructed with vertical faces and Rittenhouse almost necessarily followed suit in aligning the small orrery of his 1767 clock. However, he multiplied his problems when he decided to place the orbits of his planets in a vertical plane.

Further difficulties were introduced by every increase in accuracy of representation which he decided to include. Around a gilded brass ball representing the sun, the known planets would not be permitted to revolve in circles as they did in the common orrery—they must follow elliptical paths. Neither would Rittenhouse countenance motion at a uniform rate of speed; each planet must conform as closely as possible to Kepler's law that it sweep out equal sectors in equal times. Again, he would not be content to place the planetary orbits in the same plane; each must be inclined by the proper angle to the others, and each must have its nodes, aphelion, and perihelion at the proper points. The speed of rotation of each planet on its axis would also be reproduced accurately—when it was known. Every planet would be placed in its orbit in proper relationship to every other planet and the wheelwork would be so precise that the planets would maintain their correct positions for any given moment of time to which the machinery was cranked over a span of 10,000 years. One additional variable, the precession of the equinoxes, would be introduced by giving motion to an external circular strip placed in the plane of the ecliptic. Then the observer could set a small telescope on the sphere representing the earth, sight any of the planets, and discover its celestial position against a graduated scale.

No mortal mind and hands could have confronted this great project without hesitation. It was more than enough to intensify duodenal pains in a man who had had earlier ulcer symptoms. It was—in plain words—project impossible to fulfill as Rittenhouse conceived it. But this was not all.

In addition to the planetarium proper, the orrery would contain two side panels, one displaying all the aspects of Jupiter with its satellites and Saturn with its ring and satellites; the other comprising a lunarium. Lunaria, showing the motion and phases of the moon and even her apogee and nodes, were familiar models. Some of the authors with whom Rittenhouse was familiar described such devices but, here again, Rittenhouse intended to exceed them all. Not only would such events as eclipses be displayed but their time and duration would be presented "exactly."

The project absorbed a large part of Rittenhouse's attention for years to come. A vast amount of calculation, planning, construction, and adaptation was necessary. It was not difficult to set down the basic facts, the mean distances of the planets from the sun, the inclination and eccentricity of the orbits, the planetary speeds, speeds of rotation, and such information. But how to reproduce all of these motions in a machine of the limited size projected by Rittenhouse and operated by a single motive force—whether by winch or clock-driven mechanism—was a problem to tax his utmost ingenuity.

Even before he began to calculate gear ratios, it became apparent that he could not be as realistic as he desired. It was feasible enough, for example, to think in terms of placing the planets at their proper relative distances from the sun, but if this were done the planets themselves could not be represented by balls of the correct magnitude nor could the planetary satellites be placed at the correct distances from each planet. It would not have been useful to represent the earth any smaller than one-fifth of an inch in diameter, but even on that diminutive scale, its distance from the sun would have been one hundred-eighty feet and the sun's diameter twenty inches! Saturn would have had to be placed over seventeen hundred feet away from the sun. The speed differentials presented similar impossibilities. What could be done with the closest of the five known satellites of Saturn, which circles the planet 6,000 times during one Saturnian year? Rittenhouse could no more handle such multiplications of speed than he could preserve relative sizes and distances. He had to give up elliptical orbits, although he gave the orbits an eccentric displacement and to Mercury he gave a proportioned orbital speed—according to Kepler's second law. Despite his intense desire to achieve realism, he was forced, as all other orrery builders had been, to compromise.

Although he resisted each necessary compromise, the resultant design was still so difficult that its completion would demand his maximum skill. He came to resent other demands which kept impinging on his time, writing Barton that his friends would have to wait for awhile to be supplied with clocks because the orrery came first. He also reported reluctance to undertake a big job on Reading's town clock because that would "retard the great work." [10]

Close as he stuck to this project, Rittenhouse's world continued to expand in other directions. This was partly the influence of the orrery itself, which subtly led his thoughts to broader questions of astronomy, mathematics, and fundamental science. At the same time, he was encouraged in more intellectual activities by his friends, who were as delighted by his command of mathematics and science as they were by his craftsmanship. The route he followed in improving his knowledge was altogether appropriate to a fine clockmaker but different from the path an academic philosopher might have chosen.

His understanding of science was derived from competent

[10] Barton, *Memoirs*, 205.

syntheses and from the writings of the masters themselves—especially Newton—but the range of his resources was small. Rittenhouse had little access to the best current books and journals, often hearing of their contents from second- and third-hand sources. The *Philosophical Transactions* of the Royal Society, for example, was less familiar to him at this stage of his career than *The General Magazine of Arts and Sciences*. Significantly, this periodical was issued in London by the instrument maker, Benjamin Martin, who used the magazine as one of his vehicles for communicating scientific ideas to a wide audience. In a regular section entitled "Miscellaneous Correspondence," Martin presented everything from poetry to politics but concentrated upon diagrams of new scientific devices and mathematical problems which he seldom pursued to the point of tedium.

When Barton called his brother-in-law's attention to experiments on the compressibility of water made by Ebenezer Kinnersely of the Academy of Philadelphia, Rittenhouse was able to recall similar investigations by John Canton which he had read in Martin's *Magazine*. Martin had, in fact, lifted the account from the *Philosophical Transactions*, which Rittenhouse had no way of knowing. He confronted respectfully Canton's experiments performed with the conventional equipment of air pump and glass tubes and balls, and he accepted the compressibility of water as a reasonable conclusion. He leaped beyond the described experiments to worry about the possible structure of matter that could explain the phenomenon of compressibility. How, he wondered, could particles in actual contact be further compressed? How, in fact, could gold exceed water in specific gravity by the margin it did if the fundamental particles were in contact in each case? [11]

More often, Rittenhouse was stimulated by nothing more

[11] John Canton, "Experiments to Prove that Water is not Incompressible," *General Magazine of Arts and Sciences*, 4 (1762), 1071–72; *Phil. Trans.*, 52 (1762), 640–43; Barton, *Memoirs*, 156–57.

specialized than a local newspaper. In the colonies, of course, the newspapers were much more than purveyors of news, serving some of the functions performed by general magazines in England. They printed poetry, literary essays, and even scientific essays which were often copied from some other source. The freshest viewpoints were usually expressed in letters to the editor—although sometimes even these were copied. Rittenhouse regularly read the *Pennsylvania Gazette*, the paper founded by Benjamin Franklin and still one of the better journals in the colonies.

There, on one occasion, the Norriton clockmaker found an anonymous letter on the determination of longitude at sea which angered him. The need for a better means of finding longitude had been recognized by great prizes offered for such a discovery by the British Board of Longitude and was ultimately met by John Harrison's chronometers. It was just the sort of problem that was likely to catch Rittenhouse's attention. The letter had been written in response to a *Pennsylvania Chronicle* essay advocating the use of a sand glass which Rittenhouse recognized as having appeared before in a London paper. Neither the *Gazette* letter, which ridiculed the sand glass but also heaped scorn on Harrison's chronometers, nor the essay was the work of a scientist or even of a man of keen perceptions. Rittenhouse confined his acid remarks to his private correspondence.[12]

Another *Pennsylvania Gazette* letter, by "T. T.," provoked him to a rejoinder which became his first essay in print. Bearing all the marks of having been prompted by his friends, his letter appeared on October 8, 1767, over the signature "A Mechanic." Rittenhouse attacked T. T.'s denial of the practicability of Archimedes' assertion that, given a place to stand, he could move the earth. He did not impugn T. T.'s unsubstantiated figures (to the effect that a man exerting a two hundred-pound force through a rigid lever twelve million billion billion

[12] *Ibid.*, 582–83; *Pa. Chronicle*, June 20, 1768; *Pa. Gaz.*, July 14, 1768.

miles in length could move the earth no more than an inch in two hundred seventy million billion years). Instead, he leaped to a new plane of consideration in a way that became characteristic.[13]

Drawing upon a level of understanding attained after Archimedes' time, Rittenhouse viewed the question in the light of Newtonian mechanics. He pointed out that a two hundred-pound weight falling toward the earth would move the earth toward it even without the intervention of a lever, a fulcrum, or a place to stand. Using T. T.'s estimate of the weight of the earth, Rittenhouse calculated that such a two hundred-pound force would require only one hundred five years to move the earth an inch. This abruptly struck away the vast magnitudes that T. T. had used to reduce the Archimedean statement to an absurdity. Rittenhouse did not, however, present a practical means of moving the earth; he only placed an ancient maxim in a refreshing light.

Rittenhouse's grasp of mathematics, physics, and astronomy so far surpassed that of the men with whom he came in contact that he seldom failed to awaken admiration. Recurring efforts were made to recognize his talents, to bring him into the intellectually richer Philadelphia milieu, and to place him in a remunerative position that would free him for creative activities. Barton and Peters both toyed with projects of this character. From at least as early as 1764, the Proprietary-Anglican group sought some way of providing for the accomplished clockmaker in a fashion familiar to those who knew England. There the creative use of sinecures was practiced in a way that was rarely possible in America.[14]

The Reverend William Smith took up Rittenhouse's cause with especial zeal. Born and educated in Scotland, Smith was a man of conspicuous energy and talent. As provost of the College of Philadelphia, he was the leading intellectual in the church

[13] *Ibid.*, Aug. 20, Oct. 8, 1767.
[14] Barton, *Memoirs*, 150.

circle to which Barton had introduced his brother-in-law. Only five years older than Rittenhouse, Smith had already given clear evidence of his devotion to science by establishing a college curriculum which leaned further in this direction than any other in America. In the city, his success in cultivating a small group of literary aspirants revealed his desire to uncover talent and kindle it into creativeness. Among those he "discovered" in America, none was so promising as David Rittenhouse.

Smith was so impressed by the native-born astronomer that he continuously sought a place for him in the city, although a satisfactory solution eluded him. He was, however, in a position to confer a rather remarkable accolade upon the man. At this time, Rittenhouse had almost no concrete accomplishments. He had written nothing to speak of; he had discovered nothing in science. He had constructed superior clocks and instruments, but his intellectual attainments were visible only to those who could confront him directly. Yet Smith won the approval of the College trustees and faculty to confer upon Rittenhouse an honorary Master of Arts degree. On November 17, 1767, Smith saluted the man he had come to regard as his friend, hailing him before the commencement audience for "extraordinary Merit, and the vast Progress and Improvement . . . made by a Felicity of native Genius, in Mechanics, Mathematics, Astronomy and other liberal Arts; all . . . adorned by singular modesty and irreproachable Morals." [15]

Meanwhile Thomas Barton had taken another route to promote "Davy's" interests by writing directly to Pennsylvania's proprietor in London. He sent Thomas Penn Rittenhouse's description of his projected orrery and received an enthusiastic response. Penn, indeed, seemed to confuse somewhat the plan with the accomplishment, but this may have reflected the manner in which Barton presented it. Penn remarked, "The account you give me of Mr. Rittenhouse's Orrery, is what I could

[15] William Smith, Notes, William Smith Papers, vi, 28, HSP; Trustees Mins., i, 328, 329, 331, Univ. of Pa.; *Pa. Chronicle*, Nov. 23, 1767.

not have imagined could be executed in Pennsylvania; and I shall be much pleased to see a copper-plate of it, for which I would make that gentleman a present, for his encouragement; or, perhaps he may be induced to bring it hither, and exhibit it, by publicly lecturing on it."

Rittenhouse was pleased both by the degree and by the proprietor's letter. He felt he should send Penn "some little instrument" and responded measurably to the thought of visiting England. Most of all, he felt more keenly than ever the urgency of completing his orrery.[16]

His feeling of pressure was increased by the honors he received from Philadelphia's two vigorously contesting scientific societies. The American Society, held at Philadelphia, for Promoting and Propagating Useful Knowledge elected Rittenhouse a corresponding member in its very first selection of non-resident members on March 27, 1767. This group had recently expanded its scope to include broad intellectual objectives and science of all sorts, but its focus remained upon mechanics, agriculture, and advances that might improve the economy. Rittenhouse was exactly the sort of practical man of science it was most anxious to encourage and from whom it expected most.[17]

Rittenhouse was also elected at the first general meeting of the American Philosophical Society on January 19, 1768, his name appearing at the head of a list of eighteen new members. William Smith quickly became one of the leaders of this organization, which proclaimed itself a continuation of Franklin's society of 1743 but which, essentially, began anew at this time. Partly because of Smith's influence, this society was heavily supported by the Anglican-Proprietary-College circles which had been active in promoting Rittenhouse. At the same time, the Philosophical Society boasted several members interested in science and astronomy.[18]

[16] Barton, *Memoirs,* 204n.
[17] Am. Soc. Mins., Mar. 27, 1767, APS.
[18] APS Mins., 1768-69, 6, APS.

Rittenhouse's background and trade gave him more in common with the Quaker, craftsman, merchant group active in the American Society, but his closest intellectual friends were in the Philosophical Society. At Norriton, he was far enough away to escape the sometimes bitter competition between the two groups and to avoid being tarred with either political brush. Before long, however, he was drawn most actively into the circuit of the American Philosophical Society—almost entirely through the assiduous efforts of Smith.

As secretary, Smith was able to introduce Rittenhouse's description of his orrery as the first scientific paper read before the society. This the society heard on March 22 and ordered published in the newspaper the following month after receiving an enthusiastic committee report. The endorsement ran: "Mr. Rittenhouse deserves great applause for having projected so useful and curious a machine, and . . . if it shall answer his Intention, which they have the greatest Reason to expect from his Known abilities, they are of opinion that it will do honor to himself and to this Province." [19]

Publication of the orrery paper in the *Pennsylvania Gazette*, from which it was copied by the *Chronicle*, gave the Philosophical Society a distinct lift in its contest with the rival organization. The American Society enjoyed a temporary advantage because it had been hearing papers for a somewhat longer period and therefore had more of a backlog to present to the public through the press. But because the Philosophical Society had so far produced nothing but political manifestos, Rittenhouse's contribution was the more valuable.[20]

The American Society continued to regard Rittenhouse as one of its own members but had little to document this connection. A mild beat was scored in May by the *Chronicle*, which had become that group's primary organ. It published an extract of a letter from an unnamed but "eminent" London philosopher: "I received yours of Nov. 20, with the Description

[19] *Ibid.*, 15.
[20] *Pa. Gaz.*, Apr. 28, 1768; *Pa. Chronicle*, May 16, 1768.

of a new Orrery, making by Mr. Rittenhouse. I had before heard much of his *Ingenuity;* but this is quite wonderful, to be performed by an American, as it seems to exceed any thing of the Kind that has yet appear'd in Europe." The *Gazette* could then do no better than to reprint the story in its next issue.[21]

Rittenhouse's reputation had been made, but it leaned heavily upon unfulfilled plans. He knew that he could never rest easy until he finished the orrery. Before that major effort could be completed, however, his time was diverted to a project that would brook no excuses and no temporizing. On the very day that his orrery paper was read to the Philosophical Society, the Reverend John Ewing called attention to the transit of Venus, which would occur on June 3, 1769. Rittenhouse was not at liberty to choose. He was expected to rise to this new opportunity and he had no thought of failing to do so.

At Norriton, he scarcely noticed the continuing competition between the two Philadelphia societies or their merger at the end of the year under the comprehensive name, the American Philosophical Society, held at Philadelphia, for Promoting Useful Knowledge. His awakened interest in the coming transit grew without interruption under the stimulus of the united society which, also, became popularly known as the American Philosophical Society.

[21] *Ibid.,* May 16, 1768; *Pa. Gaz.,* May 19, 1768.

CHAPTER IV

Transit of Venus
1769

ON both sides of the Atlantic, remarkable enthusiasm surrounded preparations for observing the transit of Venus of June 3, 1769. This exceedingly rare astronomical event differed from an eclipse only in that Venus appeared so small that it made but a little black dot as it passed across the face of the sun. European nations lavished even more attention on the transit of 1769 than they had on the transit of 1761 in the knowledge that the phenomenon would not recur for another 105 years.

The scientific importance of the event arose from its use in determining the distance, in miles, from the earth to the sun. Once this value was obtained, all of the other distances in the solar system, which were then accurately known only relative to one another, would be known in absolute terms. The techniques of this calculation had not been fully worked out until the eighteenth century, and they embraced two principal methods. The method of durations required that the time needed for Venus to pass across the face of the sun be measured at a known geographical position and compared with similar observations made at another point on the earth. The second method called for recording the exact local time that Venus touched the limb of the sun and comparing it with the same information obtained at a second location. In both cases, the data was used to determine the displacement of the path of Venus seen at one place on the earth's surface from the path seen at another. This yielded the solar parallax, or the angle of the earth's semidiameter seen from the sun, which could easily be expressed in terms of actual distance from the earth to the sun.[1]

In Philadelphia, several factors generated greater interest in the 1769 transit than had arisen in 1761. The rise of two vigorously competing scientific societies following the first transit was one of these. Another was that, although no part of the 1761 transit had been visible in Philadelphia, three-quarters of it could be expected to be visible in 1769. Indeed, in 1761, it had not been possible to see the transit anywhere along the seaboard; the only American observations were made by an expedition to Newfoundland headed by Professor John Winthrop of Harvard College.

Additional impetus came from the greater British effort, which now paced the world. Nevil Maskelyne, astronomer royal of England, prepared instructions for observing the transit in the hope of encouraging Americans as well as other Britishers to participate in the enterprise. However, he did not include Philadelphia among the five American locations for which he predicted the times of contact of Venus with the sun. Indeed, when Maskelyne consulted Benjamin Franklin in an effort to promote an American expedition to observe the transit near Lake Superior, the American agent advised him that Massachusetts was the only province likely to be able to undertake it. The extent of Philadelphia's response surprised both of them.[2]

There, a personal rivalry between the Reverend John Ewing and the Reverend William Smith was almost as effective in stimulating interest as any of the more deep-seated factors— and Smith's involvement guaranteed Rittenhouse's early participation. John Ewing, a very ambitious Presbyterian clergyman with an interest in science, was Smith's subordinate on the College faculty and, like Smith, a secretary of the Philo-

[1] See Harry Woolf, *The Transits of Venus* (Princeton, 1959), 3–22, 148–49; Brooke Hindle, *The Pursuit of Science in Revolutionary America* (Chapel Hill, 1956), 98–99, 146–47.
[2] A. H. Smyth, ed., *The Writings of Benjamin Franklin* (N.Y., 1905–7), v, 137.

sophical Society. On April 19, 1768, he read to the society a letter calling attention to the importance of the coming transit of Venus and urging that the society make "effectual provision" for observing it. He pointed out that the beginning and a great part of the transit would be visible at Philadelphia—barring bad weather. He stressed the benefit to astronomy from a multiplicity of accurate observations made in different parts of the world and compared. The matter was referred to the committee on natural philosophy and astronomy which formulated several plans.[3]

At the ensuing meeting of the society, on May 19, David Rittenhouse made one of his infrequent appearances. Only coincidental business in the city or matters of the highest importance brought him in from Norriton. This time, his interest in the transit was vigorously engaged, and he went to work on the problem immediately.

Rittenhouse did not attend the June meeting, but Smith appeared with several of the aspiring clockmaker's papers. With great delight, he presented his protégé's work, although he was censured by some for using Rittenhouse in this way. There was no doubt that Rittenhouse had now contributed at least as much to buttress Smith's reputation as the College provost could offer in return. Smith reported Rittenhouse's readiness to cooperate in the transit effort by providing much of the equipment needed to conduct observations from his farm. Smith also read and described his friend's projection of Venus' path across the sun, calculated not for Norriton but for Philadelphia.

As soon as Smith had completed his presentation, Ewing took the floor to read the results of his own projection of the transit of Venus. This he offered in the form of a literary essay, whereas Rittenhouse had jotted down little more than the estimate of the time of Venus' initial external contact with the sun derived from data presented in Halley's tables. Ewing went into detail about how he calculated his figures, and he supplied several of

[3] APS Mins., 1768–69, 15.

the parameters. He worked out his answers to many more places than Rittenhouse. Where Rittenhouse gave the initial external ingress contact at 2h. 11 min., Ewing estimated it, with a wholly unwarranted precision, at 2h. 13′ 49″ 28‴. Ewing was careful to remind the society that it was he who had first proposed the transit observations, and he now urged action. He then took advantage of his service as secretary to inscribe his entire paper into the minutes—the only paper so copied except for his original transit proposal of April 19! [4]

Confronted with this vigorous personal competition, the society ordered both the Rittenhouse and the Ewing projections published and appointed two committees to observe, one headed by Ewing and the other by Smith. Ewing, aided by Hugh Williamson, Joseph Shippen, and Thomas Prior, would conduct observations in the city. Smith, accompanied by John Lukens, surveyor general of Pennsylvania, and James Dickinson, would take advantage of Rittenhouse's offer to provide for observations at Norriton. This solution had the scientific merit of avoiding the danger Ewing feared, that a single set of observers might inadvertently lose visual contact with the transit at a critical moment. In addition, the Philadelphia-Norriton split also provided some protection against local cloud cover obscuring the event. The society accepted responsibility for expenses incurred by both groups.

A new element was injected into the discussions in September when James Dickinson proposed a western expedition to observe the transit from James Bay, an arm of Hudson's Bay. He stressed the obvious need for observations made at widely separated points throughout the world. At the same time, he urged the opportunities thus presented for exploring the country. Curiously, he did not mention the one great advantage James Bay observations possessed over any observations that could be made at Philadelphia or at Norriton. The entire transit would be visible there—not just the beginning, which could

[4] *Ibid.*, 16, 17–18; *Pa. Gaz.*, Sep. 15, 1768.

be seen anywhere along the Atlantic coast. For this reason, the Royal Society of London had already planned an expedition to the area—plans which were apparently unknown in Philadelphia.[5]

If the issue of whether to observe a partial transit near the coast or a complete transit far in the American West was ever squarely debated, the debates were not published. There were advantages and disadvantages to each approach. The complete transit had to be observed in order to use the method of durations, and at the same time one set of contacts from the complete transit might also be used in the method of comparing contact times. Hence the observation of the complete transit provided more flexible information. However, scientists seldom used the method of durations. When they could depend upon the precision with which the observatory's longitude had been determined, they preferred to use the method of comparing contact times which rested more heavily upon the longitude factor. Since the longitude of the eastern cities was well established, the method of comparing contact times obtained from observing a partial transit was wholly satisfactory.

There were some reasons, therefore, for favoring eastern observations even over James Bay observations, but it does not appear that these considerations determined the decision. The immediate effect of the Dickinson proposal was to hasten and to color a petition seeking financial support from the Pennsylvania Assembly for observing the transit. Presented by the Philosophical Society on October 15, this paper offered an honest statement of the basic importance of the transit observations as "the best Method of determining the Dimensions of the solar System." At the same time, it contained distinct distortions designed to influence the commercially minded legislators with expectations of utilitarian advantage. With respect to the observations, the casual reader would have assumed that

[5] APS Mins., 1768–69, 24–25; Royal Society Council Minutes, 268, 283, Copy APS.

the society limited its plans to observations at *"Pittsburgh,* Fort *Chartres,* or at any Place on the *Mississippi,* or *Hudson's Bay."* No distinction was made between the first three suggested spots, where the transit would be partial, and the fourth, where it would be total and where—in addition—it would be further displaced in latitude from observations to be made in the southern hemisphere. No mention was made of the well-advanced plans for establishing observatories at Philadelphia and Norriton.[6]

But the petition was well-designed. The Assembly unhesitatingly appropriated £100 for the purchase of a reflecting telescope equipped with micrometer, precisely as requested. It did not immediately respond to the stated need for "proper Provision to defray the Expences of making the necessary observations in as many of the above-mentioned Places as shall appear to them most for the Benefit of the Public in general, and for the Reputation of this Province in particular," but viewed the request for support favorably. The petition stressed as urgent only the need to send to England as soon as possible for a proper telescope. The Assembly deferred action on the less immediate necessity.

The western expedition suffered a curious fate. Unofficially, the Assembly was reported in December to be quite willing to contribute £100 toward an expedition to James Bay, and in February the society submitted a new petition requesting further provision for two projects: the erection of an observatory on State House Square and a western expedition. Without specification, the Assembly granted its second £100, of which the society applied £60 for the construction of the Philadelphia observatory but nothing for the expedition.[7]

Somewhere along the line, the western expedition was lost in the shuffle. The reason given, after the shadowy James Dick-

<hr/>

[6] *Pa. Arch.,* 8th ser., VII, 6288–89.
[7] *Ibid.,* 6359; William Smith to James Hamilton, Dec. 18, 1768, APS Arch.; APS Mins., 1769–74, 17; *Pa. Gaz.,* Mar. 30, 1769.

inson withdrew from the picture, was that John Lukens was not able to make the trip and no other volunteers could be found. At the same time, it was clear that the remaining £40 was not adequate to pay for the proposed trip—in any case, it might better be used for the Norriton observatory.

More important, neither Smith nor Ewing supported the enterprise. Each used all his efforts to advance the observations for which he had specific responsibility. Smith, in particular, with Rittenhouse in his pocket, was not interested in encouraging another competing effort.

Even with Rittenhouse, Smith was faced with difficulty in trying to match the support Ewing had mustered for the Philadelphia observations. All of the money thus far appropriated had gone to Ewing's committee: £100 for the telescope and £60 for the observatory. Against that accomplishment, Rittenhouse was Smith's principal resource. Rittenhouse would build the observatory and manufacture the accessory instruments, but he did not own and could not supply a telescope to match the one ordered by the Assembly. For this, Smith made another approach.

He turned to Thomas Penn, to whose political interests he had already demonstrated a strong attachment and who might readily respond in a competitive fashion to the Assembly's action. Penn did not want the Proprietary interest to suffer by comparison with the party which clustered about Assembly leadership. Even aside from political considerations, the Penns liked to think of themselves as patrons of culture in the province. Besides, Thomas Penn had specifically demonstrated his interest in promoting Pennsylvania observations of the transit. In an earlier letter to Smith, he wrote of Maskelyne's desire that Pennsylvania participate and enclosed some of the astronomer royal's printed directions for observing the event.[8]

Under circumstances that could not have been more encouraging, Smith wrote his appeal immediately following the

[8] APS, *Trans.*, 1 (1771), 10.

Assembly's appropriation for the city telescope. He requested a similar reflecting telescope for the Norriton observatory, and, without a question, Penn donated one, "exact" to Smith's specifications. In the middle of May 1769, it reached Philadelphia, a two-foot Gregorian reflector made by Edward Nairne and equipped with a Dolland micrometer. Penn offered it for the Norriton observations, after which he requested that it be turned over to the College. It was reputed to have cost seventy guineas and provoked much favorable comment in Philadelphia, where it was only slightly exceeded in size and power by the Assembly's telescope.[9]

The rest was up to Rittenhouse. Every piece of equipment that could be found in the city was diverted to the Philadelphia observers in the expectation that Rittenhouse would provide for Norriton's needs. Even several Proprietary instruments were turned over to Ewing: a large astronomical sector, an equal altitude instrument, and a transit instrument. Smith, with many expressions of confidence in his protégé's capacity and reliability, left to him the provision of similar equipment for Norriton.

As early as November 1768, Rittenhouse selected an elevated piece of ground close to his farm house and began to erect a wooden observatory designed to house the new telescope, a clock, and accessory equipment. The roof was provided with a shutter so the telescope might be trained on the sun while the observer stayed inside. Although it was an unpretentious building, a combination of poor weather and disappointing workmen delayed its completion until the middle of April—nearly two months after the Philadelphia observatory was finished.[10]

While this work dragged on, Rittenhouse assembled the needed equipment. He was given some initial hope that an equal altitude instrument might be obtained in Philadelphia.

[9] *Ibid.*, 10–11; Penn to Smith, Mar. 3, 1769, William Smith Papers, Penn Letters, II, 57, HSP; Joseph Shippen, Jr., to Edward Shippen, May 29, 1769, Edward Shippen Papers, LC.
[10] APS, *Trans.*, I (1771), 13.

When this failed to materialize, he set to work on one of very simple construction. Basically, it consisted of a refracting telescope of three-and-one-half-foot focal length with one vertical and two horizontal hairs fixed at its focus. He intended to place it inside the observatory, but because that was not finished in time, he had to put it outside where he affixed it firmly to a stone pedestal. He mounted it so that one screw rotated the instrument on a north-south axis and another on an east-west axis.[11]

This instrument would indicate the time the sun attained the same altitude in the afternoon that it had had at any measured time in the morning. Local noon was established as the point halfway between these recorded times. This was one of the essentials required to give value to the proposed observations of Venus' contacts with the sun.

Rittenhouse also constructed a transit instrument or meridian telescope, which was another small telescope, but mounted so that it rotated on fine steel bearings along the meridian line only. At its focal point, it was equipped with a single vertical hair. To keep the instrument in adjustment, Rittenhouse set up two marks about 330 yards distant—one to the north and the other to the south in an exact meridian line. This device also was intended to check the time of true local noon. By observing the times the eastern and then the western limbs of the sun touched the vertical crosshair in the instrument, the time of noon could be established.

The clock he constructed differed from most of those he had built for sale in that it was designed not for appearance but for precision. A tall clock with a flat steel bar and a twelve-pound bob serving as the pendulum, it had a dead-beat escapement. This was an improved form of the anchor escapement in which there was no recoil or reverse rotation by the clock, a refinement of construction reserved for astronomical clocks. The clock was designed so the pendulum would oscillate in seconds

[11] *Ibid.*, 11.

and so it would not stop or lose time when being wound up. Rittenhouse regretted that he did not have time to install any of the numerous compensating devices that had been invented to correct against expansion and contraction of the pendulum rod with temperature.[12]

One piece of accessory equipment was borrowed for him by John Lukens from William Alexander, self-styled Earl of Stirling and surveyor general of the Province of New Jersey. This was a two-and-one-half-foot astronomical quadrant made by Sisson and belonging to the proprietors of East New Jersey. It was an effective instrument for measuring star angles and useful on this occasion for establishing the latitude of the Norriton observatory.

The major telescopes were less trouble for Rittenhouse. He managed to assemble and set up three which might be used to observe the transit. The reflector sent by Penn remained the best of these—not because of its magnifying power but because of a variety of characteristics including versatility. It had magnifying powers of 55, 95, 130, and 200, but, more important, it was equipped with a superior micrometer permitting a series of measurements that could not be made with the others. Measurement of the distances from one limb of Venus to a limb of the sun would permit determination of the time Venus reached the midpoint of her transit. It would also yield the angular displacement of Venus' path from the sun's limb. As a reflector, the instrument was, in addition, free of the color distortion present in both of the other instruments, which were nonachromatic refractors.

Both of these were substantially similar, one belonging to Rittenhouse himself and the other assembled by him from lenses belonging to Harvard College. The Harvard lenses reached Philadelphia from London in May, too late to be forwarded to Cambridge in time for the transit, whereupon the Philosophical Society leaders decided to "borrow" them for their observa-

[12] *Ibid.*, 12.

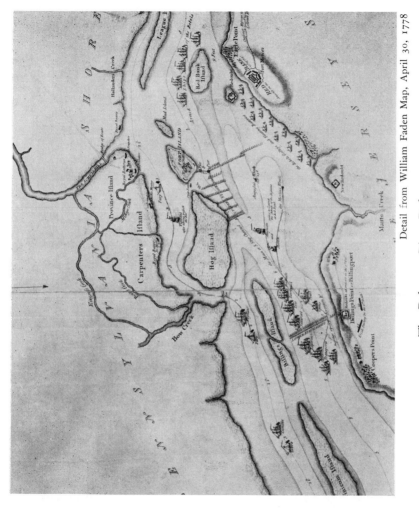

Detail from William Faden Map, April 30, 1778

The Delaware River Defenses

An engraving of a drawing by Benjamin Smith Barton
based on Rittenhouse's memory and "rude sketch."

Ohiopyle Falls
Photograph by the Author

Rittenhouse's Home, Seventh and Mulberry Streets
Watercolor by C. H. Wells, 1857

The Liberty Cap Penny
(enlarged)

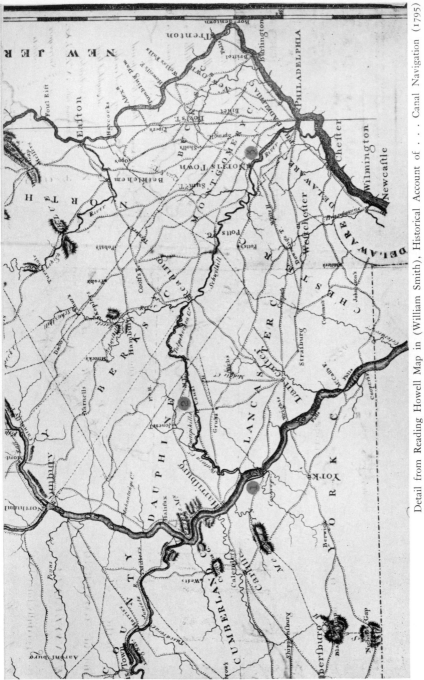

Detail from Reading Howell Map in (William Smith), Historical Account of . . . Canal Navigation (1795)

The Canal Projects of 1792

The projected canals are located at: (1) The Conewago Canal around the Conewago Falls of the Susquehanna River (2) The Susquehanna and Schuylkill Canal between the mouth of the Swatara Creek and Reading (3) The Delaware and Schuylkill Canal from Norristown to Philadelphia.

tions and then to ship them on. Rittenhouse assembled them as a telescope of a forty-two-foot focal length and about 140 power, comparing with his own telescope's thirty-six-foot focal length and power of about 144. When the observatory was ready, he mounted the reflector inside and placed both refractors outside the building.

In February, long before the equipment was in order, Rittenhouse began to make observations preparatory to the transit. His first objective was to establish the longitude of the observatory. To this end, he recorded a series of immersions of the first satellite of Jupiter—that is, he recorded the times at which the satellite moved out of sight behind the body of Jupiter. When he began these observations, he was still unable to establish his local time accurately because his equal altitude telescope was not ready. This was finally mounted on March 19, enabling him to take a series of equal altitudes of the sun approximately three hours before and three hours after noon, yielding for him the time of local noon. With the added assistance of fixed star observations made continuously since February, he was able to convert his initial observations of Jupiter's satellite into accurate local time. It was then necessary only to compare this with the local time of the same events recorded at Greenwich, the zero line of longitude, in order to determine the longitude of Rittenhouse's observatory.[13]

The latitude of the observatory was determined more easily than the longitude by a very direct method. Between May 25 and June 14, Rittenhouse took several observations of the angular distance from the zenith to both the lower and upper limbs of the sun at noon. This, of course, would have yielded the complementary angle to the actual latitude if the readings had been taken at the time of one of the equinoxes. They could be readily adjusted to that season.

A constant error in the quadrant required calibration and correction. By measuring the zenith distances of several stars

[13] *Ibid.*, 14–22.

when facing eastward and comparing these readings with those obtained by facing westward, Rittenhouse discovered an error of 3.5″ in the instrument. This had to be subtracted from all readings obtained when facing west and added to those obtained when facing east. The resultant latitude was 40° 9′ 56.10″.

Rittenhouse discovered a similar constant error in the micrometer of the reflecting telescope, which he checked against a terrestrial mark some 330 yards away. Before sunrise, when the air was most free of distortion and motion, he took ten micrometer readings approaching the mark from the left and ten more approaching it from the right. He established a correction of 1.12″, which had thereafter to be applied to all measurements made with the micrometer.

From April 3 to May 15, Rittenhouse recorded observations of equal altitudes of the sun during the day and immersions of Jupiter's first satellite at night. During this period, he altered the clock several times, cleaned it, installed it finally in the observatory, and regulated it anew. On May 20, he set the clock for the last time as close as he could to mean local time as he had determined it. Thereafter, he did nothing more with the clock except to refine still further his figures on its rate of "going." On May 20, also, he replaced the hairs in the equal altitude instrument with very fine wires.

Then, for several weeks—until over a month after the transit took place—Rittenhouse attempted to take three continuing series of observations. In addition to the equal altitudes of the sun and the immersions of Jupiter's satellite, he recorded meridian observations of the sun made with the transit instrument. Unfortunately, his health interfered with this strenuous schedule. From May 21 until two days after the transit, he was too ill to sit up at night for the observations of Jupiter's satellite. He continued the daytime observations, and nothing was lost from his failure to observe at night; the longitude of Norriton could be obtained at any time.

Yet, Rittenhouse's illness was significant. It began just about two weeks before the event for which he had been preparing so energetically. There is no indication of the nature of this sickness, but he frequently suffered from colds and coughs and he would not have been likely to give up night observations merely because of increased duodenal pains. More probably, he had a respiratory complaint with attendant fever which made a long vigil in the night air seem foolhardy.

On Thursday afternoon, June 1, William Smith and John Lukens rode up to the Norriton farm, ready to take part in the transit observations. They were delighted to find the instruments in the finest condition and state of readiness. Little remained to be done except to adjust each piece to the vision and preference of the observer who was going to use it. Smith would be stationed at the reflector in the observatory and Rittenhouse and Lukens at the refractors outside.

Despite the perfection of preparations, a deep gloom surrounded the men as they contemplated the weather, which might so easily frustrate all of their hopes. That day and several preceding had been generally overcast with frequent heavy rains. In fact, since the Wednesday of the week before, Rittenhouse had been able to get equal altitudes of the sun on only one day. Then suddenly, on Thursday evening, "the weather became perfectly clear, and continued the day following, as well as the day of the Transit, in such a state of serenity, splendor of sunshine, and purity of atmosphere, that not the least appearance of a cloud was to be seen." [14]

On Friday and on Saturday, the transit day, last-minute adjustments were made. The foci of the telescopes were marked, supports were contrived for the ends of the refractors which would permit them to move in an approximation of an arc paralleling the ecliptic, and the micrometer of the reflector was tested by taking several measurements of the diameter of the sun. Smoked glasses were mounted on all the telescopes.

By Saturday, many people had congregated at the Norriton

[14] *Ibid.*, 23; Smith to Penn, June 8, 1769, Smith Papers, III, 96, HSP.

farm, and several of them were assigned important duties in connection with the crucial observations. Smith, inside the observatory, would require no aid for he could hear the second ticks of the clock and would record his own times. Lukens and Rittenhouse, at some distance from the building, each planned to use three assistants. One assistant was required to bolster the observer's head as he lay on the flat of his back, a position forced by the great altitude of the sun at the time the transit was expected to begin. This service was performed for Rittenhouse by his brother-in-law, Thomas Barton, who had come in from Lancaster for the occasion. Two additional assistants were required for each telescope to stand at an observatory window and receive the visual signal of contact. Members of Rittenhouse's family performed this service for him while John Sellers, a member of the Norriton observation committee, and Archibald McClean, a surveyor, aided Lukens.[15]

Smith was perturbed by the growing crowd of people who hung around without any duties to perform and without any clear understanding of what was going on. Most of them were local farmers who had been excited by the bustle of preparation and by what they had heard of the plans. They were not at all unruly, but there was serious danger that someone might call out when the observers gave their visual signals of contact. If that should happen, the hope of three entirely independent observations would be destroyed. The people were strictly warned, therefore, that they must maintain a profound silence until the contacts were over; this they did with an exemplary patience. Not a whisper or a word was heard for several critical minutes.

Rittenhouse had predicted the initial, external contact of Venus with the sun at 2:11 P.M., but long before that time the observers were eagerly scanning the sun's limb for the first hint of an impression by the planet. The field of the refracting telescopes was so small that there was a chance the observers

[15] APS, *Trans.*, 1 (1771), 24-25.

might be looking at the wrong spot when Venus first came into view. This, in fact, is just what happened to Lukens, and he missed the initial indications of contact. Smith used the 95 power magnification of his telescope—rather than the two more powerful combinations available to him—precisely so that the larger size of his field would provide protection against this sort of hazard. Within a half minute of 2:11 P.M., Smith called out to the watchers at the observatory windows, warning them to be attentive.

At this crucial moment of anticipation, something happened to David Rittenhouse. Benjamin Rush later said, "it excited—in the instant of one of the contacts of the planet with the sun, an emotion of delight so exquisite and powerful, as to induce fainting." William Barton was ready to accept that explanation for he reprinted it without demur. Such a lapse of consciousness is all the more believable in view of the illness Rittenhouse had been fighting for the preceding week.[16]

His own report of the observation was eloquent in its omissions. The second, internal contact he described in elaborate detail. Of the nature of the initial, external contact, he said absolutely nothing. He remarked curiously that—to the best of his judgment—the contact occurred three seconds before the signal Barton reported to the assistants at the observatory window.[17]

Yet, the signal Barton transmitted from Rittenhouse was given much earlier than the corresponding signal from either Smith or Lukens, whose telescope had almost identical optical characteristics, and who delayed reporting contact some seconds after he finally got Venus in his field of vision. Rittenhouse's signal came thirty seconds before Lukens' and thirty-two before Smith's. He must have been alert up to that point, but afterward he recorded no impressions until Venus had advanced about one-third of its diameter over the surface of

[16] Rush, *Eulogium*, 12; Barton, *Memoirs*, 183.
[17] APS, *Trans.*, 1 (1771), 26–28.

the sun—about six or seven minutes later. This complete lack of comment upon phenomena which were unexpected and much debated was utterly unlike Rittenhouse. There is little doubt that he was unconscious as Rush reported, or otherwise disengaged from visual observation, for this period of six or seven minutes.

The tension and emotional strain upon Rittenhouse had been enormous. He was more deeply involved and more personally committed than any of the other observers. He alone had built and prepared the observatory. He had made the preliminary calculations and projections upon which the entire group based its efforts. He was regarded as the expert. He must in his observations sustain his remarkable reputation for genius in astronomy which was up to now based upon very little in the way of concrete accomplishment.

Rittenhouse was a man of strong and deep-running, but suppressed, feelings. His ulcer indicates an ability to keep a tight grip upon his external emotions but not to prevent their breaking out in psychosomatic effects. His illness at the time of the transit made some sort of uncontrollable reaction still more understandable. Not only was his own personal reputation at stake in this event but his sense of history weighed heavily upon him. Precise observations were essential for the advancement of science and for the maintenance of national and provincial reputations. There was no question of his will breaking under the strain, but, by comparison with his will, his body was feeble.

This crisis of tension was brought to an almost intolerable intensity in the terrifying appearance of Venus on the sun. Whatever he had read about the experiences of observers of the 1761 transit, Rittenhouse was unprepared for the yawning uncertainty of the exact moment at which he must declare that Venus had first touched the sun. There was no single, identifiable point of time at which he could pronounce the two in contact. The phenomenon was not one of two circles moving toward one another until they attained a moment of tangency. Venus, in fact, was altogether invisible as it approached the sun. The first hint of its presence reported by any of the observers was a faint, tremulous motion which appeared at one portion of the firmly defined limb of the sun. This was followed by a pointed, jagged, slowly growing shadow and by a larger arc of the sun's limb becoming tremulous. Finally, a sharp black dent appeared on the sun, but, by that time, the moment of tangency had clearly passed.

When should the contact be reported? The first tremor seemed too early but surely the black dent was too late and there was a long period of time between them. Smith said that the first indications he had of Venus' presence appeared twenty-two seconds before he reported contact. But Rittenhouse demanded of himself and of his instrument a precise moment of time. A contact reported with a margin of error of twenty or thirty seconds would be so fuzzy as to have little value. Moreover, he had no time to think about it or to weigh the possibilities. He had only one chance to report the time of this contact for the phenomenon would not recur in his lifetime.

He waited for three seconds after he had seen the first tremor and then reported his contact. Apparently, his keener, more practiced eye picked up an indication of Venus before either of his colleagues, but this greater skill was not enough to convince him that he had judged correctly. After giving his signal, he fainted—not as Rush said in "an emotion of delight"—but in an agony of uncertainty.

By the time he had recovered sufficiently to be able to continue his observations, he found that Venus had advanced one-third of her diameter over the face of the sun. Suddenly, he perceived a pyramid of light on the side of Venus not yet entered on the sun, the base of which was an arc of the limb of Venus. The light did not yet entirely surround Venus, but the pyramid slowly decreased in height and its base increased in length as another arm of light reached around the off-side of Venus from the opposite direction. By the time half of Venus was on the sun, the other half was surrounded by an unbroken halo of light.

European scientists had placed more emphasis upon the second contact because they felt it could be identified with greater precision. The tension mounted again. The presence of the halo seemed to Rittenhouse to obscure the moment of internal contact of Venus and the sun—but it was only a relatively minor hazard. More ominous was the "black drop" effect which plagued all of the observers. Even after Venus appeared to have entered fully onto the face of the sun, it remained connected to the outer void beyond by a black thread or ligament. Long after the limbs of Venus and the sun appeared to have passed their moment of interior tangency, the black ligament remained. When it finally broke, Venus showed as a black circle some distance within the outer periphery of the sun.

Rittenhouse attempted to judge the moment at which the limb of Venus became tangent to an imaginary projection of the limb of the sun—projected through the halo surrounding the planet and prior to the formation of the black drop. He counted off no less than 1′ 32″ after this instant before the black drop disappeared "leaving that part of the limb as well defined as the rest." When he learned the contact times reported by his colleagues, he was forced to conclude that he had again reported the contact too early.

This was the great moment! Beyond recall, it quickly slipped off into the deep abyss of time past. Nothing could be changed; nothing repeated. What was done was past, and each of the observers had a sinking sensation as he realized that the transit contacts had been recorded with none of the hoped for precision and decisiveness. How could they know which of them had judged correctly? They spoke of the effects of Venus' atmosphere, of the effects of the different optical characteristics of the telescopes, and of the still different times that would have been yielded if the sun had been lower in the sky, but they remained uncertain.

Rittenhouse's predictions had turned out brilliantly, his instruments had performed perfectly, and his own skill of eye was manifestly superlative. Yet this, he now knew, was not enough. Not only were his contacts and the contacts of his colleagues of dubious certainty but so must be all those obtained throughout the world. Every contact time would have to be stated in terms of a margin of error which removed it from any hope of pinpoint accuracy. Even accepting this ludicrously large margin of error, he was uncertain whether he had chosen the same phase of the phenomenon to brand the contact as other observers had.

In fact, he had not. Astronomers generally agreed that the internal contact occurred when the black drop broke. They were wrong, because this phenomenon varied in time with optical factors. Nevertheless, Rittenhouse's internal contact was rendered less comparable to others by his failure to follow the trend. Realizing this possibility, he also set down his black drop time but that was not the one usually picked up for comparative calculations.[18]

The Norriton astronomer's thoughts were so tangled with emotion that it was fortunate he still had a large amount of routine work to complete before the enterprise would be over.

[18] Simon Newcomb, "Discussion of Observations of the Transits of Venus in 1761 and 1769," *Astronomical Papers Prepared for the Use of the American Ephemeris and Nautical Almanac* (Washington, 1891), II, 265.

CHAPTER V

Astronomy and Reputation

1769–1770

FOR David Rittenhouse, the transit of Venus was the great moment from which all roads to the future led. The critical minutes of contact were quickly passed, but, in another sense, the transit of Venus would remain part of David Rittenhouse for the rest of his life. For a time, however, it was not clear what meaning his participation in the great event would assume.

Much depended upon the manner in which the supplemental observations connected with the transit were completed and even more upon their interpretation and presentation both to the lay public and to the learned world. All the observers participated in the first phase of the additional observations.

Even after the contacts, observations of Venus on the sun were continued until both dropped below the horizon. For this work, neither Rittenhouse's nor Lukens' telescope had any value for neither was equipped with a micrometer and thus could not be used to measure angular distances. Now, the greatest advantage of Smith's instrument became effective, enabling him to supply most of the values recorded during the afternoon. Rittenhouse and Lukens took their turns at the reflector, and both obtained some readings in each of three series of measurements. Most useful were the distances, measured every eight or ten minutes, between the nearest limbs of Venus and the sun. Occasionally, measurements were also made of the distances of the limbs along a line parallel to the equator. Finally, the diameters of Venus and the sun were measured several times—yielding results that showed the sun to be more than a second of arc larger than predicted and Venus about a second smaller.[1]

With the reflecting telescope in Smith's hands for most of the afternoon, Rittenhouse attempted to extract similar measurements from his equal altitude instrument. He gathered a series of values for the distances from the limb of the sun to the center of Venus. Later comparisons revealed these measurements to be so inferior to those obtained with Smith's telescope that they were discarded.[2] No other result could have been anticipated, but Rittenhouse did obtain alternative data for plotting the path of Venus across the sun from a rather unlikely source. More important, he kept himself occupied.

When at last the sun set, the observers divided up the work that remained. As "chairman" of the Norriton observation group, Smith planned to write the final report and for that purpose collected copies of all the data obtained. Rittenhouse would carry through some of the computations and all of the additional observations needed to establish the longitude of the observatory.

Rittenhouse devoted over a month to this tedious business. He continued to shoot the sun with his equal altitude instrument and his meridian telescope. Many nights he spent observing the eclipses of Jupiter's satellites. Once his attention was directed to the reflector in response to a letter from Smith. The Philadelphian was still concerned about the one second difference between his measurement of the sun's diameter and the value given in the *Nautical Almanac*. Rittenhouse's recheck yielded the same figure once again.[3] Before the middle of July, he completed all of the calculations he could undertake without transit data from other parts of the world.

The micrometer measurements produced a satisfying and consistent track of Venus across the sun, which Rittenhouse

[1] APS, *Trans.*, 1 (1771), 33–34.
[2] *Ibid.*, 35.
[3] Barton, *Memoirs*, 173n.

plotted on paper with some pleasure. Using his best figure for the closest observed approach of centers of Venus and the sun, he laid off a chord to represent the path of Venus across the face of the sun. Then, marking distances based on the theoretical speed of Venus, he plotted the successive positions of the planet according to the Norriton measurements of least distances of the limbs of the two bodies. The results were beautiful. Fourteen of the eighteen measurements placed Venus' center almost exactly on the projected transit line. The others were not more than a second off and equally divided in their divergences. The less frequent measurements made from the sun's equator also checked closely.[4]

On the basis of this graphic projection and the figures behind it, Rittenhouse then calculated several of the elements of Venus' orbit. They had all been previously estimated, but he discovered one discrepancy with the value derived from Halley's tables for the place of Venus at the time of the ecliptic conjunction. His figure differed from this by ten seconds of time—an opportunity to make a slight adjustment in the theory of Venus' orbit.

Working through the summer in Norriton, Rittenhouse was removed from the emotion and intrigue that surrounded the disposition of the transit reports in Philadelphia. One of the Philadelphia observers made an immediate error in reporting contact times "within a few seconds" in the *Pennsylvania Chronicle* of June 5. The paper was called to account because of the looseness of this language; so large and indefinite a margin of error was simply not acceptable. The damage done was not rectified by the explanation run in the following issue, to the effect that the imprecise language had been necessary because the going of the clock had not then been positively verified. The much more guarded statement in the *Gazette* of June 8 reflected an agreement among the three groups of observers to withhold "an authentic Account" until all the information had

[4] APS, *Trans.*, I (1771), 36–38, Plate III.

been digested. Ewing and Smith were especially determined to take no misstep. Each intended to use the observations to bolster his own reputation.

On the same day that the *Gazette* denied specific information to the public, Smith sent a very detailed report to Thomas Penn in London. He included numerical details and dwelt extensively upon the contributions of David Rittenhouse, "a Gentleman who to a complete skill in Mechanics, has joined so deep a Skill in Mathematical and Astronomical Subjects that the Construction Use and Management of all the necessary Instruments were perfectly familiar to Him." His "Skill and Exactness" in calculation was equally noteworthy.[5] Smith was not as generous to the Philadelphia observers, whom he did not inform of this letter and whose work he did not mention to Penn.

The rivalry between Smith and Ewing came into the open at the June 16 meeting of the American Philosophical Society, when each man reported himself unready to give an account of the transit observation.[6] Their motives were worthy enough; they wanted to complete several sets of calculations and to have their reports in good form. At the same time, their guarded behavior contrasted sharply with that of Owen Biddle, who gave a report on the society's third set of observations which he and Joel Bailey had made at the Delaware Capes. The Biddle and Bailey report was not nearly so complete as those ultimately made by Smith and Ewing. Indeed, it contained errors which soon required an amended report.

Yet this episode merely confirmed the suspicions of that vinegary old Quaker, Dr. Cadwalader Evans, who knew much more of the human character than he did of the science of astronomy. On his own, and unannounced to the society, he forwarded a copy of the Biddle and Bailey report to Franklin in London four days before it was presented at the meeting. He conveyed at the same time his revulsion against the behavior

[5] Smith to Penn, June 8, 1769, Smith Papers, III, 97, HSP.
[6] APS Mins., 1769-74, 33-43.

of Smith and Ewing, whom he felt ever ready to "filch reputation" from their associates in order to advance themselves. Totally unacquainted with the techniques of observation, he interpreted the fact that Smith and Ewing each lagged behind some of their fellows in reporting the first contact of Venus with the sun as an indication of their ineptitude. He bridled at newspaper accounts which always placed Smith's and Ewing's names first in their lists of observers. This he considered an affront to all the other observers but to none so much as David Rittenhouse, who was "incompareably the best Mathematician, and [who] used ye instrument with the utmost dexterity." [7]

A month later at the Philosophical Society meeting of July 20, both Smith and Ewing presented their completed reports.[8] Smith's account included much of Rittenhouse's work: the fundamentally important projection of the transit and the calculation of the elements of Venus' orbit as well as Rittenhouse's own account of instruments and observations. Throughout, Smith was assiduous in giving credit to his associate. Nevertheless, Rittenhouse was not entirely satisfied and may have been afflicted by some of the doubts old Evans expressed so openly. He wrote to his brother-in-law, "The Doctor has constantly seemed so desirous of doing me justice in the whole affair, that I suppose I must not think of transmitting any separate account to England." [9] Obviously, he had thought of just this and had decided against it.

Smith's next move was to oppose Dr. Thomas Bond's suggestion that both the Philadelphia and Norriton accounts now be sent to Franklin for publication in the *Philosophical Transactions* of the Royal Society. He argued that the transit observations would shortly appear as the nucleus of the first volume of the society's *Transactions* and that preliminary publication elsewhere would lessen the value of this work. His view

[7] Evans to Franklin, June 11, 1769, Franklin Papers, II, 180, APS.
[8] APS Mins., 1769–74, 48–71.
[9] Barton, *Memoirs*, 174n.

carried the meeting, but the failure to transmit the accounts did not have precisely the effect Smith predicted.[10] The Norriton account, sent privately by Smith, and the Lewes account, sent privately by Evans, both reached the Royal Society and were published in the fifty-ninth volume of the *Philosophical Transactions*. Bound by the Philosophical Society vote, Ewing did not forward the Philadelphia account until January 1770, when he informed Franklin of the "rash decision" to withhold the accounts.[11] His arrived too late to be included with the other accounts and consequently never appeared in that journal. This unfortunate result might more readily be interpreted as a matter of miscalculation except for other cases of duplicity attached to the activities of William Smith.

One effect of these maneuvers was to bring Smith and his Norriton associates more specific accolades from the astronomer royal than he gave to the other groups. In response to Penn's initial communication of the skeletal results, Nevil Maskelyne declared, "[the observations] seem *excellent* and *compleat*, and do honor to the gentlemen who made them." When Smith sent him the full report, he returned his personal thanks for "the account of the *valuable* observations." He was especially pleased with the description of optical phenomena attributed to Venus' atmosphere by the Norriton observers because he himself had not observed these appearances in England, where the transit had occurred at a very low altitude. With growing satisfaction, he compared the immersions and emersions of Jupiter's first satellite, most of them obtained by Rittenhouse, with both the *Nautical Almanac* and his own personal observations. The resulting longitude agreed "to a second" with that derived in the Norriton report.[12]

One distinct error he charged, and that attributable to David Rittenhouse. Rittenhouse, he said, had based his projection

[10] Evans to Franklin, Nov. 27, 1769, Franklin Papers, II, 201, APS.
[11] Ewing to Franklin, Jan. 4, 1770, Franklin Papers, III, 1, APS.
[12] APS, *Trans.*, 1 (1771), 40-41, Appendix, 1-4.

upon an estimated 8.65″ for the sun's mean horizontal parallax, but 8.65″ was the parallax of the day of the transit of 1761 as determined by Short—and by himself. Based on this figure, the mean parallax would then have been 8.84″. Rittenhouse had taken the wrong figure!

The charge was easy to refute. Smith and Rittenhouse conferred about this, but Smith wrote the reply which was published with Maskelyne's letter in the Philosophical Society's *Transactions* of 1771. He had only to refer directly to the *Philosophical Transactions*, where Short had stated baldly, "The parallax of the Sun being thus found by the observations of the internal contact at the egress 8″,52, on the day of the transit, the mean horizontal parallax of the Sun is 8″,65." [13] Had Maskelyne been napping? Had he taken a figure from a different set of data? In any case, there could be no question but that Rittenhouse had used the best figure offered in the Short article.

Toward the end of the transit summer, Rittenhouse was pulled out of Pennsylvania to participate in the drawing of the New York-New Jersey boundary line. He was not a boundary commissioner of either colony nor did he remain for the tedious process of marking off the line. He was called upon for the essential determination of the latitude at either end of the line. In this work, he cooperated with some of the most distinguished army surveyors and engineers in America.

The beginning was made on September 10 at a temporary observatory established near the Hudson River at an approximation of the forty-first parallel, the point defined as the eastern extremity of the boundary. There Rittenhouse spent four days with Captain John Montresor, Captain Samuel Holland, and Alexander McClean, whom Rittenhouse had brought along as an assistant. Rittenhouse used the best available instrument— the same astronomical sector Mason and Dixon had depended upon in marking the Pennsylvania-Maryland boundary. He

[13] *Ibid.*, Appendix, 3n.; *Phil. Trans.*, 52 (1762), 621.

was surprised, however, to find that Holland's smaller quadrant, made by Bird, had the same order of accuracy. The two did not differ by more than 17".[14]

Subsequent calculations revealed that the forty-first parallel was located 1' 22" south of the observatory. With one end of the line established, Montresor, McClean, and Rittenhouse set out for the other end, the junction of the present Neversink River with the Delaware. By September 24, they were taking observations there. They found this latitude more quickly, and after leaving the line, returned to the New York area again.[15]

Two more latitudes were established, neither of them related to the boundary line. On October 4 and 5, the group took observations at the Sandy Hook lighthouse, fixing its latitude at 40° 27' 40". Four days later, at the request of the newly formed Chamber of Commerce of the City of New York, they established the latitude of the southwest bastion of Fort George —then scheduled for renovation under Montresor's direction.[16] After much more riding, conversation, and sightseeing than was usual with him, Rittenhouse returned to Norriton leaving behind him an aura of esteem.

He got home less than a month before the transit of Mercury of November 9, 1769, laid new demands upon him and upon most of those who had participated in the transit of Venus observations. The observatories, instruments, and techniques used for the transit of Venus were all equally suitable for observing the transit of Mercury. In both events, the planet passed between the earth and the sun, but the transit of Mercury did not offer comparable data because the planet remained too far from the earth. Observations of Mercury's transit would be valuable primarily for correcting or verifying the theory of Mercury's

[14] *Ibid.*, 64 (1774), 173; Willis Chipman, "The Life and Times of Major Samuel Holland," Ontario Hist. Soc., *Papers and Records*, 21 (1924), 34; *N. J. Arch.*, 1st ser., xxvi, 462.
[15] William Alexander, Journal, 91, 99, NYHS.
[16] *Ibid.*, 102; I. N. Phelps Stokes, *Iconography of Manhattan Island* (N.Y., 1902), IV, 798; V, 1593, 2056.

orbit and at another time might not have attracted much attention. On this occasion, the opportunity for exercising available facilities upon a second astronomical event was too obvious to be permitted to pass.

Widely heralded in the newspapers, the occasion generated renewed interest in astronomy throughout the colonies. This time the weather was less favorable, totally frustrating the New York and Connecticut efforts. Successful observations were made in Massachusetts, Rhode Island, and Pennsylvania, where the Philosophical Society again took command.[17]

The Philadelphia and Norriton observatories were manned much as before, but no third expedition was sent out. Philadelphia was in some respects better equipped than it had been during the transit of Venus observations. Ewing, again in charge of that post, emphasized especially the new astronomical clock constructed by Samuel Duffield, which was equipped with a compensating pendulum.[18] Not even Rittenhouse's clock could yet boast such a device. In addition, the Philadelphians had the use of the Library Company's 150-power reflecting telescope, which Owen Biddle had used at the Capes in June.

Biddle himself went to Norriton to observe with Smith, Lukens, and Rittenhouse. Thus, except for Ewing, all of the more qualified observers were concentrated at Rittenhouse's farm, where there were not enough telescopes to go around. Biddle helped out in a variety of ways and the other three used the instruments assembled for the transit of Venus. Surprisingly, the telescope constructed with the Harvard lenses had not yet been disassembled and sent on. Indeed, Franklin in London continued to be at a loss to account to John Winthrop for the whereabouts of the lenses.[19] After the transit of Mer-

---

[17] N.Y. Gaz. and Weekly Mercury, Oct. 30, Nov. 13, 1769; Pa. Gaz., Oct. 26, 1769; Conn. Courant, Nov. 13, 1769; Phil. Trans., 61 (1771), 51–52; APS Mins., 1769–74, 78–80; Ezra Stiles, Notes on Transit of Mercury, Stiles MSS, Yale.
[18] APS, Trans., 1 (1771), 82.
[19] MHS, Proc., 15 (1876–77), 12.

cury, they were forwarded—but not in any great hurry for they did not reach Cambridge till the end of the following May.

The transit of Mercury did not present the same observational difficulties involved in the transit of Venus. Primarily because Mercury has no atmosphere, it made a sharper and less uncertain contact with the sun's limb. The result was apparent in the contact times reported. All three observers agreed to the second on the external contact and differed by only two seconds on the internal contact. This simultaneity might have cast doubt on the independence of the observations except for Smith's stress on the measures taken to avoid any communication and for similar results obtained at other stations.[20]

Despite intermittent clouds which prevented micrometer measurements of Mercury's position on the sun for about an hour, a good track of the transit was obtained. Again, Rittenhouse's transit telescope yielded data of secondary importance. The most significant result of the Norriton observations was the discovery that Mercury made her contacts with the sun about four minutes ahead of the times predicted by Edmund Halley. This discrepancy led Lalande to examine the American observations with considerable care. In the end, however, he decided not to correct the tables.[21]

In these observations, Smith again made good use of Rittenhouse to boost his own reputation but at the same time he, more than anyone else, was responsible for establishing the reputation of David Rittenhouse. He not only brought him to the attention of Pennsylvania's proprietor and defended him from an unjust accusation by the astronomer royal, but he did much to create an adulatory attitude in Philadelphia. Rittenhouse emerged as the greatest single hero of the transit observations, and his projected orrery appeared a design that almost passed understanding. In so favorable an atmosphere, Smith decided

[20] APS, *Trans.*, 1 (1771), 50–54.
[21] *Mémoires de l'Acadèmie* (1772), 451.

to strike for a more substantial and useful accolade than any yet bestowed upon the Norriton clockmaker.

For many reasons, Smith had long desired to have his friend move to the city, where he could enhance Philadelphia's intellectual circle at the same time that he improved his own opportunities. The chief problem had always been economic. At Norriton, Rittenhouse lived comfortably, supported by the sale of clocks and the produce of his farm, to which he added more acreage early in 1770.[22] Not only would this pattern be disrupted by a move, but city living costs were distinctly higher. To Smith, the answer seemed obvious. Rittenhouse's worth called out for public encouragement and his need demanded financial aid. Surely some office within the gift of the Pennsylvania government could be offered to the talented clockmaker. It would not have to be a sinecure without duties for such posts were almost non-existent in the colonies. Yet, some appointments carried relatively light duties which would have freed Rittenhouse to devote a significant portion of his time to science.

In January, Smith heard of just such an office. His opportunity was created when the Pennsylvania Assembly took up a resolution calling for the emission of £120,000 in bills of credit secured by loans on real property and requiring the appointment of Loan Office trustees to handle the business involved.[23] This was a post similar to that projected by Barton and Peters for Rittenhouse back in 1767. Now Rittenhouse was more favorable to the project and external circumstances were very much more promising.

Smith lobbied effectively at several levels. He began by suggesting to his neighbors, "the Wissahickon millers," that Rittenhouse's name be put into the bill as Loan Office trustee.[24] He then called upon the speaker of the Assembly, Joseph Gal-

[22] Indenture between David Rittenhouse and Matthias and Elizabeth Rittenhouse, Jan. 12, 1770, Photocopy, HSP.

[23] Pa. Arch., 8th ser., VII, 6473, 6476.

[24] Barton, Memoirs, 209.

70

loway, to whom he presented the same sort of pragmatic arguments he had used so successfully in getting money from the Assembly for the transit of Venus observations. He suggested that Rittenhouse might inaugurate the manufacture of optical and mathematical instruments in Philadelphia. This would be a new enterprise in colonial America and would save some of the thousands of pounds drained off to England each year in the purchase of such items. Like everyone else approached, Galloway responded enthusiastically. When the vote was taken, the house unanimously approved Rittenhouse—although not the other two trustees nominated. Chief Justice William Allen observed, "Our name is Legion for this vote," and the Council was "hearty" for Rittenhouse. Even Governor John Penn protested his desire to show his regard for Rittenhouse when Smith cornered him on the subject.[25]

Thomas Barton wrote to Smith, "I cannot think of words strong enough to express my gratitude," and Rittenhouse's sister, Esther, "shed tears of gratitude." [26] The prospect of an undemanding job which carried a £200 salary was enough to awaken such delight—but, unfortunately, it all came to naught. It was wrecked upon the shoals of the perennial conflict between assembly and governor.

The trouble lay in the Assembly's demand that it name appointees to offices created by its legislation—a demand rejected by the governor. The governor refused his assent to the Loan Office bill because it was cast in this form, and the Assembly refused to delete the names of the trustees. Thus the bill did not become law, the office was not created, and Rittenhouse was denied an appointment which men of opposing political allegiances had united in seeking for him.

William Smith was by no means deterred by this setback. He continued to urge Rittenhouse to move to the city, predicting that something else of a similar character would be found

[25] *Ibid.*, 210–11.
[26] *Ibid.*, 212, 213.

for him. More and more, Rittenhouse bent to these entreaties, but in February he was so depressed by poor health and by the failure of the Loan Office project that he wrote Barton, "If I live to write again, you shall know more of my mind." [27] Meanwhile, he devoted every extra minute to the orrery.

The long-extended transit demands had impeded this work but, except for brief periods, had not brought it to a stop. Those who observed the transit at Norriton had an opportunity to examine and admire the work already completed on the incredible machine. Everyone offered encouragement but no one was ready with a firm commitment of purchase. Smith continued to assert that, if the Assembly did not take it, the College of Philadelphia would. Yet, especially after the failure of the Loan Office project, his will seemed something distinctly different from accomplished fact.

At this point, the Reverend John Witherspoon entered the picture. Witherspoon was a Scottish Presbyterian minister, recently come to America to assume the presidency of the College of New Jersey. He immediately recognized the importance of the orrery, and his interest rose despite the meager resources of his College. One Saturday in April he rode out to Norriton with a few of the College trustees to discuss the matter with Rittenhouse.[28] After bestowing effusive praise upon the machine, he quickly offered to purchase it if Rittenhouse were not under any other obligation. The aspiring clockmaker said he was not and soon agreed to sell it for the sum of £300. He agreed also to several conditions: he would not sell another orrery for a smaller sum, he would complete this device in accord with the account presented to the Philosophical Society, and he would add any improvements he later devised.[29]

The sale price was large on two counts. First, the trustees of the College of New Jersey had just a few months earlier appro-

[27] *Ibid.*, 214n.
[28] *Pa. Gaz.*, Apr. 26, 1770.
[29] Barton, *Memoirs*, 215.

priated £250 for the purchase of all the "philosophical apparatus" required.[30] At the time, the College was woefully deficient in all sorts of instruments and equipment. Just as striking was the comparison with the price of European orreries which could be purchased for a fraction of the sum offered for Rittenhouse's machine; Benjamin Martin offered none at a higher rate than £150.[31] The belief that Rittenhouse's orrery would be "more complete than anything of the Kind ever made in Europe" did not entirely account for the price differential. Witherspoon was sincerely anxious to "encourage so truly great a Genius." [32] He also understood that his action would bring a measure of credit to the College which no collection of common instruments and no orrery of Martin's manufacture could have accomplished.

William Smith was furious about the transaction. "I never met with greater mortification," he wrote to Barton and immediately visited Rittenhouse in an effort to straighten the matter out. He blamed his friend directly only to the extent of saying, "[he] was never so little *himself*, as to suffer himself to be taken off guard on this occasion." Witherspoon was the real serpent. According to Smith, Rittenhouse on his own came to the conclusion "that he had gone too far" and readily agreed to write Witherspoon "that Smith claimed a former promise." [33] Witherspoon remained unmoved in the certain confidence that Rittenhouse would never think of backing out of his agreement.

Much disturbed, Rittenhouse wrote to his brother-in-law, "I would not, on any account, incur the imputation of cunning; nor are there, probably many persons living who deserve it less." Indeed, Smith did not press an earlier agreement upon

[30] Howard Rice, Notes on Mins. of Trustees, College of N.J. for Sep. 29, 1769, Princeton.

[31] Benjamin Martin, *The Description and Use of Both the Globes, the Armillary Sphere, and Orrery* (London, n.d.), Appendix, 1–3.

[32] *Pa. Gaz.*, Apr. 26, 1770.

[33] Barton, *Memoirs*, 215n.–16n.; William Shippen to Edward Shippen, Jr., May 3, 1770, Shippen Papers, VII, 23, HSP.

73

Rittenhouse for there had been none. He stressed instead the foolishness of letting this magnificent device go to a "village" before any genuine effort had been made to sell it to his friends in the city. More petulantly still, he suggested that the craftsman had injured himself in making an arrangement which would remove the orrery from display in the city where it might have generated commissions for instruments. Not accepting this line of argument, Rittenhouse responded, "I am greatly mistaken if this matter does not, in the end, turn out to my advantage." [34]

Good reason for such a prediction appeared in the arrangement he eventually concluded with Smith, which took advantage of the only large loophole in the Witherspoon agreement —the failure to mention a delivery date. On this basis, Rittenhouse promised to make Smith a second orrery, keeping the first on hand as a model until the second was completed. Building another machine, he felt, would "be but an amusement, compared with the first." [35] Besides, he could not complete the first, anyway, until he received an important shipment of brass from England.

Smith went away with the impression that both orreries might be ready for delivery sometime the following winter. Under the circumstances, he was content to take the second orrery for his College, but he was a little apprehensive that even this arrangement would irk the College of New Jersey authorities. He assured Rittenhouse that if Witherspoon should refuse to accept his orrery, he had reason to suppose that it might be sold in New York.

No one was entirely satisfied. With a whole catalogue of political and religious antagonisms behind their feelings, the New Jersey leaders resented Smith's action—"his usual Effrontery," Dr. Shippen called it—but they had no thought of

[34] Barton, *Memoirs*, 215.
[35] *Ibid.*

voiding their purchase of Rittenhouse's instrument.[36] If anything, the other camp was even more annoyed. Governor John Penn caught some of Smith's anger and announced that the College of Philadelphia should have "the *first* Orrery, and not the second,—even if the second should be the best." [37] He went to the length of suggesting that he might pay for the machine himself. But the agreements held, the governor notwithstanding.

Now, Rittenhouse's work upon the orreries assumed an especially compelling character that could only be interrupted for even more urgent activities. The first extended occasion of this sort following the transits was his exciting discovery of a comet on June 25. Later known as Lexell's Comet, it was of diminutive size but exceedingly high velocity. For three days, he recorded its distance from two stellar reference points with a common Hadley's quadrant. On July 1, the good weather gave way to clouds, but at last Rittenhouse was able to catch another glimpse of the comet, brighter than before and far across the sky. In only twenty-five hours, it had moved forty-five degrees! On July 3, he saw it once again and then it disappeared. Search as he would, he could not discover it, and, when he calculated its path, he concluded that he would not be likely to see it again.[38]

He applied the data he had collected to discover the elements of the comet's orbit, calculating the heliocentric and geocentric place of the comet on the basis of Halley's *Tabula Generalis Motuum Cometarum, in Orbe Parabolico*. Surprisingly he found that on subsequent returns it would not again come as close to the earth as it had on July 1.

General confirmation of his theory appeared when the *Gentleman's Magazine* for July 1770 arrived with a report of Messier's earlier discovery of the comet on June 15. Rittenhouse calculated that Messier's observations confirmed the magnitude

---

[36] William Shippen to Edward Shippen, Jr., May 3, 1770, Shippen Papers, VII, 23, HSP.
[37] Barton, *Memoirs*, 217n.
[38] APS, *Trans.*, I (1771), Appendix, 37–41.

he had assigned to the comet and its time of perihelion but required an increase of four or five degrees in the inclination of its orbit. The August issue of the same magazine carried a report that James Six had sighted the comet on its return from perihelion on August 22. Rittenhouse had been quite unable to see the comet himself but his theory placed it almost precisely where Six had found it in declination and about two degrees off in right ascension.[39]

Other Americans watched the comet too. Lord Stirling found it on June 28 but lost it on July 2. Newspaper correspondents in Williamsburg, New York, and Connecticut reported its position. In Cambridge, John Winthrop discovered it on June 26 —the day after Rittenhouse found it—but his theory conflicted sharply with Rittenhouse's. The Pennsylvanian emphatically denied Winthrop's assertions that the comet passed the meridian between twelve and one each day and that it reached its perihelion before July 30. He also denied a late New York report that the comet had been sighted near the spot where it was originally discovered. None of the Americans had so good an observational or theoretical picture of the comet as Rittenhouse.[40]

So much work upon the comet so shortly after the transit observations led Rittenhouse to an idea coupling the two. Why not take advantage of the close approach of the comet to the earth to measure the sun's parallax? He would have established the comet's absolute distance from the earth by a series of micrometer measurements of the angular distance of the comet's nucleus from fixed stars taken at different points on the earth's surface.[41] If one assumed that the relative distance of comet from sun and earth were known, the sun's distance could then be calculated. Theoretically, of course, he was right. However,

[39] *Ibid.*, 41–45.
[40] *Ibid.*, 45–46; *Conn. Courant*, July 2, 9, 16, 1770; *Va. Gaz.*, Sep. 13, 20, 1770, Oct. 25, 1770; Barton, *Memoirs*, 221–22.
[41] APS, *Trans.*, 1 (1771), Appendix, 40.

his knowledge of the comet's orbit was not as precise as needed, and the required terrestrial observations were not made. Rittenhouse could not pursue his thought.

This activity was very much pleasanter than the harrowing conflict which continued in Philadelphia over the disposition of some of his work. Fortunately Rittenhouse was spared direct involvement in the arguments within the Philosophical Society over the publication of the transit of Venus and transit of Mercury accounts. Smith, however, took his part and, after "a good deal of debate," succeeded in winning precedence for Rittenhouse's orrery paper and for all of the Norriton observations over Ewing's papers.[42] Biddle's report was placed last in the transit of Venus section. All doubt about the completeness of Smith's victory was removed when preparation of copy for the press was placed in his hands.

Before the printing could be completed, more field work was required. Nevil Maskelyne called upon the Philosophical Society to obtain terrestrial measurements linking the three posts from which the transit of Venus had been observed to the point in Philadelphia for which Mason and Dixon had established the latitude and longitude. The society responded immediately, appointing Biddle, Bailey, and Richard Thomas to take the courses and distances from the New Castle courthouse to the State House observatory and Smith, Lukens, and Rittenhouse to undertake the same measurement from Norriton. Both groups were promised, "the Society will defray the Expence of these Measurem[ts]." [43]

As usual, Biddle completed his assignment with a minimum of fanfare and was back within two weeks claiming expenses of £11..14..4.[44] Smith did not take the project so lightly. He proceeded to develop a major operation which offered the op-

[42] APS Mins., 1769-74, 102, 107, 110.
[43] Ibid., 107.
[44] Ibid.

portunity for publishing another paper over his signature. A month after Biddle had finished his survey, Smith was ready to begin.

On July 2, 1770, Smith and Lukens reached Rittenhouse's farm, accompanied by two "experienced Surveyors," Archibald McClean and Jesse Lukens.[45] First, they established the magnetic variation by checking their compasses against Rittenhouse's astronomically determined meridian line. Then, they adjusted their chain to the standard sixty-six-foot length. Finally, all five set off, each of the three principals keeping separate records of every bearing and distance taken after having checked and rechecked each leveling and plumbing. Two days later, they reached the city.

Rittenhouse did not participate in the subsequent calculation of the distance separating Norriton from Philadelphia. Two different determinations of this value were made, one by Smith and the other by McClean and Jesse Lukens. The results were very satisfying. In no comparison did Norriton's longitude differ by more than 4″ from Rittenhouse's earlier figures obtained from immersions of Jupiter's satellites and from the transit of Mercury. The difference in Norriton's latitude was expectedly greater, the survey figure showing it to be 25.09″ less north than Rittenhouse had made it.[46] Even this was not a large difference, and although no one could know whether Rittenhouse's or Mason's and Dixon's figures were better, the correspondence between the two gave confidence.

Even after this work was completed, the transit of Venus story could not be finished until a sufficient number of observations from other parts of the world were received. The Philosophical Society was too anxious to get its efforts in print to wait for these or for parallax determinations based upon them.

On September 22, 1770, copies of the transit accounts were presented to the Pennsylvania Assembly along with a memorial

[45] APS, *Trans.*, 1 (1771), Appendix, 5.
[46] *Ibid.*, 9.

of thanks for its patronage.[47] This publication was so far incomplete that it did not include the paper on the recently finished terrestrial survey or the report on the Norriton transit of Venus observations. On the other hand, the Philadelphia transit of Venus papers included two rather odd determinations of the sun's parallax—each of which met the deficiency of observational data from distant parts of the world with a different solution. Ewing presented his own calculation of parallax based on long familiar figures obtained from the transit of 1761. This was of little use because other astronomers with more authority had already worked out values based on the same data. Hugh Williamson projected the Philadelphia 1769 figures to the time he assumed the full transit would have taken if he had been able to see it. His result, 8.685″, was too close for coincidence to the 8.65″ found by Short on the basis of 1761 data and used by Williamson as his beginning point. Not even the authors took these determinations seriously and neither Rittenhouse nor Smith bothered to concoct similar values.[48]

The Pennsylvania Assembly had been advised that the transit observations were likely to be "of great Service" in determining the sun's parallax. With this hope in mind, the Philosophical Society in November instructed its committee on astronomy to extract the times of transit contacts presented in the Royal Society's latest volume of *Philosophical Transactions*.[49] Rittenhouse served on the committee which reported its compilation two weeks later. The more laborious task of actually calculating the parallax was assumed by William Smith, who appealed to Rittenhouse at several points and followed methods suggested by his friend. Smith said that Rittenhouse and he made some of the calculations together, but that most of them he did unaided. Together, they rechecked much of the work. From what Rittenhouse later told John Page, the project seems to have

[47] *Pa. Arch.*, 8th ser., VII, 6537–38.
[48] APS, *Trans.*, I (1771), 67–76, 81.
[49] APS Mins., 1769–74, 113.

been his in plan and direction, even though Smith performed most of the arithmetical drudgery.[50]

Smith began by comparing the contact times obtained in Norriton and in Philadelphia with the contacts reported from ten distant posts. The external contact and two phases of the internal contact were used—both the time of coincidence of the limbs of the sun and Venus and the end of the black drop effect. The average of these comparisons yielded a mean horizontal parallax of 8.6045″—a figure with which Smith publicly expressed dissatisfaction. He echoed the fears of Maskelyne and Ferner that some of the European observations had been obtained when the sun was too low in the sky and that the longitude of some of the posts was not sufficiently reliable.[51] To avoid errors that would have resulted from such faulty data, Smith presented as a better figure, a corrected value for the parallax based upon the Norriton and Greenwich contacts alone. The minor correction he made represented an application of the assumption that the earth was an oblate spheroid rather than a sphere as the other calculations assumed. The result was a mean horizontal parallax of 8.805″.[52]

This value is surprising—especially in retrospect—because of its correspondence with more recent estimates of the sun's parallax. In 1890, Simon Newcomb used the same eighteenth-century transit data to produce a figure of 8.79″. In the twentieth century, measurements by H. Spencer Jones yielded the striking value of 8.806″! [53]

Of course, the coincidence of the Norriton-Greenwich value with modern estimates is not as meaningful as the bare figures suggest. Eighteenth-century Europeans obtained much more divergent figures from a wider range of reliable observational data. Smith, indeed, recognized that his calculations were an

[50] Rittenhouse to Page, Aug. 19, 1777, Photocopy, HSP.
[51] APS, *Trans.*, 1 (1771), Appendix, 67.
[52] *Ibid.*, 70.
[53] Simon Newcomb, "Discussion of Observations," 402; H. Spencer Jones, "The Distance of the Sun," *Endeavour*, 1 (1942), 17.

exercise rather than a determination that would be followed in Europe. Certainly he should have circumscribed his value for the parallax within a rather wide margin of error. The degree of coincidence owes much to chance. Nevertheless, it remains an arresting result which was not dependent upon chance alone.

Even without this dramatic coincidence of figures, Rittenhouse's contemporaries had no trouble in identifying him as the most important single figure in the series of astronomical observations completed in Pennsylvania during 1769 and 1770. None of the ill-will generated in several quarters attached to him. He enjoyed a reputation that shone more brightly than ever.

CHAPTER VI

Philadelphia

1770–1773

Toward the end of 1770, David Rittenhouse finally moved his little family to Philadelphia. No position awaited him there despite the readiness of all elements of the Pennsylvania government to see him comfortably placed. He was drawn to the provincial metropolis, regardless. The more he achieved and the more his work was recognized, the more it became apparent that he could never fulfill his potentialities at Norriton. Smith would not permit him to ignore these facts. Scientific attainment, financial success, and the society of the learned and the powerful all drew Rittenhouse to the city.

The parting was difficult; the Norriton farm had been his childhood home and no other residence would ever replace it in his affection. He had accomplished much there, although his ulcer attacks testified that the farm had never been the haven of tranquility it later came to seem. Ever after, he used it as a retreat from a world in which he played a role to the accompaniment of applause but also of continuing overtones of discomfort. Whenever he could justify it, he returned. He spent many summers there and sometimes stayed for longer periods— but the 1770 move was permanent. He lived out the rest of his life as a resident of Philadelphia.

The move was complicated by Eleanor's condition. She was expecting another child in the late winter and the two girls were no more than babies themselves—two and four years old. The orreries, too, were in an uncomfortable state of pregnancy. Because they were so close to completion, it would have been better on some counts to finish them without having to build and equip a new workshop in an altogether new setting. On the other hand, it was easier to obtain materials and competent workmen in the city.

Rittenhouse leased a brick house on the southeast corner of Seventh and Mulberry Streets from the prominent merchant, Thomas Clifford.[1] Over the years, this proved to be a very satisfactory location. The section was residential, toward the outskirts of the settled part of the city, but within an easy walk of the business center.

Once in the city, Rittenhouse found the Philosophical Society a major recourse. At the first meeting in January 1771, he was elected secretary and in February, he read a paper on the fascinating power of snakes. The paper itself has since disappeared but his rejection of the popular superstition is clear from a bird-charming episode he passed on to his nephew, Benjamin Smith Barton. Rittenhouse told of a highly agitated redwinged black bird which apparently had been captured by the charm of a snake, but on closer inspection turned out to be attacking the snake because it had found her nest and was devouring her brood. Rittenhouse fully enjoyed the new accessibility of curious men.[2]

But, whatever he seemed to his admirers, Rittenhouse thought of himself as a "mechanic." His livelihood depended upon the practice of his trade and, for some years to come, only occasional supplements to his income arose from other sources. Many of the surviving Rittenhouse clocks date from the Philadelphia period of his craftsmanship. So too, do various other products that were described collectively under the term "mathematical instruments." Indeed, the move to the city was undertaken in anticipation of an expanding demand for mathematical instruments.

Perhaps the biggest part of this trade lay in supplying sur-

---

[1] Barton, *Memoirs*, 325.
[2] APS Mins., 1769–74, 119; APS, *Trans.*, IV (1799), 108.

veyors with their principal needs: compasses, levels, and chains. Rittenhouse probably did not manufacture the standard Gunter's chain but, on occasion, he did supply them.[3] More worthy of an instrument maker were the surveyor's levels he manufactured and the compasses of which he made many, some equipped with spirit levels, some set in gimbals, many fitted with covers or boxes for portability, and all of them finished with a finesse which still distinguishes them. Sometime after moving to Philadelphia, he introduced his greatest innovation—the compass equipped with a vernier and thereafter sometimes referred to as the "Rittenhouse compass." The vernier improved the ease and accuracy of laying off magnetic declination.[4]

For surveyors, he also made leveling instruments, or small telescopes equipped with spirit levels. He made separate levels and levels to be used in a variety of ways. For celestial surveying, he made zenith sectors of varying dimensions.[5] He was equipped to make or repair any sort of instrument involving refracting lens systems, compasses, levels, scales, or clockwork. Almost immediately he emerged not only as the outstanding clockmaker but also as Philadelphia's greatest instrument maker.

During a long career, the variety of his manufactures grew to large proportions. He made common eyeglasses. He made at least one set of fine scales. He made mercury barometers, mercury thermometers, and he constructed one hygrometer of his own design. In this device, he glued two strips of mahogany together, each about five inches long, three-quarters of an inch wide, and one-tenth of an inch thick. One he had cut with the grain and the other against it. Increased humidity swelled the strip cut against the grain and curled the coupled pair toward the strip cut with the grain; decreased humidity had the reverse

[3] One attributed to him is preserved in the Rittenhouse Room at Mill Grove, Pa.; DR, Notebook, 1785–92, Oct. 20, 1791, APS.

[4] See below pp. 246–47.

[5] The Smithsonian Institution owns two of his zenith sectors; Benjamin Lightfoot to Samuel Coats, Aug. 18, 1771, Gratz Collection, HSP; APS, *Trans.*, III (1793), 116; V (1802), 204.

84

effect. The coupled strips were then placed before a graduated arc and served as a pointer to yield a quantitative reading.[6]

Completion of the orreries diverted him from his trade but at the same time supported it. Orreries of such unprecedented refinement were a demonstration of the best of the clock and mathematical instrument maker's technique. Although not conceived as an advertising device, no better advertisement could have been offered.

By the middle of February, the Princeton orrery was ready but not free of Smith's clutches. Witherspoon agreed that the planetarium might be used in Philadelphia through the winter in conjunction with a lecture series planned to raise money for the College of Philadelphia orrery. He made a quick trip to Philadelphia, however, to see the completed orrery and to make a down payment of £20 as tangible evidence of his contract with Rittenhouse. Meanwhile, Rittenhouse drew up a little paper describing the orrery for his friend Israel Jacobs, who was a member of the Pennsylvania Assembly and who was planning, with Smith, to bring the orrery to that body's attention. On February 21, Smith wrote out a brief testimonial of his own to supplement Rittenhouse's paper, apologizing for his handwriting with the comment that the ink froze in his pen as he wrote! [7]

However cold Smith's study was, it was incomparably colder that day in the Rittenhouse home. There, the first blow of a double tragedy fell with a ferociousness that destroyed the meaning of the successes piling up in every other sphere of his life. Eleanor was delivered of a stillborn child, lingered herself for two days more, and then expired.

In three brief days, Rittenhouse's life was wrenched from its moorings, and he nearly foundered. "How irksome does

---

[6] Barton, *Memoirs*, 139n., 207n., 585-86; John C. Fitzpatrick, ed., *The Writings of George Washington* (Washington, 1931-44), XXVI, 27; Boyd, ed., *Papers of Jefferson*, X, 647.

[7] DR, Little Paper, Jacobs Papers, II, 437, HSP; Smith to DR, Feb. 21, 1771, Photocopy, Princeton; College of N.J. Ledger, 1769, 46, Photocopy, Princeton.

everything seem," he cried out. "Nothing interesting, nothing entertaining! except my two little girls; and yet my reflecting on their loss sinks me the deeper in affliction." He could not think. He certainly could not plan. The only necessity he accepted was that his children remain beside him. He looked all about him for some means of escape—perhaps now he would take that "ramble to Europe" Smith had talked about.[8]

Life only appeared to stop. The days went by inexorably bringing new rewards in their train. Even as Eleanor died, copies of the first volume of the *Transactions* of the American Philosophical Society were received from the printer and distributed through the city. More than any other man, David Rittenhouse was celebrated by this volume. It began with the description of his orrery and reached its climax in the lengthy accounts of the observations of the transit of Venus which left readers with the distinct impression that Rittenhouse was the dominant figure involved.

Nothing could have been less important to him at the moment, but, while he was free to neglect the Philosophical Society, some obligations held him captive. His work commitments were extensive, and Smith had already announced the series of twenty-three public lectures, scheduled to begin on February 28. Of these, Rittenhouse was to give only two—those demonstrating the orrery. The rest, dealing with a variety of topics in natural philosophy, would be offered by Smith, by Benjamin Rush, and by Ebenezer Kinnersley.[9]

The series drew crowds, which Smith captured in his introductory lecture. According to the Reverend Richard Peters, "[the audience] swallowed every word he said, with the pleasure that attends eating the choicest viands." [10] The very success of the venture placed an additional burden on Rittenhouse who was forced to break up the whole assembly into small demon-

---

[8] Barton, *Memoirs*, 219.
[9] *Pa. Gaz.*, Feb. 28, 1771.
[10] Barton, *Memoirs*, 217.

stration groups. Listlessly, he complained of "the drudgery of explaining the Orrery to two hundred persons, in small companies of ten or twelve, each." He did concede, "The satisfaction they universally express, makes however some amends." [11]

To members of the Pennsylvania Assembly, he gave other orrery demonstrations which, in the end, proved more remunerative than the money-making lecture series. On March 8, the legislature passed an unprecedented resolution awarding £300 to David Rittenhouse, "as a Testimony of the high Sense which this House entertain of his Mathematical Genius and Mechanical Abilities in constructing the said Orrery." In addition, they agreed to contract with the ingenious mechanic for the construction of another orrery, "for the Use of the Public," at any sum not exceeding £400.[12]

Now more than ever were his friends incapable of comprehending the depth of Rittenhouse's continuing depression. The £300 award had no more meaning than the *Transactions* or the success of the lectures. To Barton, he commented quietly, "This would have been very agreeable to me, if my poor Eleanor had lived; but now, neither money—nor reputation—has any charms; though I must still think them valuable, because absolutely necessary in this unhappy life." [13]

Smith was so elated himself with results which "succeeded to our utmost wishes," that he did not even see the expression on Rittenhouse's face. He perceived, "The loss of his wife has greatly disconcerted him," but, altogether too lightly, remarked, "we try to keep up his spirits, under it." [14]

Rittenhouse returned to work and routine after a relatively brief interval. Early in April, he received a £200 payment on the Princeton orrery and packed it off to the College.[15] The

[11] *Ibid.*
[12] *Pa. Arch.*, 8th ser., VIII, 6662.
[13] Barton, *Memoirs*, 219.
[14] *Ibid.*, 218n.
[15] *Pa. Gaz.*, Apr. 4, 1771; College of N.J. Ledger, 1769, 46, Photocopy, Princeton.

central planetarium was complete according to his plans and so was one side panel, which, presumably, contained a lunarium. He never did complete the projected second side panel. He probably completed the Philadelphia orrery by August 20, when Smith paid him £109..10, on account. Of this, £65 was applied to pay for the cabinet. He never received any additional payments from the College of Philadelphia even though their orrery contained a second side panel, displaying Jupiter and Saturn. For the Philadelphia orrery, he received £44..10; for the Princeton orrery, £220.[16]

Rittenhouse found interest in the Philosophical Society again after having missed only three meetings. In June, he served on a committee to examine flint glass specimens manufactured by William Henry Stiegel. The society's endorsement was printed in the newspapers and followed by a legislative award of £150 in the same pattern as Rittenhouse's orrery grant. Before the summer was out, Rittenhouse was ordering glass tubes from Stiegel's Manheim, Pennsylvania, glasshouse.[17] He also attended the society's one social occasion, the annual dinner, eliciting John Murgatroyd's compliment, "The greatest Honor of the Repast was the presence of Doct: [Thomas] Graeme and the Modesty of Mr Rittenhouse." [18] The following January, he was elected curator of the society.

Smith's departure in the fall of 1771 on an expedition through the South created still another opportunity for Rittenhouse. On November 19, he was asked to take charge of the scientific apparatus belonging to the College and to exhibit experiments each week paralleling the lectures heard by the students. Rittenhouse had not enjoyed giving the orrery lectures, and he did not enjoy this service, but he stuck it out till Smith returned in February.[19]

[16] DR to Smith, Aug. 20, 1771, Univ. of Pa.; Howard C. Rice, Jr., *The Rittenhouse Orrery* (Princeton, 1954), 38–39.

[17] APS Mins., 1769–74, 125; *Pa. Gaz.*, June 27, 1771; *Pa. Chronicle*, July 1, 1771; *Pa. Arch.*, 8th ser., VIII, 6857; Barton, *Memoirs*, 207n.

[18] *PMHB*, XXIV, 369.

[19] Trustees Mins., II, 33, Univ. of Pa.

He had resumed an active life, but he enjoyed nothing. One year after Eleanor's death, the wound remained so painful that his friends were still unable to reach him. He bridled at Barton's continuing complaints of his failure to write, announcing, "That you may not be disappointed, I would have you to expect nothing of me, in the future. I no longer feel any inducement to exert myself: every thing—even life itself—is insipid." [20]

He flailed out at his brother-in-law's submission of a set of mathematical problems, "I entreat you not to insist on my measuring heads with any pragmatical Schoolmaster, who is heartily welcome, for me, to divert himself with his $x.y.z.'s$, at which he may be very expert, and yet be, as you say, both ignorant and conceited." One by one, he contemptuously catalogued and dismissed each question, underlining his refusal to answer with scorn, "You cannot conceive how much I despise this kind of juggle, where no use is proposed." [21]

In happier days, Rittenhouse would not have responded so unpleasantly, although the tedium of extensive mathematical operations never failed to annoy him. Much that he did was laborious and repetitive but that part of his work he always resented.

On this point as on every other, Barton misunderstood. He imagined that Rittenhouse was annoyed at the apparent trial of his abilities, but at this stage of his depression Rittenhouse was too disinterested to care about that. He was annoyed at the effort to make him focus his attention, especially when there was no purpose to it. He resisted any need to direct his efforts and spent his evenings in desultory reading of poetry and books of "amusement"—still trying to escape.

Curiously, Barton made no attempt to console his brother-in-law through appeals to God, to divine love, to reunion in another life, or to any of the consolations of religion. At least, no such allusions have been preserved. He quoted Shakespeare, he quoted the physician, Dr. William Cadogan, and he quoted

[20] Barton, *Memoirs,* 231.
[21] *Ibid.,* 234n.–35n.

an anonymous poet. He even quoted his daughter, who attributed her uncle's distress to love, for he had admitted that he was now paying his addresses to "someone." Barton also referred to temporal comforts, but he never approached within an arm's length of understanding.[22]

The dimensions of Rittenhouse's despondency resist precise measurement, but a few factors are significantly related. Eleanor had moved to Philadelphia at a stage of pregnancy late enough that her troubles may have been caused by the resulting stress. Even if the move itself had not been harmful, she had faced that series of physical and emotional demands that must always follow efforts to reform a household within another house. Rittenhouse could not know whether the move had caused her death. The thought clearly haunted him. It was no help that rewards had been showered on him ever since he reached the city. That made it even worse. Because the honors were related to the death, in time sequence if in nothing more, Rittenhouse could not permit himself to enjoy them.

Although he might not have emerged unscarred from so serious a depression, time seems finally to have relieved his misery. He had not only honors to sustain him, but many of them were presented with a personal friendliness that could not be mistaken. In 1772, Charles Willson Peale painted his portrait, from which he planned to produce engravings to be sold to a friendly public. The painting still reflects the warmth of Peale's feelings even as it displays the somber mood of its subject.[23]

Accolades from across the sea had a special significance in colonial America, and delightful praise was received late in April by the hands of Benjamin Franklin. From London, he sent a box of books for the Philosophical Society and a letter from the Reverend William Ludlam, fellow of St. John's College, Cambridge, with specific directions that the letter be com-

[22] *Ibid.*, 232–34.

[23] Portrait owned by Univ. of Pa.; Charles Coleman Sellers, *Charles Willson Peale* (Phila., 1947), I, 110.

municated to David Rittenhouse. On May 1, it was read to the society.

After expressing general enthusiasm for the society's *Transactions,* Ludlam especially singled out the work of Rittenhouse, *"There is not another Society in the world that can boast of a member such as* Mr. RITTENHOUSE: theorist enough to encounter the problems of determining (from a few Observations) the Orbit of a Comet; and also mechanic enough to make, with his own hands, an Equal-Altitude Instrument, a Transit-Telescope, and a Timepiece. I wish I was near enough to see his mechanical apparatus." [24]

In September, Rittenhouse went down to Princeton to receive the degree of Master of Arts. In this way, the College not only honored Rittenhouse but emphasized again their possession of his orrery, which they even mentioned in newspaper advertising designed to attract students. Witherspoon was still anxious to have the inventor complete the missing portion of the orrery, but the degree did not stimulate him to that end.[25]

In the city, Rittenhouse's horizons continued to expand. He undertook an altogether new endeavor when he provided the astronomical calculations for James Humphreys' *Universal Almanack* for 1773. He worked out risings and settings of the sun, the length of the days, much data on the moon, and a little on the movements of the planets. The publisher was conscious that Rittenhouse's name was worth as much as the data he submitted. He advertised, "The calculations of this Almanack may be depended upon, as performed with the greatest exactness and truth, being the performance of that ingenious master of mathematics Mr. DAVID RITTENHOUSE, of this City." [26]

As recently as 1760, Philadelphia almanacs had merely copied the calculations they presented, admitting that they were "fitted for the Latitude of Boston." [27] When they began to introduce

[24] Barton, *Memoirs,* 181n.
[25] *Va. Gaz.* (Purdie and Dixon), Oct. 29, 1772.
[26] *Pa. Chronicle,* Nov. 7, 1772.
[27] *Father Abraham's Almanack . . . 1760* [Phila., 1759], title page.

astronomical information calculated for the situation of Philadelphia, they gave no hint of the source. Now Rittenhouse's name became a kind of stamp of authenticity, and one almanac after another announced that he had supplied the astronomical data included. The following year, *The Virginia Almanack*, issued in Williamsburg, touted data "By the celebrated Mr. Rittenhouse, Philomath." John Dunlap, the Philadelphia printer, next fell in line, using Rittenhouse's work for his *Father Abraham's Almanack* for 1775 and adding *Father Abraham's Pocket Almanack* the following year. By 1775, Rittenhouse was still satisfying the needs of all these publishers plus Francis Bailey's for his *The Lancaster Almanack* and his German language *Der Gantz Neue Verbesserte Nord-Americanische Calendar*.

Demands for Rittenhouse's calculations continued to expand until he began to decline this service in 1780. By then, his name had become indissolubly connected with the almanac throughout Pennsylvania and the Chesapeake region.

In Philadelphia, he served both as a manufacturer of surveying instruments and as a surveyor. He was better able to use the instruments he made than the surveyors to whom he sold them; he was at home both in the techniques of common, terrestrial surveying—which meant little more than taking bearings, levels, and distances—and in the more demanding art of obtaining fixes by astronomical observations.

This mastery of surveying brought him into the bitter intercolonial boundary dispute between Pennsylvania and Virginia in 1772. By that time, about twelve hundred families lived in uneasy circumstances bordering on anarchy within a region claimed by both provinces—most of them inside what is now southwestern Pennsylvania. Some had land patents from Virginia, some from Pennsylvania, and some had none at all. The governors of both provinces were disposed to maintain the claims of their people but neither had a firm grasp of the facts because they had never been established. The key to many aspects of the problem was whether Fort Pitt lay on the Pennsylvania or the Virginia side of the border. This was the answer William Smith and David Rittenhouse proposed to find in a plan they submitted to Governor John Penn.

Pennsylvania and Virginia had not yet reached agreement about their conflicting charter claims but, if Pennsylvania's charter were to be followed literally, her western boundary would have fallen exactly five degrees west of the Delaware River at every point along its course. Such a western line would turn and wander in exact duplication of the course of the river that marked the province's eastern boundary. The question, then, reduced to this: at the latitude of Fort Pitt, was the center of the Delaware River more or less than five degrees of longitude distant? The Pennsylvania authorities were convinced that Fort Pitt lay within these five degrees. The Virginians were dubious but less concerned. Regardless of the facts under the Pennsylvania charter, Virginia's 1609 "west and northwest" grant certainly included Fort Pitt. Besides, the Virginians were less legalistically inclined. Governor Lord Dunmore was ready to take what he could hold and let others argue about rights.

Smith and Rittenhouse urged an astronomical survey—surreptitiously conducted—which would fix the position of Fort Pitt with respect to the boundary. Smith, who penned the proposal, optimistically predicted that this "would serve to quiet matters." [28] He expected that even if it did not, it would provide the Pennsylvania governor with valuable data for bargaining.

The plan was well conceived. Surveyor General John Lukens would be sent quietly to Fort Pitt with a minimum of equipment including an equal altitude instrument, a telescope, a quadrant, and a timepiece, "which Mr. *Rittenhouse* can fit up in

[28] Memorial by William Smith and David Rittenhouse, [Oct.-Nov. 1772], Burd-Shippen Papers, ii, 64, APS.

93

two or three Days, so as to be carried to *fort-Pitt*, & be ready for Use by only hanging on the Pendulum of it." [29] For two months, Lukens would observe immersions and emersions of Jupiter's satellites; at the same time, Smith and Rittenhouse would make parallel observations in Philadelphia. If as few as five or six matching observations could be obtained, the two men predicted accuracy to within a mile.

Sometime in late 1772 or early 1773, the plan was executed. The parallel observations placed Fort Pitt six miles within the western boundary. This was close but decisive.

Penn did not use his ammunition immediately but waited until Virginia made her most aggressive move. On January 1, 1774, Dr. John Connolly announced the formation of a new Virginia county which would include Fort Pitt. Penn then fired his new evidence at Lord Dunmore, convinced that it was "abundantly sufficient to satisfy you that the Place is, beyond all doubt, within this Province." [30] Predictably, Dunmore was unimpressed, but before the situation could deteriorate further, it was eclipsed in importance by the Revolutionary crisis. Solution awaited other, and greater, events.

Less dramatic but no less valued, were the canal surveys in which Rittenhouse played a leading part. He was first engaged early in 1772 by an Assembly committee charged with the task of taking the levels of the Susquehanna, Schuylkill, and Lehigh Rivers. The purpose of this work was to study the possibility of a canal connection between the Delaware River system and the Susquehanna in order to keep the western trade within the province. Rittenhouse's initial expedition in this service ended abruptly when he was taken sick in the field. That September, he was added to the committee which was in addition jogged by the demand that they proceed "with all convenient Dispatch." [31]

[29] *Ibid.*
[30] *Pa. Arch.*, 4th ser., III, 458–59.
[31] *Ibid.*, 8th ser., VIII, 6748, 6853; *PMHB*, XIX, 70.

The work was begun in November by Samuel Rhoads and David Rittenhouse and completed in time for the two men to submit a comprehensive report on January 30, 1773. At times, they were aided by other members of the committee: by John Sellers briefly and for several days by William Henry of Lancaster. Henry was a mechanic, a gunsmith who shared many of Rittenhouse's interests and became his fast friend.

The survey sought to go beyond previous investigations in providing specific, quantitative information about the physical relationship of the Delaware River system to the Susquehanna River system. The surveyors carefully measured at successive stations the levels of the Schuylkill and the Lehigh, the two great westward leading tributaries of the Delaware, and the levels of the Susquehanna. This resulted in the expected conclusion that the Susquehanna was upwards of two hundred feet higher than the Delaware tidewater. The hills between the two systems they explored at several points, recording the heights of this middle ground. There was ample water, they concluded, to supply "the Canal of Partition." They did not attempt to choose between two routes they explored or a third which they felt should be explored. Nor did they attempt any estimate of costs. Instead, they recommended "procuring from *Europe* such Assistance as the Importance of the work may require." This was the advice Franklin had sent Rhoads, and Rittenhouse was happy to concur. They had demonstrated the feasibility of a canal and felt that the next step called for a man with canal-building experience.[32]

This survey was an excellent example of the role in which Rittenhouse increasingly found himself cast. The Assembly called him in as an expert to a service other men had failed to perform. More was expected of him than was at all reasonable. He had had absolutely no experience with canals; he had never seen a canal, much less built one. The growing assumption was

[32] *Pa. Arch.*, 8th ser., VIII, 6894, 6931–34, 7022; DR, Notebook, 1785–92, n.p., n.d., APS; Franklin to Samuel Rhoads, Aug. 22, 1772, APS.

that as a mathematical scientist he could apply his knowledge to almost any practical problem. Had he not demonstrated this capacity in the case of his orrery and his astronomical surveys? Somehow, he lived up to the misguided expectations. Acquainted with the methods of orderly approach which had so expanded man's knowledge of nature, he always expected regularity and matched his expectations with a disciplined approach to each new problem. He completed his assignment efficiently but stopped short of attempting evaluations for which he had no basis in experience. Rittenhouse continued to extend the improbable legend which surrounded him.

As Eleanor's death receded into the past, his depression eased, but the decisive end was given to it by his second marriage. At the close of 1772, David Rittenhouse married Hannah Jacobs, a friend of long standing and sister of John and Israel Jacobs. Hannah was three years younger than Rittenhouse and was, as Eleanor had been, a member of the Society of Friends. When she too was disowned for her marriage, she made no effort to reinstate herself but followed her husband in occasional attendance at Presbyterian services.[33]

Hannah was a very capable, efficient wife. Well-informed and bright, she was able to offer many kinds of help in addition to providing a warm, comfortable home. She even succeeded in the well-nigh impossible task of raising two step-daughters. In October, a child was born to the couple but died in its infancy and they had no others. All his subsequent life gives evidence that Rittenhouse had found as good a solution to his domestic needs as the circumstances permitted.

[33] *Pa. Gaz.*, Dec. 23, 1772.

CHAPTER VII

Science and Service

1773–1775

RITTENHOUSE's first years in Philadelphia were not filled with creative scientific work. Even after his domestic life had been reordered and his livelihood assured, he found only limited encouragement for the sort of contribution to knowledge his friends anticipated. The bulk of his time was necessarily applied to his trade and to the varied commissions he had to accept. The community, although universally proud of Rittenhouse, little understood the conditions required for effective work in science. Men did not distinguish easily between science and technics, and, while Rittenhouse confronted both with a similarly ordered attitude, the sources of support in the two areas were totally different.

The most obvious place to look for help in carrying through scientific work was the American Philosophical Society. Here he was always welcome; reelected a curator each year and librarian in 1775, he had direct access to the society's meager resources. The book collection was almost negligible, but, after the distribution of the first volume of *Transactions*, exchange journals and book gifts trickled in.

Rittenhouse's attendance at the declining meetings became more sporadic, especially during 1774. He continued to be relied upon for advice in the committees to which papers were submitted. As a member of the standing committee on geography, mathematics, natural philosophy, and astronomy, he usually saw all items related to astronomy. These, however, even Benjamin Thompson's paper on an aurora borealis and Humphry Marshall's on sunspots, were of limited value.[1] In

[1] APS Mins., 1769–74, 115, 133, 145, and *passim*.

fact, the society received fewer stimulating communications in the basic sciences than in mechanics and practical affairs.

An example of the latter was the steam engine Christopher Colles demonstrated before a committee appointed to view it. Rittenhouse and his fellow committeemen saw the engine perform several strokes although it "did not long continue." Nevertheless, they concluded that Colles was familiar with the basic principles, capable of building an effective engine, and "worthy of Public encouragement." [2] They were well acquainted with the application of the steam engine to the drainage of mines and were convinced of its utility in this service.

On another ad hoc committee, Rittenhouse observed Arthur Donaldson's dredge, or dock cleaning machine. The committee not only approved of this machine but appeared before the Pennsylvania Assembly to support the inventor's request for encouragement. Like Rittenhouse and Stiegel before him, Donaldson was honored with a grant, his in the amount of £100.[3]

One popular scientific fad brought Rittenhouse and members of the society to experiments which were genuinely scientific in character. The initial stimulus within the society came from William Bryant of Trenton, who submitted a paper on the electrical eel (*Gymnotus electricus*), a specimen of which he had obtained on a recent trip to Surinam. He was rightly convinced that it was a different fish from the torpedo with which several European savants were then experimenting.[4] His investigations convinced him that the shock it communicated was electrical in character. Henry Collins Flagg, of South Carolina, sent the society another paper on the fish.[5]

An opportunity to do more than speculate upon this phenomenon was presented to the society in July 1773 when one of the eels was imported to Philadelphia. A committee was

[2] *Ibid.*, 149.
[3] *Ibid.*, 144, 146; *Pa. Arch.*, 8th ser., VIII, 7063, 7143, 7191; *Pa. Chronicle,* Feb. 1, 1774.
[4] APS, *Trans.*, II (1786), 166–69.
[5] *Ibid.*, 170–73.

speedily appointed to agree with the owner "on terms to make a set of Experiments, with a view to determine the nature of the shocks which it communicates."[6] The committee consisted of Ebenezer Kinnersley, the most prominent "electrician" in the city; David Rittenhouse; Isaac Bartram, son of John and by profession a druggist; Levi Hollingsworth, a merchant; and Owen Biddle.

On August 17 and 19, a series of experiments was performed, most of them conscious duplications of familiar electrical experiments.[7] Two pith ball attempts failed to produce any result, but three conventional human circuit experiments demonstrated that the eel's shock was transmitted through a circle of men holding hands, the first of whom touched also the eel's head and the last his tail. When this circle was interrupted by a conductor, the shock still passed but not when a non-conductor was inserted. A Leiden jar transmitted the shock and so did a chain. It was discovered that actual contact with the fish did not have to be established but only with the water close to it.

A living fish placed in the water was stunned by the eel's shock, but it revived after being removed from the tank. Identical results were obtained when the fish was shocked instead with a small electrical charge from a Leiden jar.

Several attempts were made to produce a visible spark. In one experiment, the circuit included a gap between two rounded points of brass wire which was narrowed to as little as one-hundredth of an inch. In another, the gilding on a book served as part of the circuit. None of these efforts produced either a shock or a spark. Rittenhouse told both his nephew and Hugh Williamson that in a similar experiment carried on at a later time he distinctly saw a spark, but none of the other experimenters in either series had that experience.[8]

[6] APS Mins., 1769–74, 148.
[7] *Phila. Medical and Physical Journal,* 1 (1805), Pt. 2, 96–100, 159–61.
[8] *Ibid.,* 161n.; Barton mistakenly thought he referred to the first series;

The committee was convinced that the eel's shock was electrical. It did not, however, attempt a comprehensive statement, concluding only, "No shock from the fish can be communicated through dry wood, glass, or any other substance, so far as we have tried, that will not conduct electricity." [9] The report was never put in literary form or published until Benjamin Smith Barton printed it in 1805, by which time it had only historical interest.

The committee's work reached other experimenters through different channels. Hugh Williamson wrote Rush from England in 1774 to request a copy of the committee's report, and evidence that he received it appears in his paper on the electrical eel published in the *Philosophical Transactions* for 1775.[10] Henry Cavendish knew of the Philadelphia experiments when he carried through his own significant work on the subject. He wrote in 1776, "It was found, both by Dr. Williamson and by a committee appointed by the Philosophical Society of Pennsylvania, that the shock of the *Gymnotus* would sometimes pass through a chain, though they never perceived any light." [11] Cavendish demonstrated the importance of controlling experimental conditions when he applied a recognized source of electricity to similar experiments using a chain as a part of the circuit. Depending upon the tension placed on the chain, he was able to obtain no shock at all, a shock, or a shock plus a spark.

Despite its limitations, the Philosophical Society offered Rittenhouse opportunities to expand his acquaintances. On June 15, 1774, he was honored by association with another philosophical society formed the preceding year in Williamsburg, Virginia. In company with four other Philadelphians, Franklin, Smith, Morgan, and Rush, he was elected to corresponding member-

---

Williamson paper read June 15, 1804, MS Communications in Natural History, I, 27, APS.

[9] *Phila. Medical and Physical Journal*, I (1805), Pt. 2, 161.

[10] Williamson to Rush, Feb. 19, 1774, Rush Papers, LCP; *Phil. Trans.*, 65 (1775), 94–101.

[11] *Ibid.*, 66 (1776), 224.

ship in the Virginia Society for Promoting Useful Knowledge.[12] The chief force behind this organization was John Page, who had been a great admirer of Rittenhouse ever since the transit of Venus observations. The society was never able to offer stimulus or help, although Page's interest did lead Rittenhouse to later accomplishments.

His most fundamental scientific work of this period owed nothing to either society or to any of his friends. In 1774, Rittenhouse carried through a series of experiments and observations which had their origin in phenomena he had observed in using the telescope and in material published in the *Philosophical Transactions*. His investigation concerned an "optical deception" encountered in the use of microscopes and telescopes and later described as the cameo-intaglio illusion or the illusion of reversible relief. The effect of this illusion is to reverse the relief of a three-dimensional surface; to make the raised parts appear depressed and the depressed parts raised.

He began his experiments under the impression that they related to the behavior of light and the laws of optics. Only as he proceeded did it become clear that he was dealing with human behavior, or psychology, instead. The spilling over of a problem in physics to the realm of psychology is not surprising in the field of vision. Investigators ever since the fifteenth century had been using optical instruments in their search for the laws of optics, and the human factor in the use of these instruments had readily occurred to them. Even the analysis of the human eye as an optical instrument was undertaken early.

Rittenhouse's interest in reversible relief was not awakened by work then in progress anywhere in the world. His stimulus, insofar as he was influenced by anything beyond his native curiosity, was the paper submitted in 1745 to the Royal Society by Philip Frederick Gmelin of Würtemberg and published in English in 1756. Gmelin examined the reversal of re-

[12] *Va. Gaz.* (Purdie and Dixon), June 16, 1774; see Hindle, *Pursuit*, 213-15.

lief in seals, carvings, and other objects observed through both microscopes and telescopes. His investigation, conducted under varied conditions, led him to "suspect, that all those fallacies were owing to shade." But he concluded, "why all these things happen exactly after the same manner, I do not pretend to determine." [13]

By 1774, Rittenhouse was still justified in declaring, "The cause of this appearance, for any thing I know, remains still to be explained." [14] He began his study by observing a series of three-dimensional objects through a tube containing two convex lenses separated by a distance equivalent to the sum of their focal lengths. Always the image was inverted and often the raised portions appeared depressed and the depressed portions raised. Thinking about it, he discarded his initial notion that the reversed relief was caused by the near points of the object becoming the far points in the optical image. He finally discarded the assumption that the reversal depended upon any of the laws of optics. The best alternative left was that the reversal was the result of the *interpretation* of the inverted image, an idea supported by the moon's appearance through a telescope. To his trained eye, cognizant of the source of light, the heights and valleys of the surface were well-defined. From personal experience, he had found that the untrained observer seldom saw anything but dark and light patches.

His resultant hypothesis was that the illusion depended upon rules of judging "imperceptibly formed in the mind." [15] He postulated that the key to the perception of the relief of a three-dimensional surface was the interpretation of shadows in relation to the perceived direction of illumination. As a test, he looked through his inverting tube at a brick hearth illuminated from a single window opposite the chimney. The relief reversed as he expected, "all the bricks appeared depressed and the clefts

[13] John Martyn, ed., *Phil. Trans. Abridged*, 10 (1756), 31, 32; *Phil. Trans.*, 43 (1745), 385–91.
[14] APS, *Trans.*, II (1786), 37.
[15] *Ibid.*, 38.

between them elevated." [16] He then blocked direct light from the window by a board and placed a mirror opposite the window to reverse the direction of light falling on the hearth. This reversed the actual direction of light but not the perceived or imagined direction with the result that the relief reversed again to appear in its normal condition with the mortar depressed and the bricks raised.

A second experiment revealed that a tube without lenses produced the reversed relief illusion when the direction of incident light was altered 180° by using the mirror and board. The surface assumed its normal appearance when the light actually came from the window. The two experiments convincingly supported Rittenhouse's hypothesis that the illusion resulted from miscuing the interpretive faculties of the mind with a perceived direction of light different from the actual direction.

Rittenhouse went on to investigate the strength of the illusion, discovering that the insertion of a finger, pen, or pencil in the field was sufficient to destroy it and to reestablish the correct interpretation of the surface. After breaking the illusion once or twice in this manner, he found it difficult to regain.

Although he served as his own subject and obtained his data through introspection, Rittenhouse performed wholly satisfactory psychological experiments. His questions were limited in range; for example, he concerned himself exclusively with monocular vision, for that was the experience of the eighteenth-century astronomer. But he found his way, with little or nothing of structured theory to guide him, to satisfying answers. He placed the illusion of reversible relief firmly within the larger field of perception and underlined the contribution of past experience in this process. His conclusions have had permanent validity.

Despite the quality of this work, it had strikingly little influence. The war delayed its publication until 1786, when his

[16] *Ibid.,* 39.

paper appeared in the Philosophical Society's *Transactions* without provoking significant reaction. Investigators of a later era sometimes referred back to his work but usually without much understanding.[17] As no one had been interested in the problem when Rittenhouse took it up, so no one was much interested when he solved it.

To the extent that the Pennsylvanians knew about this work, they applauded. The community was seldom surprised now by his scientific accomplishments; it expected this and regarded it as confirmation of his reputation. It had implicit faith, moreover, that his science added to his ability to perform useful services. Sometimes for good reason and sometimes on general principles, Rittenhouse received an increasing number of appointments from the community, from both city and provincial governments.

A minor city assignment was given him on June 25, 1774, when, with four other men, he was added to the number of "Regulators of Party Walls, Buildings, and Partition Fences in the City of Philadelphia." [18] This appointment was made with the thought that his skill as a surveyor might be useful to the group; the same sort of reasoning led to the inclusion of Robert Smith, whose skill as a carpenter or builder might aid in this duty.

The Common Council of the city turned to Rittenhouse for advice on another matter with which he had had no related experience. Complaints had been received against the accuracy of the copper half-bushel measure, long used by the city as the standard of dry measure. It was said to contain more than the legal volume to the clear loss of merchants involved in the wheat trade, a serious matter which justified the attention of the city's best scientist. A Council committee consulted Rittenhouse on the replacement of the battered copper measure, and a few

[17] Brooke Hindle and Helen M. Hindle, "David Rittenhouse and the Illusion of Reversible Relief," *Isis*, 50 (1959), 138–40.
[18] *Minutes of the Common Council of . . . Phila. 1704 to 1776* (Phila., 1847), 795.

months later reported back with a new brass standard measure.[19]

With equal confidence, the Pennsylvania governor turned to Rittenhouse when the northern border erupted into a vastly more serious problem. The proprietors had consistently opposed Connecticut's interpretation of her charter, in which she asserted claim to the northern third of Pennsylvania by jumping over New York and New Jersey. The Penns obtained a crown order in 1763 directing Connecticut to stop the movement of her people to the Wyoming Valley and, in 1768, the Treaty of Fort Stanwix disavowed an Indian sale of the valley to Connecticut's Susquehanna Company. During these sparring contests, the government of Connecticut affected not to be involved in the squabbles of a private land company. Now, in 1774, the colony abandoned that pretense by erecting the town of Westmoreland in the valley and annexing it to the Connecticut county of Litchfield.[20]

In August, Thomas and John Penn sent proposals for marking the northern boundary of Pennsylvania to Privy Council and to Lieutenant Governor Cadwallader Colden of New York. This, of course, was a means of bringing the dispute to a head without admitting the existence of Connecticut claims. Colden, personally friendly to Pennsylvania and politically hostile to Connecticut, responded quickly and enthusiastically. Rather than wait for Privy Council to take action, he urged that the two colonies begin immediately by determining the eastern end of the boundary at the Delaware River. As a former surveyor general, he even suggested how this point should be established: on the basis of elevations of the pole star taken during November and December.[21]

The Penns were delighted to have a New York settlement which they could add to their case against Connecticut. John

[19] *Ibid.*, 793, 800.

[20] Julian P. Boyd, ed., *The Susquehanna Company Papers* (Wilkes-Barre, 1930–31), 195; Oscar Zeichner, *Connecticut's Years of Controversy, 1750–1776* (Chapel Hill, 1949), 146.

[21] *Report of the Regents of the University on the Boundaries of the State of N.Y.* (Albany, 1874), 241, 244.

Penn appointed David Rittenhouse on October 24 to this service and, at the same time, to survey the Delaware River.[22] By November 8, when Captain Samuel Holland was appointed to act for New York, Rittenhouse was already on his way to the northeast corner of the colony. Holland was an experienced army engineer who had participated in the marking of several colonial boundaries while engaged in a survey of the New England coast.[23] Rittenhouse had met him on the New York-New Jersey line in 1769, and they became congenial companions.

The two men quickly got to work on observations designed to fix the "beginning of the 43ᵈ degree of latitude," which was interpreted to mean forty-two degrees north latitude.[24] They proceeded up the Delaware River taking star elevations with a common Hadley's quadrant until they reached approximately the required latitude. Then, using an excellent six-foot astronomical sector made by Edward Bird, they took a series of observations of Lyra, Cygni, and Castor—not of Polaris. It mattered little which stars were used since they were able to compare their results with the accurate, corrected tables of star declination prepared by James Bradley. This comparison placed their station only 1.3″ or 132 feet too far north.

The only remaining problem was to mark the established point. Since the boundary began in the middle of the river, the markers had to be placed on either bank, where the forty-second parallel crossed. On the east bank on top of a heap of stones, they placed a small stone with "New-York, 1774" cut on its north side and on top, "Lat. 42° Var. 4° 20′," the last term referring to the magnetic variation. The west bank was similarly marked with the top stone lettered "Pennsylvania, 1774" on its south side.[25]

[22] Ibid., 247; Barton, Memoirs, 237; PMHB, xv, 246.
[23] Chipman, "Holland," xxi, 12.
[24] Report of the Secretary of Internal Affairs of . . . Pennsylvania, Containing Reports of the Surveys and Re-surveys of the Boundary Lines (Harrisburg, 1887), 495.
[25] Ibid.

As he retraced his path back to Philadelphia, Rittenhouse returned to the second commission he had received from the governor. He surveyed the course of the Delaware River from the New York line to Philadelphia, a task which occupied him till the end of December. The following spring, he took five days to complete the river survey from Philadelphia to the New Castle circle. This work was intended only to plot the course of the river and to record its outstanding features. It provided the most accurate information then available and became the foundation of later cartography of the region.[26]

In accepting this continuing series of commissions and the honor that accompanied them, Rittenhouse might easily have abandoned any attempt to cultivate the basic sciences. The community would not have minded; would not, for the most part, even have noticed. The clockmaker, however, had no difficulty distinguishing between creative science and the professional skills of instrument making or surveying. In February 1775, he succeeded brilliantly in communicating some of this understanding and some of his own enthusiasm for the study of astronomy through a public oration he delivered to the American Philosophical Society. His address on the history and present state of astronomy stimulated a movement to offer him the opportunity of devoting his major effort to the advancement of science. Springing from the fertile brain of William Smith, the plan sought to place Rittenhouse in a new post as "Public Astronomical Observer." [27]

The idea of a public observatory in Pennsylvania had still earlier roots. Relying upon the enthusiasm awakened by the transit of Venus observations, John Ewing had launched such an enterprise in 1770. In this cause, he wrote to both Franklin and Maskelyne, but he studiously avoided bringing it to the at-

[26] DR to the Proprietors, Aug. 25, 1775, Penn-Physick Papers, IV, 89, HSP; Robert Erskine, Plan of the River Delaware, 1779, Copied from DR Plan of August 1773, Photocopy, Pa. Hist. and Museum Commission; Reading Howell, *A Map of Pennsylvania*, 1793.
[27] *Pa. Arch.*, 8th ser., VIII, 1208.

tention of Philadelphians who might challenge his leadership in the project. Ewing sought English initiative to establish a Philadelphia observatory that would be administered from Greenwich. He unquestionably saw himself associated with the observatory in a major role. Maskelyne was not unreceptive, but Franklin reported that the cost of the establishment would probably defeat it.[28]

Smith made a far more sophisticated approach in 1775. He understood as well as Rittenhouse the distinction between science and "practice," but he also realized that it was necessary to clothe basic science in practical garb. Especially if he were to gain approval of the commercially minded Assembly, he had to demonstrate the utilitarian value of a public observatory. He also understood the appeal of patriotism in stressing the advantages America had for astronomy. His timing was perfect. Just seven days after Rittenhouse's oration had evoked an emotional response to the pursuit of astronomy, Smith brought before the Philosophical Society a petition to the Assembly calling for the erection of a public observatory. The society enthusiastically approved the idea, requested Smith to prepare a similar petition to the governor, and instructed the officers of the society to present both petitions in the name of the society.[29]

On March 7, Smith's masterpiece was unveiled before the Assembly; truly a remarkable performance. Whereas Ewing had convinced himself of the "unreasonableness" of asking the Assembly to "lay out public Money for such a Purpose," Smith assaulted the body without apology. He deftly tied together Pennsylvania's growing reputation for public-spirited institutions, such as the Philosophical Society, with her "rapid Improvements in all useful arts." He expressed gratitude for Assembly aid in the past but promised that the society would

[28] Ewing to Franklin, Jan. 4, 1770, Franklin Papers, III, 1, APS; Smyth, ed., *Writings of Franklin*, v, 270.
[29] APS Mins., 1774-87, 20.

not ask for further help except for "the Encouragement of useful Inventions, and the patronizing Undertakings beneficial to the whole Community." [30] He told the Assembly it must regard the establishment of an observatory in this light.

With a genuine understanding of the character of science, he sketched the possible contributions to knowledge which might be expected to follow from regular astronomical observations. He twisted the truth slightly when he related this basic science directly to the improvement of navigation and geography. When he turned to the man he hoped to place in the position of public observer, he lapsed again into uncolored translation of the truth as he saw it.

Smith felt too strongly to dissemble when he spoke of Rittenhouse: "It would be inexcusable, therefore, in your Petitioners to neglect the present Opportunity of endeavouring to set such a Design on Foot, when we have a Gentleman among us, whose Abilities, speculative as well as practical, would do Honour to any Country, and who is nevertheless indebted for Bread to his daily Toil, in an Occupation the most unfriendly both to Health and Study. Under his Auspices the Work may now be undertaken with the greatest Advantages, and others may be bred up by him to prosecute it in future Times; but if the present Opportunity is neglected, perhaps whole Centuries may not afford such another. To rescue such a Man from the Drudgery of *manual Labour*, and give him an Occasion of indulging his bent of Genius, with Advantage to his Country, is an Honour which crowned Heads might glory in." [31]

He next turned to the task of matching the bait to the fish. He planned things so he could tell the Assembly that it would not be asked to bear the cost of erecting the observatory. The proprietors would be asked to donate suitable land. A public subscription would take care of the building and the needed instruments—although most of the instruments could be made

[30] *Pa. Arch.*, 8th ser., VIII, 7205.
[31] *Ibid.*, 7206.

by Rittenhouse himself. The only contribution required from the Assembly would be an annual salary for the "Public Astronomical Observer."

Tangible, practical benefits could be promised, too. The observatory would be open at all times to mariners and those who wished to learn navigation. Specifically, instruction would be offered in those methods of finding longitude at sea for which the British Parliament had paid such handsome rewards. If desired, the observer might also be appointed "Surveyor of High-Roads and Waters" and be always available to conduct canal and road surveys and to advise on these matters.[32]

Almost as an aside, Smith proposed the annual publication of observations. This would fulfill the scientific objectives of the plan by circulating through Europe the data collected at the observatory. It would enhance the prestige of America, of Pennsylvania, and of the Philosophical Society, which would supervise this publication.

At least one man was greatly disturbed by the entire project. John Ewing saw himself shunted aside as astronomer in charge of the observatory. He would even be deprived of any credit for its establishment. He quickly wrote to Maskelyne to see whether the Smith plan could not be forestalled by speedy English action in establishing a Philadelphia observatory. Could not a memorial be laid before Lord North? Maskelyne replied flatteringly, "Were an Observatory to be erected at Philadelphia I do not know any person at Philadelphia more capable of taking care of it than yourself." [33]

This was small comfort under the circumstances, for Maskelyne's evaluation of political realities destroyed Ewing's last glimmer of hope. Conscious that men had already died on Lexington Green, the astronomer royal wrote, "In the present unhappy situation of American affairs I have not the least idea

---

[32] *Ibid.*, 7208.
[33] Maskelyne to Ewing, Aug. 4, 1775, APS.

that any thing can be done towards erecting an Observatory at Philadelphia." [34]

The war killed all hope of aid from England. It killed, also, any chance that Pennsylvania would take the required action. It killed much more; it killed much of the remaining encouragement and peace of mind that permitted the growth of a creative science.

[34] *Ibid.*

CHAPTER VIII

Confession of Faith

1775

RITTENHOUSE's oration of February 24, 1775, had a deeper significance than the impetus it gave to the public observatory project, and it endured longer.[1] It revealed much of the mind and character of David Rittenhouse. He offered there far more than a narrative of the history and present state of astronomy, which was its nominal theme. He presented the essence of his own aspirations and beliefs, his own philosophy and religion, questions of unending concern to the community. The oration was a public confession of faith.

This was the third annual oration of the American Philosophical Society, the first of which had been given by William Smith and the second by Benjamin Rush.[2] By 1775, the society was in a declining state, not having met at all for eight months prior to the meeting which formulated oration plans.[3] Nevertheless, Rittenhouse drew an audience that crowded the facilities of a hall in the College seating 150. In attendance were the governor, the speaker and members of the Assembly, the society, and citizens who had applied early enough for tickets.

Although he spoke with a feeble voice, Rittenhouse communicated an infectious enthusiasm. Far from puncturing the sometimes unrealistic illusions men held of him and of his powers, he strengthened them. The *Journal* reflected the prevailing

[1] DR, *An Oration Delivered February 24, 1775, before the American Philosophical Society* (Phila., 1775).
[2] William Smith, *An Oration Delivered January 22, 1773, before the . . . American Philosophical Society* (Phila., 1773); Benjamin Rush, *An Oration Delivered before the American Philosophical Society* (Phila., 1774).
[3] APS Mins., 1774–87, 1–5, and *passim*.

reaction, "The topic was astronomy, which was treated in that accurate, sublime, and masterly manner, which might have been expected from the celebrated inventor of the AMERICAN ORRERY; and the whole was enlivened with beautiful digressions, and benevolent moral reflections drawn from the subject, which gave universal satisfaction." [4]

Rittenhouse surveyed the history of astronomy in traditional terms, adding only his interpretations and reactions. He ran through the chronology twice—almost as if he had relied upon two major sources. His essay cannot be documented in detail, but some of the books he used can be identified. Among them were Francis Bacon's *Advancement of Learning*, Pierre Bayle's *Historical and Critical Dictionary*, and Newton's *Principia* and *Opticks*. He drew upon a variety of articles which had appeared in the *Philosophical Transactions*. He must have used general accounts from the *Encyclopedia Britannica*, Chambers' *Universal Dictionary of Arts and Sciences*, William Derham's *Astro-Theology*, or similar works which were available to him.[5]

Rittenhouse rejected the suggestion that astronomy had sprung from astrology, which he tagged, instead, "a spurious offspring of Astronomy." [6] He regarded astrology as another evidence of human depravity, which revealed his own curious readiness to accept the doctrine of man's fall. As a matter of faith, he acceded to the idea that man had lived initially in a state of rectitude. Whether he accepted this because it was a part of the Bible, because it had pre-Christian origins, or because it had non-Christian sustenance, he did not indicate.

Reasonably enough for his day, he dismissed the astronomy of the Chaldeans, the Egyptians, the Arabs, and the Chinese on the grounds that the evidence was unsatisfactory. He cast doubt especially upon Chinese achievements because knowledge of them had come through Jesuit channels. In his mind, as-

[4] *Pa. Jour.*, Feb. 22, Mar. 1, 1775; Rush, *Eulogium*, 13.
[5] DR, *Oration*, 10, 14, 15, 16, and *passim*.
[6] *Ibid.*, 5.

tronomy began with the Greeks, but, aside from familiar references to Hipparchus, Pythagoras, Thales, and Ptolemy, he did not develop their story. The succeeding ages he gave even less attention, mentioning only Roger Bacon and Regiomontanus before Copernicus.

In effect, Rittenhouse began his account with Copernicus, who had "explained the true system of the universe" against the "objection of the Aristotelians." [7] Tycho Brahe deserved praise for his accuracy and discoveries despite his error in imagining the sun to revolve about the earth, while permitting the other planets to go about the sun. Rittenhouse could not freely admire the "whimsical" Kepler, but he recognized that his love of harmony had led to fundamental advances of knowledge. Galileo was much more to his taste. Here was a hard-headed observational astronomer who had brilliantly used the telescope, very shortly after its invention, to discover numerous significant facts, some of which demonstrated the truth of the Copernican system.

The materials had thus been collected, but the magnificent edifice of astronomical philosophy could not be constructed until the master builder appeared. Here, Rittenhouse's emotional admiration escaped all bounds, "And it was, I make no doubt, by a particular appointment of Providence, that at this time the immortal Newton appeared." With "more than mortal sagacity," he discovered the laws of motion governing even the minutest irregularities of the heavenly bodies "and reduced them to the most beautiful simplicity." [8]

The crystalline spheres of the ancients, the vortices of Descartes, and the music of Kepler were now superseded by a system based upon the principle of gravity, the laws of motion, and the direct observation of nature. "Other systems of Philosophy have been spun out of the fertile brain of some great genius or other; and for want of a foundation in nature, have

[7] *Ibid.*, 7.
[8] *Ibid.*, 14, 15.

had their rise and fall, succeeding each other by turns. But this will be as durable as science, and can never sink into neglect, until 'universal darkness buries all.' " [9]

Newton represented attained perfection, but not the end of seeking for man's mind would never be satiated. Rittenhouse went on to describe astronomical advances of more recent years, concentrating on a few episodes. He used James Bradley's discovery of the aberration of light to illustrate the indeterminacy of scientific methods. In looking for stellar parallax, Bradley had stumbled upon the aberration of light from which one could deduce the velocity of light. This value had previously eluded the best efforts of experimental science. Truth might emerge from a variety of sources, but Rittenhouse never doubted that an absolute truth existed and that man could and would perceive it.

In a brief digression on the theories of light, he revealed a willingness to live with contradictions—in anticipation, of course, that the apparent contradictions would be resolved once the full truth were known. When he turned to the doctrine that differing velocities accounted for the variation in the refraction of different colors, he found three telling objections. Two he could answer. The third he could not, and he commented, characteristically, "This objection I shall for the present leave in its full force." [10]

Rittenhouse then conducted his audience on a tour of the solar system, in which he described the visible universe from the vantage point of one planet or satellite after another. He had certainly made this trip many times while building his orreries. It was also a journey that bore a striking similarity to the section in the *Encyclopedia Britannica* entitled, "The Phenomena of the Heavens as seen from different parts of the Solar System." [11]

[9] *Ibid.*, 14.
[10] *Ibid.*, 16n.
[11] *Encyclopedia Britannica* (Edinbh., 1771), I, 441–49.

When he turned to the current state of astronomy, Rittenhouse speculated freely in something of the manner of the
"Queries" appended to Newton's *Opticks*. He commented, "I
shall hazard some conjectures of my own; which, if they have
but novelty to recommend them, may perhaps be more acceptable than retailing the conjectures of others." [12]

Not for the first time but with unusual penetration, he pointed
to the peculiar advantage of position enjoyed by America in the
study of astronomy. It enjoyed a serenity of atmosphere and a
geographical displacement from the principal observatories of
the world that encouraged major contributions. He did not
doubt that enough men of genius were produced to fulfill the
opportunities. The question was whether American society
would tempt them forth from obscurity and persuade them
away from other pursuits.

Among fertile fields for research, he urged the study of
comets. Their composition and nature was not known, and Rittenhouse even cast doubt upon the certainty of the orbits
ascribed to them. The data on which the calculations had been
based were so uncertain that he felt it was possible to choose
whatever values suited one's purpose.

When he made suggestions, he usually urged the sort of study
required to test them. Was it possible, he asked, that the foci of
the admittedly changing planetary orbits revolved about some
common center? This must be discovered from "observation,
and not from theory alone." [13] Was the moon really increasing
in velocity, or did this appearance reflect a change in the diurnal
rotation of the earth? Many defects of astronomy could be
supplied by optical advances: the periods of rotation of
Venus, Saturn, and Mercury, for example. If Alexander Wilson were correct that sun spots had sloping sides, perhaps they
were permanent and solid like the moon's craters. In any case,
what was called for here and throughout the study of astronomy
was more observation. Except for a few comments on the Milky

[12] DR, *Oration*, 5.
[13] *Ibid.*, 23.

Way, he speculated little on the fixed stars, contenting himself with the prediction that there, "amazing discoveries may yet be made." [14]

Toward the end of his address, Rittenhouse tried to demonstrate the harmony of astronomy and religion. This was not merely an attempt to justify the best hopes and allay the worst fears of his audience. It was an honest report on his own personal travail. The creed he recited was the one to which he sincerely subscribed.

His belief in God he stated explicitly. He referred to God the creator, the divine architect, the Deity, the almighty Power, the divinity, and the divine Providence. His God was an impersonal God, at times almost indistinguishable from nature itself. He was never God the redeemer or the savior, and Rittenhouse never, anywhere, suggested that he would accept the divinity of Christ. Indeed, the dogmas of salvation, of works, and of grace were altogether outside his area of concern.

His affirmation of belief in immortality before this audience was only the most specific and detailed he made. Twenty years before, he had given unequivocal testimony in favor of it.[15] On his deathbed, he would repeat this anticipation and there is no record that he ever doubted the reality of life after death—specifically in a future state of rewards and punishment.[16]

Surprisingly, however, he accepted the possibility of miracles. The attack on miracles had been a jumping-off point for deistic thinkers, and Rittenhouse's beliefs in many respects could be tagged as deistic. Yet he here demonstrated a greater capacity to accommodate his views to those of Christianity than had many European deists. By the same token, he had fewer hopes that wholly mechanistic explanations would suffice to describe all that could be described.

As it had been for Christian thinkers, so it was easy for Rittenhouse to think on the one hand of a system of natural law

---

[14] *Ibid.*, 24–25.
[15] Barton, *Memoirs*, 503.
[16] *Ibid.*, 444.

by which the universe was regulated but on the other of divine and extra-legal interference in this system. "Neither Religion nor Philosophy," he declared, "forbids us to believe that infinite wisdom and power, prompted by infinite goodness, may throughout the vast extent of creation and duration, have frequently interposed in a manner quite incomprehensible to us, when it became necessary to the happiness of created beings of some other rank or degree." [17]

Rittenhouse's use of the idea of infinity was another significant key to his religious outlook. It has recently been demonstrated that the concept of an infinite universe was one of the fundamental alterations of view that accompanied and defined the scientific revolution. But, of course, infinity as an attribute and definition of God was a much older concept. Rittenhouse consistently applied infinity to God alone. The Milky Way was "of *immeasurable*, though not *infinite* extent." The regions of space were "unlimited," the stars "innumerable," but he never described them as infinite. The visible stars might "perhaps compose but the leaf of a flower in the creator's garden, or a single pillar in the immense building of the divine architect." The building was "immense," but only the architect was "infinite." [18]

In the course of his commentary on astronomy, Rittenhouse met squarely the question for which Giordano Bruno had been confined for seven years in the prisons of the Inquisition and finally burned at the stake—the plurality of worlds. "The doctrine of a plurality of worlds," he insisted, "is inseparable from the principles of Astronomy." Similarly, opposition of religious authorities to the doctrine of the earth's rotation, although based on the Bible, had been "mistaken." It had been "compelled to give way to the force of astronomical evidence." [19]

On the other hand, Rittenhouse was firmly confident that

[17] DR, *Oration,* 19.
[18] *Ibid.,* 25.
[19] *Ibid.,* 19.

any conflict between science and religion was only apparent. True science and true religion traveled the same path. Fuller understanding would reconcile any apparent difference, for there was only one truth. Yet, when he was faced with an "apparent" difference, Rittenhouse always appealed to the evidence of science—never to the revealed word of God. Science was his ultimate sanction at the same time that he asserted the truth of religion.

Science, specifically astronomy, was not limited to describing the behavior of nature. It provided a moral force, as well, which reinforced the teachings of religion. With a backhanded compliment to Christianity, he explained, "Astronomy, like the Christian religion, if you will allow me the comparison, has a much greater influence on our knowledge in general, and perhaps on our manners too, than is commonly imagined. Though but few men are its particular votaries, yet the light it affords is universally diffused amongst us; and it is difficult for us to divest ourselves of its influence so far, as to frame any competent idea of what would be our situation without it." [20]

Nothing could better demonstrate God's presence throughout the universe than the study of astronomy. Astronomy freed men from bigotry and superstition. When skeptics sought to perform the same service, their cobweb philosophies were liable to be broken by the smallest incident in nature. Astronomy encouraged universal benevolence; it favored none of man's vices; it denied none of the truths of religion.

Most revealing of the lights Rittenhouse lived by were the two utopias he sketched in the course of his talk. One was a temporal state which illustrated elements of his political creed. The other was paradise itself—the pleasantest personal mode of existence he could conceive.

He placed his political utopia on the other astronomical worlds he visited in his imaginary tour. He could not know whether the inhabitants of other planets had been created liable

[20] *Ibid.*, 7–8.

to fall, like man. If they retained their original state of rectitude, they would enjoy the creator's bounty with gratitude and adoration. They would govern themselves according to the dictates of reason for the purpose of attaining happiness for themselves and others. "We will hope that their statesmen are patriots, and that their Kings, if that order of beings has found admittance there, have the feelings of humanity." [21]

In none of their advantages would these utopian inhabitants be more fortunate than in their isolation from the vices cultivated on earth. Human slavery, Rittenhouse assaulted especially. "None of your sons and daughters, degraded from their native dignity, have been doomed to endless slavery by us in America, merely because *their* bodies may be disposed to reflect or absorb the rays of light, in a way different from *ours.*" [22]

Even the inhabitants of the moon were far enough away to be happily removed from the reach of the Spaniard, the avaricious Briton, and Frederick, "that tyrant of the north and scourge of mankind." [23] America was not so fortunate. She was even then being assaulted by evils from across the sea.

In a flush of patriotism, however, Rittenhouse recognized that good as well as ill had come from Europe. The movement of civilization had brought America to "surprising . . . advances towards the meridian of glory." But, using a familiar metaphor, he suggested that tyranny and luxury after having conquered Asia and having nearly conquered Europe were threatening America. These forces, "by a vile affectation of virtues they know not, pretend at first to be the patrons of science and philosophy, but at length fail not effectually to destroy them. . . . May the God of knowledge inspire us with wisdom to prevent it: Let our harbours, our doors, our hearts, be shut against luxury." [24]

Although a quiet man, Rittenhouse was a man of strong con-

[21] *Ibid.,* 19.
[22] *Ibid.,* 19–20.
[23] *Ibid.,* 20.
[24] *Ibid.*

victions. He felt and spoke angrily when he confronted malevolence. When he turned to the contemplation of his own personal paradise, his mood changed abruptly. Peace descended upon him.

Heaven was not, to Rittenhouse, an abrupt alteration of state but a further development—perhaps an ecstatic development—of the best the earth had offered. The meaning of life, and its goal, was found in a continually expanding knowledge of nature; a growth in truth. He thought in terms of the great chain of being which related all the forms of nature in an orderly sequence. This ladder of life, he felt, stretched beyond the earth and beyond the grave. Death, in fact, might mean promotion "to a more exalted rank amongst the creatures of God." [25]

"I must confess," he mused, "that I am not one of those sanguine spirits who seem to think that when the withered hand of death hath drawn up the curtain of eternity, almost all distance between the creature and creator, between the finite and infinite, will be annihilated. Every enlargement of our faculties, every new happiness conferred upon us, every step we advance towards the perfection of the divinity, will very probably render us more and more sensible of his inexhaustible stores of communicable bliss, and his inaccessible perfections." [26] More specifically, he hoped to have "our understandings greatly enlarged, be enabled to follow truth in all her labyrinths with a higher relish and more facility, and thus lay the foundation of an eternal improvement in knowledge and happiness." [27]

All those who heard the oration and listened; all those who read the printed version and inwardly digested it now understood the meaning of David Rittenhouse. The honors he had received and would yet receive became intelligible both to those who could make no sense of his transit papers and to those who could make sense of them but could not see why

[25] *Ibid.*, 27.
[26] *Ibid.*, 26–27.
[27] *Ibid.*, 27.

they brought him so much renown. His worth was less a matter of what he had done or of what he would accomplish than of what he was. He was the personification of the truth of science in harmonious combination with Christian humility and virtue.

Ever afterward, Rittenhouse lived encased within a strange glow that had previously been visible to only a few who knew him well. Timothy Matlack testified to the condition when he resumed the series of annual orations after a lapse of five years. As an explanation of the interval since the 1775 oration, his comment was absolutely wrong. As an expression of the pervasive view of Rittenhouse and his oration, he was precise. "This," he said, "by excelling too far, has damped and discouraged where it ought to have roused and emulated." [28]

[28] Timothy Matlack, *An Oration Delivered March 16, 1780, before the . . . American Philosophical Society* (Phila., 1780), 8.

CHAPTER IX

The Revolution
1775–1776

THE American Revolution permanently changed Rittenhouse's life. His scientific reputation proved to have distinct political value which he did not hesitate to stake on the outcome of the conflict against Britain and even to place on the line in the bitter factional battles within Pennsylvania. For the cause, he threw himself into a succession of new roles, each of which increased his stature in fields previously foreign to him.

Rittenhouse's commitment to the Revolution was complete and irrevocable. Rush later testified that he had a very early but "secret" attachment to an elective and representative form of government. Rittenhouse said almost as much himself in his oration, where he revealed a hostility to British tyranny and to monarchy. How early this attitude arose can only be guessed, but the first recorded hint of it appears in his attendance at the May Day 1773 celebration of the Sons of St. Tammany. This was not a national society but a sublimation of the Sons of Liberty of Stamp Act days. So successfully had the liberty club been muted that beside the political radicals sat such bulwarks of the old order as Governor Penn, Chief Justice Chew, and two of the Allens. More numerous among the celebrators, however, were the leaders of the current opposition to British policy.[1]

After the Boston Tea Party and the ensuing Intolerable Acts, Rittenhouse was directly caught up in the struggle. The distinctly radical Mechanics Association sponsored a meeting

[1] Rush, *Eulogium*, 35; DR, *Oration*, 19–20; *PMHB*, xxv, 446.

which brought together twelve hundred mechanics in State House Square on June 9, 1774. This mass meeting took two decisive actions. It passed a resolution supporting the call for a Continental Congress, and it appointed a Committee of Correspondence. The committee, which included David Rittenhouse, was immediately instructed to answer a communication received from the mechanics of New York. In this relationship, Rittenhouse established a strong political base as one of the most distinguished mechanics in the city.[2]

For a time, his private life was not substantially altered. He continued to spend most of his time in the manufacture of clocks and instruments. At his request, the Assembly gave him the care of the State House clock as of March 1, 1775. The job was worth £20 a year and easy to manage since he already had responsibility for the Philosophical Society's clock in the State House yard observatory. More portentious was the honor accorded him that year when a privately owned ship was named the *Rittenhouse*.[3]

The war began in April 1775. The Second Continental Congress met in May, and in June the Pennsylvania Assembly appointed a Committee of Safety to direct defense measures. One of its most unusual provisions was the construction of a group of row galleys which were demonstrated to the Congress, the Assembly, and a group of leading citizens on September 28. Among those invited was David Rittenhouse, who found himself aboard the *Bull Dog* with Owen Biddle, Michael Hillegas, and John Adams. Adams, who wrote more in his diary about his fellow passengers than he did about the boat he was inspecting, observed, "Rittenhouse is a mechanic; a mathematician, a philosopher, and an astronomer . . . [he] is a tall slender man, plain, soft, modest, no remarkable depth or thoughtfulness in his face, yet cool, attentive, and clear." [4]

[2] *Pa. Gaz.*, June 15, 1774.
[3] *Pa. Arch.*, 8th ser., VIII, 7177, 7179, 7568; *Pa. Jour.*, June 15, 1774.
[4] Charles F. Adams, ed., *The Works of John Adams* (Boston, 1850), II, 429.

On October 27, the Committee of Safety, newly enlarged, appointed Rittenhouse to be its engineer. For nearly a month no recorded demands were made of him. Then on November 25, he was engulfed with a variety of commissions, ranging from a familiar surveying operation to the wholly new field of arms and munitions production. These demands were based on a deep belief that science was practical and Rittenhouse a practical scientist.[5]

In the survey, he and three or four other men inspected the Delaware River from Marcus Hook to the city, recording information that had been of no concern to him when he surveyed the same distance for Governor Penn earlier that year.[6] Now the purpose was to discover the best means of fortifying the river approach to Philadelphia. Shoals, bars, and depths of water had to be marked. The nature of the shoreline and the elevation of the banks were also important. Rittenhouse was so well equipped for this task that it proved only the first of a succession of similar assignments.

Another commission received on November 25 took him far from his previous range of activities. He was asked to attend a subcommittee of merchants, iron masters, and army officers in their arrangements with Morgan Bustead and Samuel Potts for the casting of several heavy cannon. This was an enterprise beyond the accomplishments of the colonial economy, and even the iron masters who had produced smaller cannon in the past lacked the necessary experience. After Rittenhouse visited Potts' iron foundry, the Committee of Safety executed a contract for the cannon. On January 19, Rittenhouse was appointed with Andrew Doz, Thomas Cuthbert, Daniel Joy, and Benjamin Harbeson—none of them members of the Committee of Safety—to supervise the enterprise. The cannon committee was instructed to help, but Rittenhouse found himself with a major share of the responsibility in a quest that proved elusive. Before

[5] *Pa. Col. Recs.*, x, 383.
[6] *Ibid.*, 412, 465, 474, 619.

the problem was solved, he undertook a more exciting series of experiments in the rifling of cannon. Rifles of musket size, the famous "Pennsylvania rifles," had already had an impact on the war. The idea of rifled cannon was brilliant but required more development than could be completed during the War of the Revolution.[7]

On November 25 also, the Assembly gave Rittenhouse another assignment that took him into an unknown realm. With Owen Biddle and Peter Dehaven, he was joined in a committee to supervise the saltpeter works in Market Street, previously under Philadelphia's Committee of Inspection and Observation. The Assembly's action was based upon the recommendation of the committee, disappointed with its success in the enterprise, and upon a request from Congress that provincial assemblies take more effective measures to stimulate saltpeter production.[8]

Saltpeter, or potassium nitrate, was the most critical single ingredient in gunpowder. The colonies had not previously produced it, but no war could be fought without an adequate supply. They had not stockpiled gunpowder or saltpeter when their ports were open, and now the British embargo on American commerce made domestic production the best solution. This proved even more difficult, however, than discovering satisfactory techniques for casting large cannon. Exhortations, bounties, and published recipes all failed to produce significant quantities of saltpeter.

At the time Rittenhouse was brought into the Philadelphia project, prospects looked brighter than they had hitherto. Baltis Moody, recently engaged at the saltpeter works, had behind him an enviable record of saltpeter production. Stocks of the powder that he had made while at York, Pennsylvania, were still being brought into the city. Moody assured an Assembly committee that there were "plenty of impregnated materials in

[7] *Ibid.*, 412, 462; *Pa. Arch.*, 4th ser., III, 610; *Pa. Col. Recs.*, X, 501.
[8] *Pa. Arch.*, 8th ser., VIII, 7367–68.

the city"—that is plenty of nitrate-bearing materials such as street sweepings, stable deposits, and outhouse pits. He indicated that the rate of production could be "very fast" and would depend primarily on how much money the Assembly was ready to lay out.[9]

An enthusiastic Assembly voted Moody a £25 premium for the saltpeter he had already produced and promised another £25 above his wages after he properly trained those put under his tutelage by the committee. The Assembly placed £500 at the disposal of the committee and offered £25 a hundred weight to all individuals who produced saltpeter on their own initiative. The money required had now been provided, but the problems were not so easily solved.

For one thing, the energetic action taken by the Assembly was not equally pleasing to everyone. Benjamin Rush had been one of the committee charged with directing the works before the Assembly took over. He was not continued on the new committee although Owen Biddle was. Yet Rush was reckoned the leading expert on saltpeter in the city. He was not only professor of chemistry in the Medical School but, more specifically, he had written and published the most widely used American tract on the manufacture of saltpeter. Before the Assembly's action, Rush had been predicting that, in a year or two, enough of the nitrate would be produced to satisfy the needs of the American fleet as well as the army. Afterwards, he had little to say but sought quietly to recover the private moneys he and Biddle had advanced in the project.[10]

Rittenhouse certainly began with a limited knowledge of the manufacture of explosives, a defect he sought to remedy by characteristically dedicated study. When Charles Willson Peale and Dr. Thomas Young visited him in January, he was full of the subject. He happily offered them his own formula for gun-

[9] *Ibid.*, 7354.
[10] *Ibid.*, 7503, 7471; *Pa. Mag.*, 1 (1775), 266–68; Butterfield, ed., *Letters of Rush*, 1, 92.

powder. A few days later, Biddle, Dehaven, and he turned over eighty-eight pounds of saltpeter just produced in the Market Street factory.[11] This was not a large quantity but it seemed promising.

This promise was never fulfilled. Patriotic appeals backed by substantial rewards continued to be offered by the Assembly and to be advertised in the press along with related efforts to collect paper and sulphur. Rittenhouse was involved in the Assembly's plans for the establishment of six private powder mills. In the end, it was a futile quest. Pennsylvania produced usable quantities of both saltpeter and gunpowder, but the yield was not sufficient. As in the other colonies, the effort and the output declined sharply after the first year and a half. America had to depend on foreign sources after all.[12]

Even Rittenhouse's private time was now taken up with problems related to military combat. He worked with Peale on two rifle improvements. One was a telescopic sight, and the other an idea of Peale's for building into the stock a box large enough to carry bullets and wipers.[13] Rittenhouse set one of his journeymen to work on this invention, and, when it was ready, Peale and Rittenhouse took it out in the fields to test it. Neither inventor was disheartened when the device opened accidentally, spilling all its bullets; neither was at his best in pursuits related to soldiering.

Somehow Rittenhouse became an authority on explosives, ballistics, and other matters far removed from clocks and comets. He lectured Peale on the performance of rifles, reporting that riflemen asserted they could not shoot true when they used too heavy a charge of powder. If this were verifiable—and Rittenhouse admitted a considerable lack of experience—he suggested that it might follow from the compression and compacting of

[11] *Pa. Col. Recs.*, x, 468; *PMHB*, LVII, 160.
[12] *Pa. Arch.*, 2d ser., I, 582; *Pa. Col. Recs.*, x, 482; *Pa. Gaz.*, Jan. 24, 31, Mar. 20, 1776; Orlando W. Stephenson, "The Supply of Gunpowder in 1776," *American Historical Review*, 30 (1924-25), 277.
[13] Charles Willson Peale, Typed Diary, 15-16, APS.

air in front of the bullet, which caused it to go off in an easier direction. Not yet understanding the principles involved, he pointed to the jagged course of lightning in air compared with its straight course in a vacuum.[14]

On January 22, the Committee of Safety gave Rittenhouse another surveying assignment which proved more difficult than the first. With Samuel Morris, Jr., John McNeal, and Daniel Joy, he was directed to survey the Jersey shore from Billingsport to Newtown Creek, a stretch of about seven miles somewhat to the south of Philadelphia. This time, they were to go beyond map-making to locate the likeliest spots on the far shore for fortifications and to return estimates of expense. This was a question of military engineering which involved knowledge of strategy and tactics as well. Rittenhouse had little but surveying skills to apply to this operation, but the other members of the group could contribute from a variety of backgrounds: Morris was a member of the Committee of Safety and familiar with general defense plans, McNeal was a construction man who had just declined appointment as an engineer to the committee, and Joy was an army officer.[15]

The location of fortifications depended upon the over-all defense strategy, which had been adopted before Rittenhouse became involved. The basic plan was to close the river to invasion from downstream by sinking *chevaux-de-frise*, or obstacles which would block the passage of ships in all but a few restricted and secret channels. This tactic could be rendered effective only if complemented by an active defense which would keep an aggressor fleet under assault by cannon fire and other forms of harassment.

The committee report, signed by the three experts but not by Morris, was surprisingly bold in taking exception to the basic defense plan. There were two obvious spots for the location of forts on the Jersey shore: Billingsport, a little down-

[14] *Ibid.*, 19.
[15] *Pa. Col. Recs.*, x, 456, 474-75.

stream and across from Hog Island on the Pennsylvania side, and Red Bank, five miles upstream from Billingsport and somewhat north of Fort Island on the Pennsylvania side. The land was high at both spots, and both projected into the river. Unfortunately, neither was well situated to command the *chevaux-de-frise* already sunk out from Fort Island. Besides, only a superior army could prevent the enemy from landing below either point and capturing the fort. If turned against the Americans, the fort might then become a serious danger.

Instead of building such a fort, the survey committee urged the development of a mobile defense. A number of twelve or eighteen pounders should be mounted on strong traveling carriages and used behind breastworks previously prepared at the best spots. Then the enemy could be assaulted from a series of different positions. If hard-pressed, the Americans would be able to extricate themselves without great loss.

This fascinating idea disclosed a justifiable reluctance to rely upon the superiority of American armed forces. At the same time it showed that the committee did not realize that the untrained Americans were especially deficient in the mobility called for. The question was not resolved until months later when General Washington and his staff inspected the ground and reversed the committee's recommendation. After he understood the military considerations, Rittenhouse was not at all reluctant to vote in favor of fortifying Billingsport and completing the fortifications on Fort Island.[16]

On March 2, the quiet clockmaker was handed his most challenging assignment. In a special election, he was chosen to fill Franklin's unexpired term in the Pennsylvania Assembly. Franklin had resigned his seat and also his place on the Committee of Safety on the plea that his age required him to concentrate all his energies on his service as delegate to the Continental Congress.[17]

[16] *Pa. Arch.*, 8th ser., VIII, 7530, 7537–38.
[17] *Ibid.*, 7411, 7428; *Pa. Jour.*, Mar. 6, 1776; Marshall, *Diary*, 61.

Rittenhouse's election was eloquent testimony to the satisfaction with which his fulfillment of the parade of unfamiliar commissions had been received. It indicated, too, the colors to be seen in the first flames of the Revolution. His qualities were more valued as the Revolutionary fervor grew: a man of the people; a child of nature unspoiled by schools or kings or churches; a man of natural dignity and self-evident virtue. Virtue! a quality increasingly cherished by the Revolution and before long adopted by Pennsylvania as the first word of its tripartite motto. The American cause had already benefited from the application of Rittenhouse's honored science. Politically, the radical faction felt they could count on his support of the most positive measures against Britain. Finally, who could more fittingly succeed Benjamin Franklin? To ask the question on March 2, 1776, was to answer it.

"Attending the House, he was qualified as a Member, and took his seat accordingly" on March 5.[18] With so little ceremony, Rittenhouse was suddenly projected into the middle of one of the most active political cauldrons in an erupting nation. Usually, a fledgling burgess was introduced slowly at the beginning of the session to unfolding problems, but Rittenhouse met them first in a virulent state. A vigorous minority, intent upon independence, counted Rittenhouse's victory as evidence of their popularity and as an accession to their strength. This compounded a crisis which the war alone raised to a high pitch; Rittenhouse's first day was a sufficient trial for any man.

Some of the business on this day was routine. A reward was voted to two claimants who had apprehended a man charged with murder. Three private petitions were considered: two of them referred to committee and a third tabled. The house listened to a letter from the governor to the magistrates of Northumberland County, directing them to execute the laws of the province despite the Connecticut settlers. Penn reported that he was not yet able to submit an account of the expenses

[18] *Pa. Arch.*, 8th ser., VIII, 7428.

of a recent expedition to Wyoming to maintain Pennsylvania authority.

More important were matters concerning the war against Britain in which the province was heavily engaged. A petition from Reading complained of the number of captured British regulars quartered in private houses throughout the town, urging that the province build large barracks for the "Billetting of Continental Troops as well as Prisoners." [19] It was tabled. A petition from a militia battalion committee which asked several changes in the regulations governing the troops was similarly tabled. Remarkably swift action met a memorial from the Committee of Safety calling for new troops. A committee appointed in the morning reported in the afternoon with detailed estimates of the cost of maintaining fifteen hundred men. The house immediately voted to raise the men and, by the casting vote of the speaker, to enlist them until January 1, 1778.

The most divisive issue received the least attention from the house. It voted to defer till the end of the week consideration of a large number of back-country petitions for increased representation in the Assembly. This demand had agitated politics for over a decade, but now it was applied to new purposes. Initially, the agitation for greater representation for the interior counties and the city had come from the Presbyterian-Anglican-Proprietary faction and had been aimed against the "three Quaker Counties" and the Quaker-Assembly party. In 1776, the bulk of the Quakers and the Proprietary leaders found themselves united in deploring the more extreme demands of the radical Revolutionary leaders. The radicals realized that they could not effectively deploy back-country support for strong measures against Britain unless the representation were redressed. They supported this objective strenuously, using the serious threat that they could always bypass the Assembly with a provincial congress or convention.

[19] *Ibid.*, 7430.

Two days later, the Assembly devoted almost the whole day to the question of representation. The result was a resolution to give four more seats to the city, two more each to Lancaster, York, Cumberland, Berks, and Northampton, and one more to Bedford, Northumberland, and Westmoreland. The final votes, taken on the 13th and 14th, revealed better than a 2-to-1 majority in favor of the measure. Rittenhouse, of course, voted for it. Except for one man, the opposition was confined to representatives from the three eastern counties that stood to lose political influence by the revision—most of them Quakers.[20]

The success of this move brought Rittenhouse his first commission as assemblyman. With John Montgomery, representative from Cumberland County, he was directed to wait on the governor for his assent to the bill.[21] The choice of these two men was a matter of formal considerations. Rittenhouse was the only city representative sitting in the house, and the city was the largest single beneficiary of the bill; Montgomery represented the counties benefited. At the same time, there may have been some wish to introduce Rittenhouse in his new role to Governor Penn, who was well acquainted with his scientific and mechanical attainments. The bill became law on March 23.

Gradually Rittenhouse was absorbed into other house duties. Some had personal implications. He was pleased, for example, to vote for the confirmation of Hannah's brother-in-law, Caleb Parry, as lieutenant colonel of the Philadelphia County battalion. He was harrowed, on the other hand, by the results of the Congressional resolution of March 14 calling for the disarming of the "notoriously disaffected." The turmoil of conflicting loyalties was especially close to Rittenhouse because of his Quaker relatives and his many friends who hesitated to accept the Revolution. William Smith had already been found by the Committee of Safety, "from his own confession, to have

[20] *Ibid.*, 7444, 7446.
[21] *Ibid.*, 7446.

acted an unfriendly part in the present dispute between Great Britain and these Colonies." [22] This case continued to agitate the government and the press, but Rittenhouse never cut his friend off, although their old relationship was injured.

Many Assembly functions again brought him to problems for which he had had no experience or preparation. With Michael Hillegas and George Gray, Philadelphia County representatives, he was given the task of contracting for supplies to sustain the troops being raised by the province. This entailed a whole series of decisions about the character of rations required and the price levels to be permitted. The standards adopted left no grounds for complaint by the soldiers. The meat ration, for example, was calculated on the basis of a pound of beef or mutton or three-quarters of a pound of pork a day! [23]

Another popular decision in which Rittenhouse concurred showed somewhat less wisdom. As a member of the committee to settle the rank of the captains and subalterns of the Pennsylvania forces, he agreed to the proposition that promotions should be made entirely on the basis of seniority. A rigid rule had been usual in handling the promotion of the lower ranks of officers, and it was even more necessary in a popular revolution; but the committee report did not give even a nodding recognition to the need for merit.[24]

Some of Rittenhouse's jobs were merely tedious. On one occasion he had to share the duty of comparing engrossed bills with the originals, of having the seal affixed to the laws, and of carrying them for deposit to the Rolls Office. On one committee, he visited Province Island to view recent storm damage and to agree with tenants on the amount of losses sustained. On another, he visited the Pennsylvania Hospital to report on its condition. He was given a wide sampling of the business before the house.[25]

[22] *Ibid.; Pa. Gaz.*, Mar. 20, 1776; *Pa. Col. Recs.*, x, 469.
[23] *Pa. Arch.*, 8th ser., VIII, 7454.
[24] *Ibid.*, 7456, 7463–64.
[25] *Ibid.*, 7455, 7466, 7470, 7504, 7508.

When he served on the committee on the Connecticut dispute, Rittenhouse confronted a problem familiar to him from his work in establishing the pivotal point of the northern boundary. The five-man committee was directed to collect all the resolutions of Congress on the dispute and all the affidavits and petitions filed with the Assembly.[26] It was to digest and report upon them at the next sitting of the house. The report was never made—in a sense, the house never sat again. On April 6 it adjourned to May 20 to await the outcome of the elections for the newly established seats.

At this point, despite the readiness of the Assembly to extend seats to underrepresented areas and to advance such radicals as Rittenhouse, its future lay in serious doubt. On the day of adjournment, pressure from the Philadelphia Committee of Inspection and Observation forced a test vote on changing instructions to the Pennsylvania delegates in Congress which would permit them to approve independence. The attempt was defeated by "a great Majority." [27] Both the Pennsylvania minority and the Congressional majority were exceedingly disturbed and some were more than ever prepared to seek their objectives by routes which did not include the Assembly.

Before adjourning, the house added Rittenhouse, with Michael Hillegas and Joseph Parker, to the Committee of Safety. That body, already ripe with power, grew in stature whenever the Assembly was not in session and now more than ever when the future of the legislature was in doubt. As a member, Rittenhouse was assured of some voice in the critical decisions that could not much longer be postponed.[28]

He was quickly assigned duties in keeping with his experience as engineer to the committee. He was placed on the cannon committee, where he continued his efforts to solve the problems of producing large cannon and of promoting the more rapid output of brass field pieces. As a member of the Fort

[26] *Ibid.*, 7471.
[27] *Ibid.*, 7513.
[28] *Ibid.*, 7509; *Pa. Col. Recs.*, x, 537.

Island committee and the committee for further defenses, he assumed a more responsible role in enterprises to which he had already contributed.[29]

Increasingly he was joined with the other mechanic-scientist on the Committee of Safety, Owen Biddle.[30] Early in May, they were given responsibility for conducting an inventory of the shot on hand and for providing any additional supplies required. With little delay, they contracted for fifty tons of cannon balls and for lesser quantities of chain shot, bar shot, and grape shot. The two men were directed to design and procure a large quantity of iron clock weights which could then be exchanged for the lead clock weights in common use throughout the city. The Committee of Safety had long sought to collect all the lead they could find for the manufacture of bullets. This approach would tap the last large reservoir of lead held in private hands.

The Committee of Safety made progress toward the solution of some of its problems, but, when the Assembly reconvened on May 20, one difficulty worsened sharply. The committee complained to the legislature that membership in the two bodies overlapped to such an extent that, with the house in session, the committee often did not have a quorum. The memorial urged the appointment of additional committee members.[31]

The committee's troubles were mild, however, compared with those encountered by the Assembly when it faced the Revolutionary crisis anew. The elections had not gone according to the radicals' predictions. They won most of the western seats, but in the city everything went wrong. Opponents of independence won three of the four new city seats, and only George Clymer of the radical slate was elected.[32] The defeat

[29] *Ibid.*, 539, 543–44, 547.
[30] *Ibid.*, 558, 559, 561, 572; *Pa. Arch.*, 4th ser., III, 594; *Pa. Gaz.*, May 8, 22, 1776.
[31] *Pa. Arch.*, 8th ser., VIII, 7519.
[32] *Ibid.*, 7513–14; Theodore Thayer, *Pennsylvania Politics and the Growth of Democracy, 1740–1776* (Harrisburg, 1953), 179.

was narrow enough to be explained by the lost votes of those away in army service, but whether the explanation was valid or not, the advocates of independence failed to gain control of the house. There, their strength was sufficient only to nullify the legislature by preventing a quorum. Outside the chamber, there was a good chance they could act more positively.

The chief question now was whether independence could be attained at all without overthrowing the old Charter of Privileges and the existing government of Pennsylvania. Leaders in the Continental Congress were convinced that Pennsylvania's reluctance was the major bar remaining to the acceptance of independence. With this knowledge, the Pennsylvania radicals pressed hard. They found the key in John Adams' resolution of May 10, calling on "the respective Assemblies and Conventions of the United Colonies, where no government sufficient to the exigencies of their affairs hath been hitherto established, to adopt such government as shall, in the opinion of the representatives of the people best conduce to the happiness and safety of their constituents in particular, and America in general." [33]

Philadelphia had reacted violently to the resolution. There, a public meeting was held in the State House yard at which four or five thousand people overwhelmingly approved a projected convention to form a new government for Pennsylvania. Soon petitions and counterpetitions flooded the Assembly: demands that a convention be called and violent denunciations of the idea; demands for changing the instructions of the Congressional delegates and demands that they not be changed. The house sat immobilized except for perfunctory business. Occasionally, it reacted to the more dramatic military news.[34]

It opened its eyes to consider the engagement of the Pennsylvania row galleys with *H.M.S. Roebuck* and *H.M.S. Liver-*

[33] *Journals of the American Congress from 1774 to 1788* (Phila., 1800–1801), II, 158.

[34] *Pa. Gaz.*, May 1, 8, 22, 29, June 5, 1776; *Pa. Packet*, May 27, 1776; Broadside: In Committee Chamber, [Phila.], May 18, 1776, LCP.

pool. This affair had first concerned Rittenhouse early in May when the Committee of Safety ordered the Pennsylvania ships to attack British war vessels which were discovered proceeding up the Delaware. In the ensuing two-day skirmish, the *Roebuck* avoided capture or destruction despite a favorable opportunity presented when she ran aground. The committee was disappointed—probably critical—and the galley commanders reacted publicly by blaming the result on the committee's failure to provide sufficient ammunition. After investigation, the Assembly exonerated the Committee of Safety and commended it.[35]

All this was trivial compared with the great problem of independence, which the Assembly was unable to resolve and which occasioned a variously motivated absenteeism, often preventing a quorum. The impotence and frustration of the house infected the Committee of Safety, which released some of its pique in its unusually specific minutes for June 11: "Mr. Clymer, Mr. Parker, & Mr. Rittenhouse, being obliged to leave the Board to attend the House, no business could be entered into." [36] But if they did attend the Assembly, they accomplished nothing for no quorum was attained that day, nor the next, nor the day following. The province and all elements of its government were like a ship becalmed, hull down from the port she sought.

This uneasy atmosphere was disconcerting to advocates and opponents of independence alike, but especially to a man who had only recently entered politics from a quieter life and who already fully accepted the need for independence. At this juncture, Rittenhouse wrote the only scientific piece he was able to squeeze out of a hurried and harried time. It reflected his mood, revealing more bitterness and arrogance than had ever before diluted the objectivity of his science.

Under the signature "R," he replied in the *Pennsylvania*

---

[35] *Pa. Jour.*, May 13, 1776; *Pa. Arch.*, 8th ser., VIII, 7536, 7538, 7544.
[36] *Ibid.*, 7540; *Pa. Col. Recs.*, x, 598.

Magazine to a dull and muddled letter which John Wither-spoon had transparently signed "J. W." Witherspoon presumed to cast doubt on some of Newton's work and to praise Descartes by contrast. That was enough for Rittenhouse. In just two sharply etched paragraphs, he cut through Witherspoon's obfuscations to reveal the untruth of the most concrete charge presented. With biting contempt, he commented, "I wish the gentleman would be more cautious for the future; as well on his own account, as for the sake of your readers, some of whom may be misled by the weakest reasoning." [37] Witherspoon was more cautious thereafter: he never again published anything on science. Rittenhouse was more cautious too: he never again permitted himself to show such a degree of exasperation.

The tension was broken when the Assembly finally succumbed to the unrelieved pressure and caved in. On June 8, the house withdrew its opposition to independence. The Pennsylvania delegates in Congress were authorized to "concur" with other delegations, although independence was not specifically mentioned. The contest was then transferred to the Pennsylvania delegation, a majority of which still opposed independence, and to the floor of Congress. Even before that struggle for independence was won, the Assembly adjourned.[38]

The Pennsylvania radicals did not arrest their plans to replace the Assembly with a government to be designed by a convention called for that purpose. On June 18, a Conference of Provincial Committees met in Philadelphia, agreed to call a convention, and set July 8 as the date for electing delegates.[39]

Congress voted independence on July 2; on July 4 it adopted the Declaration of Independence; and on July 8 the Declaration was read to a large crowd in the State House yard. Many

[37] *Pa. Mag.*, I (June, 1776), 282–83; Brooke Hindle, "Witherspoon, Rittenhouse, and Sir Isaac Newton," *William and Mary Quar.*, 3d ser., 15 (1958), 365–72.
[38] *Pa. Arch.*, 8th ser., VIII, 7539, 7542–43; *Pa. Gaz.*, June 12, 1776.
[39] *Journals of the House of Representatives of the Commonwealth of Pennsylvania* [1776–81] (Phila., 1782), 34.

were already there to vote for convention delegates and the two events were related in more than time and place. Parades, salutes, bonfires, and ringing bells dramatized the occasion. Inside the Assembly room and the court room, the king's arms were torn down. The old order came to an end before the new order had been supplied.[40]

The still debilitated Committee of Safety exercised the last remnant of governmental authority in Pennsylvania. Many people—and not all of them Tories—had serious doubts about the wisdom of the course that had been chosen and about the end to which it might lead. To some, Rittenhouse's association with the move to independence represented a personal tragedy within a national tragedy, one poet predicting:

> Oblivion shall entomb thy name
> And from the Rolls of future fame
> Thou'll fall, to rise no more.[41]

To others, he became an increasing assurance.

[40] Marshall, *Diary*, 83; *Pa. Gaz.*, July 10, 1776.
[41] Pemberton Papers, xxx, 55, HSP.

CHAPTER X

The Constitution

1776

O N July 8, 1776, David Rittenhouse was elected a member of the Convention called to give Pennsylvania a new constitution, "on the authority of the people only." [1] This was the high tide of the Revolution in the state. The Revolutionary Convention wrote a Revolutionary constitution which represented not the fulfillment of Pennsylvania's achievements in government as a colony but the overthrow and abnegation of the old order within the state and paralleled the expulsion of external British authority. The men who had opposed compromise to push Pennsylvania through to independence, opposed compromise again when they pushed her through to a new form of government.

The conditions which led to the formation of the Convention were unique. Least important was the evident need to replace the charter of a proprietary colony with something more suitable to an independent state. Every other proprietary and royal colony in the new United States had, sooner or later, to establish a new constitution. The problem in Pennsylvania was that the independence movement was a minority movement. This factor colored the entire war. The Revolutionary leaders were hard pressed to discover governmental means of maximizing their support and minimizing their opposition sufficiently to keep Pennsylvania in the fight. This was the job of the Convention and the reason so many of its members were inexperienced and unknown.

The groundwork was laid by the Conference of Provincial

[1] *Pa. Arch.*, 2d ser., III, 639.

Committees, which had been bound by no charter or previous practice in establishing the rules for electing members of the Convention. In every way, it sought to favor the elements which supported the Revolution and to discriminate against those opposing it. The traditional property requirement for voting—fifty acres or fifty pounds personal property—was abandoned because this disfranchised large numbers of associators. The associators were the Revolutionary militia and, almost by definition, they supported the Revolution. The Conference extended to every associator the right to vote provided he was twenty-one years old, had lived in Pennsylvania for a year, and had at some time or other paid either local or provincial taxes.[2]

For the identical purpose, those unquestionably opposed to the Revolution were disfranchised. Tories and Tory sympathizers were identified by their refusal to take an oath against the king and in support of the government to be established by the Convention. The franchise was withheld from such nonjurors and in addition from anyone charged by a local committee as an enemy to the Revolution.

The deck was stacked in still another way. The western counties and Philadelphia continued to harbor grievances generated by their long struggle against underrepresentation, despite the Assembly's recent correction of that fault. More to the point, the westerners and the rank and file of the city people were commonly recognized to be very much more ardent in their support of the Revolution than the inhabitants of Bucks, Chester, and Philadelphia Counties. The Conference unblushingly, therefore, accorded gross overrepresentation to the West and the city. Regardless of population, the city and every county in the state were given equal representation— each was permitted to send eight representatives to the Convention on the lame plea that accurate information about the number of taxables was not available.

[2] Broadside: Extracts from the Proceedings of the Provincial Conference of Committees, June 18, 1776, LC.

The effects of this plotting were intensified by other factors in the political environment. The Quakers, who had long dominated Pennsylvania politics, largely withdrew from active participation. The discipline of their meetings was frequently exercised to restrict members from political action which condoned warlike measures.[3] Many no longer voted in elections. The Moravians in the state followed a somewhat similar course. Even moderate Whigs were reluctant to pursue the lead of the radicals who had forced Pennsylvania into independence. Many of them were sincerely committed to the American opposition to Britain but they did not want to go so far or so fast—and especially they did not trust the violent radical leadership. Faced with disagreeable alternatives, moderates too, in some cases, refused to vote on July 8. As a result, Charles Biddle reported, "there were very few respectable people present." [4]

The bulk of the political leadership of colonial Pennsylvania was now to be found in Tory, Quaker, or moderate Whig camps. Their withdrawal unintentionally combined with the efforts of the Conference and the radical leaders to produce a Convention lacking the necessary political experience.

One final factor vitally affected the voters who chose the Convention. On the very day independence was declared, Howe landed on Staten Island in the first step of his grimly successful New York campaign. With a trained and growing enemy army little more than a hundred miles away, the members of Convention were chosen not *because* they were radicals in any general sense, or *because* they had political experience or did not have it, but only because they were "violent partisans of the American cause." [5]

Even before the Convention met on July 15, opponents began to hammer away at the incapacity of the assembly, and, unquestionably, most of its members were unknowns, countrymen of limited knowledge. Then and thereafter, however, two an-

[3] David Hawke, *In the Midst of a Revolution* (Phila., 1961), 154.
[4] Charles Biddle, *Autobiography* (Phila., 1883), 86.
[5] *PMHB*, xii, 389.

swers proved most effective against tormentors who prattled of inexperience and lack of distinction: "They quite forget Dr. Franklin and David Rittenhouse, A.M. were in Convention." [6] Much of the respectability and prestige the Convention had came from these men, who readily pledged their reputations to a dubious cause.

Franklin was unanimously elected president, where he was visible for all to see. His name was his chief contribution to the Convention, for he was ill much of the time it met and he took a limited part in the deliberations that he attended. Alexander Graydon, an unfriendly witness, recorded Vice President George Ross's comment that Franklin left to him not only "the whole business of the department, but even declined the trouble of thinking." [7] Nevertheless, many aspects of the frame of government adopted by the Convention were in close harmony with Franklin's ideas of government—most specifically the unicameral legislature and the plural executive.[8] At a variety of points, both his known opinions and his voice proved influential.

The name of David Rittenhouse was less exalted than Franklin's, but it possessed a remarkable resilience, resisting one of the worst periods of calumny in American history. Even the veriest Tories never thought of scratching at the symbol Rittenhouse had become. They had to content themselves with plaintive laments about malevolent plotters who accomplished his "fall."

By one, he was advised,

> Labour not in State Affairs
> Keep acquaintance with the Stars
> For there thy Genius lies.[9]

---

[6] *Pa. Gaz.*, Oct. 30, 1776.
[7] [Alexander Graydon], *Memoirs of a Life, Chiefly Passed within Pennsylvania* (Harrisburgh, 1811), 286.
[8] *Pa. Gaz.*, Mar. 31, 1779.
[9] Pemberton Papers, xxx, 55, HSP.

Even the unrelenting Jonathan Odell acknowledged the symbol,

> There dwelt in Norriton's sequestered bowers,
> A mortal blessed with mathematic powers,—
> To whom was David Rittenhouse unknown?
> Fair Science saw and marked him for her own.

But,

> While thus he soared above the starry spheres,
> The word of Congress sounded in his ears;
> He listened to the voice with strange delight
> And swift descended from his dazzling height.[10]

One of the most subtle means of diminishing Franklin's and Rittenhouse's fame was the admission of their superiority "in everything else except the science of government." [11] But, although Rittenhouse's reputation derived almost wholly from fields unrelated to government, he lent far more than his name to the Convention. He was neither misled, nor duped, nor hypnotized. His eyes were open and his heart was filled with a transcendent faith in the American cause and in man's ability to govern himself. He found "numsculs" in the Convention, as Peter Grubb called them; he found men who "would go to the devil for popularity," but he was neither dismayed by incompetence nor disturbed by "leveling principles." [12] His political creed was clear-cut and simple. He was in hearty sympathy with the tendencies of the Convention to rest government upon the wisdom and virtue of the average man. He was one—perhaps one of few—who took the philosophy of the Declaration of Independence seriously.

But there is no evidence that Rittenhouse went to the Convention with the blueprint of a constitution in his mind; the

---

[10] *Royal Gaz.* (N.Y.), Sep. 8, 1779.

[11] Samuel B. Harding, "Party Struggles over the First Pennsylvania Constitution," Amer. Hist. Assn., *Annual Report for 1894* (Washington, 1895), 379n.

[12] Cited by J. Paul Selsam, *The Pennsylvania Constitution of 1776* (Phila., 1936), 149.

blueprints came from others. The limited evidence suggests that James Cannon may have been the most influential of these. An Anglican immigrant from Scotland, Cannon had taught mathematics in the College and became an important political force as secretary of the committee of privates of the associator battalions. Under his leadership, this pressure group favored annual elections, broad suffrage, and care to prevent the rule of the aristocracy.[13] Timothy Matlack, fighting Quaker much scorned by the opposition for his impecunious background, was a colonel of associators and a brawling leader inside and outside the Convention. Robert Whitehill was a new but durable politician with strong support in Cumberland County. Outside the Convention, George Bryan probably did not exercise the authority credited to him, but Thomas Paine was close to the small group of leaders and his *Common Sense* was an ever present influence.

Before the Convention had well begun the writing of a constitution, it recognized that it had another function which must be carried on concurrently. In the Assembly's default, it assumed the legislative power of the state. The Assembly had adjourned in June and, faced with continued nullification, had to adjourn again when it tried to function in August. Finally on September 26, two days ahead of the Convention, it "rose." Rittenhouse did not attend the death throes of the old order; he was absorbed in building the new.

For the first week, he almost completely ignored the meetings of the floundering Committee of Safety in order to attend the Convention.[14] On July 23, however, the Convention reorganized the committee, changing its name to the Council of Safety and directing it "to exercise the whole of the executive powers of government, so far as relates to the military defence

---

[13] Broadside: To the Several Battalions of Military Associators, June 26, 1776, HSP.
[14] *Pa. Col. Recs.*, x, 648–56.

146

and safety of the province." [15] Fifteen members were appointed from the city or its vicinity and one from each of the counties. Among them were several leaders of the Convention, including Biddle, Cannon, and Matlack, but the majority were as obscure as the generality of the Convention. Christopher Marshall complained that it was "a poor set for that important post at this time." [16]

First named among the members of the Council of Safety, Rittenhouse was raised on the crest of the Revolutionary wave to his greatest political prominence. For the first two weeks, he served as temporary chairman. On August 6, Thomas Wharton was elected president of the Council and Rittenhouse vice-president.[17] "Vice President elect," Odell moaned, "of rogues and fools." [18] Yet none ever called Rittenhouse rogue or fool, and he succeeded in transferring some part of his reputation to the newly constituted council. He gave more; he gave devotion, integrity, and direction. The complete minutes of the Council of Safety reveal that he missed very few sessions during the tenure of the Convention and that at nearly half of the sessions, he presided. This duty necessarily took him away from the Convention floor much of the time, but the imperfect Convention minutes suggest that he was frequently present and, since both bodies met in the State House, always near by. When the Convention was not sitting, he met with its committees.

Although the Convention early appointed committees to prepare a draft of the Constitution and a declaration of rights, much of its business concerned day-to-day problems of government. A minute entry that became almost standard read, "resumed the consideration of legislative and executive business." [19] When possible, the Convention turned business over

[15] *Pa. House Jours.* (1782), 52, 55.
[16] Marshall, *Diary*, 86.
[17] *Pa. Col. Recs.*, x, 672.
[18] *Royal Gaz.* (N.Y.), Sep. 8, 1779.
[19] *Pa. House Jours.* (1782), 51.

to the Council of Safety, but it retained control of policy decisions and affairs unrelated to the conduct of the war.

On July 20, the Convention replaced all the Pennsylvania delegates to Congress who had voted against the Declaration or who seemed reluctant about the Revolution and appointed a committee to prepare new instructions for the delegates. Rittenhouse served on the committee with Matlack, Cannon, Colonel Thomas Smith of Bedford County, and Colonel John Bull, chairman of the Philadelphia Committee of Inspection and Observation. The fervor they poured into a draft resolution so impressed the Convention that it passed unanimously. Delegates were exhorted to "punctual" attendance, "vigorous" exertion against the enemy, "union" of the states, the establishment of a naval force, and diplomacy worthy of "free and independent states." [20]

Rittenhouse's appointment to a committee to prepare ordinances against counterfeiting and treason proved more distressing. The first draft of the ordinance on counterfeiting did not suit the Convention, and the version it finally approved was unrestrained in severity. The counterfeiting of bills of credit of the United States, Pennsylvania, or any of the states was made punishable by death. Informers were encouraged by substantial rewards. Whipping, pillorying, cutting off the ears, *and* a fine of £100 was the penalty established for hiking denominations of bills and for knowingly passing counterfeit currency. If the fine could not be paid, the convict might be sold for up to seven years' labor.[21] The Revolutionaries did not hesitate to use the utmost power of the state in attempting to control a serious problem.

To the state, treason was the more heinous crime, but the Convention met it with a lighter scale of punishments. After rejecting the death penalty, the Convention and the committee wrestled long and hard, finally coming to a satisfactory resolu-

[20] *Ibid.*, 53, 55, 57.
[21] *Ibid.*, 54, 55, 56, 58, 60.

tion on September 5. Treason was defined, and the penalty was established as forfeiture of estate and imprisonment for a term not to exceed the length of the war. The mildness of this punishment reflected the need for some accommodation with a potentially enormous population of traitors. On September 12, an additional ordinance provided that security for good behavior might be demanded or imprisonment imposed in the case of writing or speaking against measures of the United States.[22] As a wartime restriction upon traditional freedoms, this was a remarkably loose muzzle.

Rittenhouse was not free of this problem with the passage of the ordinance, for the Convention named the members of the Council of Safety justices of the peace and gave to them responsibility for enforcement. The justices of the peace were required to exact security or to confine those who opposed United States measures. In addition, any three justices were empowered to refuse bail to a person deemed dangerous and to commit him to a common jail for the duration of the war.[23]

Rittenhouse chaired one committee assigned an impossible objective: to render the "burden and expense just and Equal" between associators and non-associators.[24] Everyone acknowledged the sacrifice of those who put their lives in jeopardy and injured their business and family to serve in the field. How could an equivalent contribution be exacted from those who did not serve? In the midst of extended efforts, reports, and recommitments, Rittenhouse presided over the Convention on several occasions when it resolved itself into a committee of the whole to discuss this problem. Another barrier that did not yield to discussion was the undoubted need for harsh discipline to get any military use out of the associators. This need was countered by the impossibility of subjecting volunteer soldiers to the maximum scale of punishments.

The most satisfactory solution lay in eliminating the prob-

[22] *Ibid.*, 61, 71; *Pa. Gaz.*, Sep. 4, 11, 25, 1776.
[23] *Ibid.*, Sep. 4, 1776.
[24] *Pa. House Jours.* (1782), 54, 62, 65, 68, 76, 77, 82, 83.

lem by dissolving the associator battalions. This was a dream the Convention clutched at when it sought to implement Congress' plan to create a 10,000-man "Flying Camp." Provision was made for the Pennsylvania contingent of 6,000 in this mobile fighting force under the impression that, once constituted, the Flying Camp would obviate the need for the associator battalions. Indeed, the associators were promised that they would be released as soon as the new force was established.

Meanwhile, however, the problem remained. Strenuous efforts were made to recover deserters, and local committees were adjured to "distribute money equitably" to keep associators' families from need.[25] Rittenhouse's committee brought forth a tax measure which laid heavy tax burdens on non-associators. It added to the twenty shilling monthly tax a new tax of four shillings in the pound on the annual output of each non-associator's estate.[26] In terms of a productive farm, this was equivalent to a 20 per cent income tax—a steep assessment.

Because of his previous involvement, Rittenhouse was projected into the Virginia boundary dispute as soon as that affair —on top of all other troubles—fell into the Convention's lap. The continuing ferment on the frontier owed as much to conflicting land claims as it did to the threat of Indian attack. The approach to a solution was undertaken on the initiative of the Virginia delegation to Congress, which in a dignified, friendly appeal urged on the Pennsylvanians the establishment of a temporary boundary between the two states. The invitation, drafted by Thomas Jefferson, breathed the emotional sense of union that had been generated by the Declaration, and the Pennsylvania Convention responded in the same spirit.[27]

Rittenhouse, Thomas Smith, Alexander Lowrey, Owen Biddle, and James Potter were appointed to meet the Virginia delegates. Weeks afterward, they reported that the Virginians had

[25] *Ibid.*, 63, 64, 66; *Pa. Gaz.*, Aug. 14, 21, 28, 1776.
[26] *Pa. House Jours.* (1782), 82–83.
[27] Boyd, ed., *Papers of Jefferson*, I, 465–66.

in mind a boundary "very wide from the true limits of *Pennsylvania,* according to the Charter." [28] Not even the committee's ardent patriotism was sufficient to lead it to compromise Pennsylvania's interests so unfavorably. It reacted strongly against a line so inconsistent with Virginia's earlier pledge and suggested a temporary line closer to the true one. The Virginia delegates responded that they had no power to negotiate. They promised to seek "counter proposals" to lay before the next Pennsylvania Assembly; and thus the question had to be left.[29]

Here for a time the matter ended. Never more than a stopgap government, the Convention was seldom able to offer the sustained initiative required to solve the more serious problems confronting it. It took action at points where action could not be avoided in the hope that the ensuing permanent government would be able to build upon beginnings it had made. The Convention never forgot that its primary purpose was to write a constitution.

Rittenhouse took no part in the initial phase of drafting the Constitution. Three days after the Convention assembled, a committee of eleven, including many of the members with legal or governmental experience, was appointed to draft a declaration of rights. The members were very shortly given, in addition, the fundamental task of writing a frame of government. On July 25, the committee was expanded by the addition of six men, including Matlack, Cannon, Whitehill, and Rittenhouse—the core of the Revolutionary leadership.[30]

Thereafter, the Convention devoted much of its attention to the declaration of rights, adopted on August 16, and to the frame of government, which took considerably longer. Sometime before the 21st, Rittenhouse became chairman of this key committee; he made its reports to the Convention, and he presided on the frequent occasions when the frame of gov-

[28] *Pa. House Jours.* (1782), 50, 53, 82.
[29] *Ibid.,* 82.
[30] *Ibid.,* 56.

ernment was debated in a committee of the whole.[31] On September 5, Franklin, Rittenhouse, and the Reverend William Vanhorn, a Baptist minister with a master's degree from the College of Rhode Island, were appointed to revise the accepted draft in style and to have four hundred copies printed for public consideration. Further debate followed, a few substantive changes were made, and the finished frame of government was published on September 18.

The preamble, oath of office, and oath of allegiance were subsequently drafted by Cannon, John Jacobs, and Rittenhouse, and were quickly approved. On the 28th, the Constitution, including preamble, declaration of rights, and frame of government was formally adopted and the Convention rose—its task completed.

As far as the record goes, no one played a more conspicuous part in forming the Pennsylvania Constitution of 1776 than David Rittenhouse. He served on the committee that prepared the declaration of rights, he chaired the committee during the most important phase of drafting the frame of government, he served on the committee that prepared the preamble and the oaths, and he served on the committee on style.[32] No other member was so involved in every single phase of the writing of the Constitution. Even so, it is impossible to know how much he contributed to the Constitution or in what particulars it may have deviated from his ideas. It is clear only, from the comments of his time and from his whole subsequent political life, that he was in harmony with the general form and the aspirations of the Constitution.

The Constitution was a Revolutionary document, a fact glossed over by contemporary opponents and underplayed by historians ever since. A product of the Revolution against Great Britain, its form was primarily determined by the need to

[31] *Ibid.*, 65, 66, 68, 69.
[32] *Ibid.*, 87.

win that war. Then and ever after it has been criticized as a party manifesto, written by men with limited knowledge of government. The criticism was not without truth but this was not the most important truth about it.

The philosophy that underlay the entire Constitution, coinciding with Rittenhouse's own philosophy, was the philosophy of the Declaration—literally transcribed. Indeed, the preamble was in large measure an inept paraphrase of the Declaration's sonorous phrases respecting the compact theory of government, natural rights, and the right of revolution. With fewer mental reservations than the Congress, the Convention accepted the assertion that "all men are created equal." The Pennsylvanians balked at the economic leveling demanded by Cannon, but they went far in the political realm.[33] They translated theoretical equalitarianism into a working political democracy which bore an uncanny resemblance to the aspirations of the English Commonwealth period. Whether manhood suffrage, a unicameral legislature, a plural executive, and rotation in office were transmitted to the Convention by the intellectuals or were a part of the folk beliefs of the delegates—or both—they constituted a consistent pattern which rested government on the wisdom and virtue of the common man.

The Pennsylvania declaration of rights has properly been described as an amended version of Virginia's bill of rights, which was written by George Mason and adopted only a month before the Pennsylvania Convention convened. Other states, too, followed this practice, leaving Pennsylvania's compilation a distinctly average and normal performance. The civil rights that became standard were included with the exception of one Virginia prohibition on government: that against excessive bail, fines, and cruel and unusual punishments. This may have been a reflection of the ardent Revolutionaries' concern for declining civic virtue and their demonstrated readiness to en-

[33] Broadside: An Essay of a Declaration of Rights [1776], HSP.

force virtue where it was insufficient. On the other hand, the declaration was notable for freeing Pennsylvania's numerous pacifists from the obligation of bearing arms. Added to the Virginia list, were the rights of petition, assembly, and "a Natural Inherent right to Emigrate from one State to another." [34]

The frame of government was the novel part of the Constitution; unquestionably it was the most democratic provided by any of the states. Perhaps its most controversial element, an object of violent dispute before it ever went into effect, was the unicameral legislature. Here especially, the Pennsylvanians were deemed by competent American political thinkers to have deviated from the best theory and practice of the age. George Ross and George Clymer headed an effort to defeat this proposal during the course of the Convention but they could not prevail—particularly when Franklin threw his weight behind the single-house legislature.[35]

The decision to have a unicameral legislature was not at all the result of inexperience and theoretical ignorance, as charged. In the first place, Pennsylvania had had a single-house legislature for seventy-five years. Not even the most experienced critic had served the state, or former province, or the United States under any form but unicameralism. The innovation of bicameralism had nothing to offer Pennsylvania's Revolutionary leaders in terms of their major objective—which, be it always remembered, was the completion of the Revolution against Britain. Indeed, there was every possibility that their opponents within the state might be better able to stalemate the Revolution if presented with two houses. They might more easily capture one of the two.

John Adams, who described the Constitution with harsh invective, divined the truth with his usual perceptiveness. He confessed, "An apprehension, that the Proprietary and Quaker

[34] Thayer, *Pa. Politics*, 214.
[35] *Pa. Gaz.*, Mar. 31, 1779; *Pa. House Jours.* (1782), 52; Harding, "Party Struggles," 378.

interest would prevail, to the election of characters disaffected to the American cause, finally preponderated against two legislative councils." [36]

This insight also explains the unprecedented liberality of the suffrage requirements. The Convention was as convinced as the Conference that the American cause was strongly supported by the associators, the disfranchised in the city, and the westerners who lacked a "stake in society." They followed the formula introduced by the Conference, anticipating that the more radical Revolutionary leadership would benefit. Property qualifications for voting were abolished. All men over twenty-one who had lived in the state for a year and had paid taxes, and all sons of voters even though they had not paid taxes, were given the franchise.[37]

Provisions for rotation in office, for written ballot, for easy naturalization, and provisions barring plural voting and plural officeholding were liberal political reforms following from the prevailing philosophy of government. At the same time, they too were presumed to favor the election of advocates of the American cause.

There was nothing liberal about the oath of allegiance; its only justification was to keep those opposed to the Revolution from getting control of the government. The form of the oath to be taken by all officers of government was specified in the frame of government. It included not only a pledge to the Commonwealth but a promise not to "do any Act or Thing prejudicial or Injurious to the Constitution or Government thereof as established by the Convention." [38] When this was interpreted to bar from office any who sought to replace the Constitution of 1776 with another, it could and did become an instrument of party tyranny.

The religious portion of the oath required of assemblymen

[36] Adams, ed., *Works of Adams*, IX, 429, 623.
[37] Thayer, *Pa. Politics*, 215.
[38] *Ibid.*, 225.

was resolved curiously. It was more liberal than the Charter of Privileges, which had required belief "in JESUS CHRIST the SAVIOUR of the world."[39] The 1776 formula represented an ambiguous compromise, the first sentence of which was in full accord with Rittenhouse's and Franklin's sentiments, if perhaps not liberal enough for Cannon. It read: "I do Believe in one God the Creator and Governor of the Universe the Rewarder of the Good and Punisher of the Wicked." Franklin opposed the second sentence, and probably Rittenhouse as well, but in vain. It went on, "I do acknowledge the Scriptures of the Old and New Testament to be given by Divine Inspiration."[40] This could mean many different things, but it was not ideally suited to a deist's beliefs.

The oath was distinctly less pleasing to the Christian clergy and laity. The Reverend Henry Melchior Muhlenberg complained bitterly, "it now seems as if a Christian people were ruled by Jews, Turks, Spinozists, Deists, perverted naturalists." When William Smith, despite the charges of Toryism rising against him, sought to rally the clergy in an effort to win more recognition of the churches, Muhlenberg responded pessimistically, "What can despised preachers effect with a Rump Parliament?"[41] His intention was to heap obloquy on the Convention, but he was perceptive in tying the Commonwealth of Pennsylvania to the Commonwealth of England.

Smith succeeded, acting largely through the clergy, in convincing Franklin and in winning a clause in which the Constitution "encouraged and protected" all religious societies.[42] The clause was extended, too, to cover bodies for the advancement of virtue and learning and for charitable purposes. Smith's powers of persuasion were still undimmed.

[39] *Ibid.*, 206.
[40] *Ibid.*, 217; Jared Sparks, ed., *The Works of Benjamin Franklin* (Chicago, 1882), x, 134.
[41] *PMHB*, XXII, 129–31.
[42] George B. Wood, *The History of the University of Pennsylvania* (Phila., 1834), 210; *Pa. Arch.*, 3d ser., x, 765.

The limited attention given the doctrine of checks and balances in the frame of government was severely "reprobated" by opponents.[43] The document clearly recognized the compartmentation of powers in specific statements giving "Supreme Legislative power" to the Assembly, "Supreme Executive power" to the president and Council, and judicial power to "Courts of Justice." [44] The compartmentation, however, was almost watertight as far as the Assembly was concerned. No individual or body was given a veto over its measures so it did in fact possess supreme legislative power. The fundamental anticipation was that the abuse of power in the Assembly would be checked by not giving special power to any group and by the exercise of a broad suffrage and annual elections. The freedoms of press, speech, assembly, and religion would guarantee a free Assembly. A further check was exercised by the people through public legislative sessions and through the requirement that all bills be printed for public consideration before the third reading. Time, too, was a check, in that all except emergency legislation was to be considered by two successive Assemblies.

The judiciary, if anything, was overbalanced by checks. Appointed by the executive arm, judges were given terms of only seven years although they might be reappointed. They might be impeached at any time by the Assembly. No court was given, explicitly or implicitly, the right to review legislation.

The executive was so weak that few checks were needed. Here especially, the Revolutionary character of the Constitution was evident, for the radicals sought not to accommodate the views of their opponents but to overcome them. As the Revolutionists did everywhere in the United States, they weakened the executive, because this had been the seat of external power, and they correspondingly strengthened the popular organ of government, the Assembly. Pennsylvania went further than

[43] [Graydon], *Memoirs*, 286.
[44] Thayer, *Pa. Politics*, 215.

any other state in this by replacing the governor altogether with a multiple executive, styled the Supreme Executive Council. Even this innovation had roots in experience for, alone of the colonies, Pennsylvania had had a council limited to administrative and executive functions—a council without legislative power. Now the proprietary governor was eliminated and the powers of the council expanded. A political necessity accounted for the disproportionate representation of the West on the Council. One member of Council was to be chosen from each county and one from the city; a sure way of strengthening the hand of those who favored the American cause.

Even when the necessities and aspirations behind the frame of government were understood, the deficiency of checks and balances was still apparent—especially the lack of restraints upon the Assembly. To remedy this fault a body wholly new to Pennsylvania was designed to restrain the abuse of power without creating a power center that might oppose the will of the people. A Council of Censors was established, "in Order that the Freedom of this Common Wealth may be preserved inviolate for ever." [45] Elected every seven years, the Council was empowered to review actions of all elements of the government to determine whether any violations of the Constitution had occurred. If violations had taken place, it could take steps to correct them. Of all the innovations of the Constitution this rootless invention was the most unsatisfactory, but how well it would work—or how well any part of the Constitution would work—depended less upon its abstract characteristics than upon the individuals who would be called upon to use it.

In the final days of the Convention, the stature to which Rittenhouse had grown became more apparent in every resolution. He was appointed chairman of a committee to settle the incidental expenses of the Convention and chairman of another committee to prepare seals for the Assembly and the Supreme Executive Council. He was associated with Cannon and Mat-

[45] *Ibid.*, 226–27.

lack in writing an address to explain why the Convention had assumed the powers of government during its sitting. With Cannon, Matlack, and Bull, he was directed to revise the minutes and have copies printed of the minutes, the ordinances, and the Constitution.[46]

Although Rittenhouse had not become a working politician, he emerged as much more than a symbol. He served actively in leading the Convention to the completion of its task. His sincerity was obvious to all; he believed in the Constitution because he believed in the cause behind it.

[46] Pa. *House Jours.* (1782), 95–96.

CHAPTER XI

The War

1776

THE Revolution did not consist alone in asserting independence and in composing frames of government. The final test lay in defending them. All the while the Convention sat, the sound of distant drums grew louder and the threat of enemy armies greater. Howe's forces on Staten Island increased until they numbered some 34,000, and the Americans could only wonder how effective the lightning would be when it struck. For weeks and months, those who held the precarious balance in favor of the Revolution in Pennsylvania were never free of threatening disaster.

In the Convention and in the Council of Safety, Rittenhouse received the full brunt of the demands for action. The Council continued to serve as the Convention's executive arm in military affairs, one knotty problem after another being referred to it for solution. Convention members remained directly and deeply concerned with defense preparations; they inspected the fortifications, ships, floating battery, and galleys in the vicinity of Fort Island, but they were not willing to accept much responsibility even for policy decisions. When the Council specifically requested a ruling on the touchy question of command of the fleet, the Convention postponed consideration, referred the question to committee, and finally directed that the matter be decided "wholly" by the Council of Safety, with the observation that seniority need not always govern such appointments. Other problems relating to raw materials, to arms, to deserters, and to the frontier, it turned over to the Council as a matter of course.[1]

[1] *Pa. House Jours.* (1782), 50, 55, 58, 61, 64, 85, 86.

Occasionally, the Convention took direct action. It sought to implement the Congressional resolution to disarm the disaffected by collecting all arms in the hands of non-associators. Rittenhouse chaired the committee charged with preparing an ordinance to execute this intention. Two days later, the Convention passed an ordinance giving the colonel of each associator battalion responsibility for taking up all arms in his district belonging to non-associators. The owners were to be given receipts and the arms appraised and repaired. The colonels would then have in their hands some means of arming associators, who were coming in much faster than they could be equipped.[2]

This supply did not begin to fill the equipment needs which Council found entirely beyond its means in almost every required item. Muskets and rifles could not be manufactured quickly, so the Convention recommended that the Council provide pikes for the unarmed—an idea Franklin had earlier urged. In an oblique response, the Council, over Rittenhouse's signature, directed Franklin and the rest of the Pennsylvania delegation to Congress to request that arms collected by Congress be made available to the Pennsylvania troops. The Council continued its efforts to collect all lead remaining in private hands in the city, spurred by advice from Congress and from the Convention. Rittenhouse was charged with arranging for an adequate supply of musket cartridge paper from the papermakers, among whom members of his family were still prominent.[3]

The still lagging program for producing cannon was further set back when Captain Benjamin Loxley, superintendent of the cannon foundry, was called up with his artillery company. Rather preemptorily, Rittenhouse directed General Daniel Roberdeau to release the captain, admonishing him, "a day's

---

[2] *Ibid.*, 51, 52–53; *Pa. Gaz.*, Aug. 7, 1776.
[3] *Pa. House Jours.* (1782), 55; *Pa. Col. Recs.*, x, 637; *Pa. Arch.*, 4th ser., III, 610–11.

delay in this business may be attended with the most Serious Consequences." [4]

The Council continued exemptions from marching with the militia for several categories of defense personnel. Men employed by the state in making guns, gunlocks, *chevaux-de-frise*, and piers had been excused by the old Committee of Safety, and the Council added papermakers to this group. Those exempted, however, were not freed from their military obligations. At the risk of incurring the disabilities attached to non-associators, they were required to enroll in one of the four guard companies which provided defense when the organized militia left the city.[5]

The Council encouraged associators to enroll in the Flying Camp by publishing the favorable rations and by offering a £3 bounty for enlistments. At the same time, the Convention offered a £3 reward for the apprehension of deserters from the associator battalions. The most constructive approach to desertion lay in the heightened liberality with which limited resources were applied to the relief of associator families.[6]

More harrowing was the identification of outright traitors, the line between treason and patriotism being almost impossible to draw in the state of tension and conflicting loyalties. Rittenhouse presided over several Council hearings which attempted to establish the truth in the escape of Colonel Joseph Kirkland from the city jail to a British ship in Delaware Bay. Interrogations revealed that several individuals aided the officer by supplying a rope ladder and hooks to permit him to get over the jail wall, a horse to make his escape, and a boat to get him out to the man-of-war. Those accused denied their complicity and, in the process, introduced a tangle of illicit personal relationships. Sometime after this rather unsatisfactory inquiry, Ritten-

[4] *Ibid.*, 610.
[5] *Pa. Col. Recs.*, x, 649, 660; *Pa. Gaz.*, July 10, Aug. 14, 1776.
[6] *Ibid.*, Aug. 10, 14, 1776; Broadside: In Convention, Aug. 9, 1776, LCP; Broadside: In Convention, Aug. 16, 1776, LCP.

house borrowed two books on criminal law from Franklin.[7]

Kirkland's escape did not seriously damage the reputation of the Philadelphia jail as a place of high security. William Livingston, governor of New Jersey, wrote Rittenhouse requesting the Council to accept one Ledwitz for confinement in their "spacious new Palace," where he could be denied communication with Tories. Ledwitz, with a group of "the most incorrigible villains in the universe belonging to the Army of the United States," had till recently been confined in the Morris County jail. His companions were turned over to the Marine Committee to serve on naval vessels, but Ledwitz was too dangerous even for this punitive treatment! [8]

On August 10, the Convention ordered the whole of the militia into New Jersey with the exception of the western companies, which were retained at home to defend the frontier. The western counties, despite their fervor for the Revolution, professed less fear of Howe than of British-inspired Indian incursions. In response to their continued pleas, the Convention released the frontier counties from the requirement that only the Council of Safety could call out their associators. This authority was given to the Council member or to a major representing each county.[9]

Howe was, in fact, the more serious threat. On August 22, he began to move off Staten Island and by the 27th had brilliantly won the battle of Long Island. He invaded Manhattan at Kips Bay on September 15 and slowly maneuvered Washington up into Westchester, where the two armies sparred in the battle of White Plains on October 28. Individual American acts of heroism and occasionally inspired tactics did not

[7] *Pa. Arch.*, 2d ser., I, 611–15, 602–4, 605–6, 617, 606–7; *Pa. Col. Recs.*, x, 662–64; Peter Force, ed., *American Archives* (Wash., 1837–53), 5th ser., III, 1308; Benjamin Franklin, Memorandum Book, opp. Oct. 21, 1776, APS.
[8] Livingston to DR, Nov. 30, 1776, Gratz Coll., HSP.
[9] *Pa. House Jours.* (1782), 80, 85, 86; Broadside: In Convention, Aug. 10, 1776, LCP.

reduce measurably the enormity of the defeat or the growing precariousness of the American army.

As news of the spreading disaster reached Philadelphia, fear arose that that city would next feel the invader's heel. The completion of defenses now became essential; particularly important was the plan to close the Delaware to enemy penetration. The Jersey anchor of this barrier, the fortifications at Billingsport, lay unfinished as a result of conflicting authority. The old Committee of Safety had begun this enterprise but then had deferred to the direction of the Congressional Board of War, which failed to convert the proffered responsibility into action. The Council of Safety, unable to act on its own, requested on September 16, through Rittenhouse and Colonel John Bayard, that the Board grant permission to proceed immediately with the construction. This time an agreement was reached, the Board lent the services of the Polish engineer, Thaddeus Kosciuszko, and the Council carried through the construction work under the superintendence of Colonel John Bull.[10]

In October, Rittenhouse headed an effort to devise the means for fixing a boom and heavy chain across the main river channel between two previously built piers. The rest of the river was reasonably well denied to enemy ships by *chevaux-de-frise*, but it was necessary to be able to close the main channel at will. A few days later, he went out with still another committee to survey all possible land approaches to the city for the purpose of designating the best locations for redoubts.[11]

The Council never imagined that the best fortifications were of much use unless held by well-led troops, but it was in no position to provide them. Rittenhouse headed a committee to seek Congressional action in stationing a body of troops near Philadelphia under the command of an experienced general

[10] *Pa. Col. Recs.*, x, 619, 631, 660, 764, 719.
[11] *Ibid.*, 750, 754–55.

officer.[12] In October, this appeared a more reasonable request to the Pennsylvanians than it could to those whose attention was focused on the dissolving army that had stood behind New York's ramparts.

A strange atmosphere settled upon Philadelphia as the Revolution approached its moment of truth. In the interregnum between the rising of the Convention and the election of a new assembly, it would have been hard to say which was more feared, British victory or the widely distasteful Constitution. The Quakers, the Tories, and all those out of sympathy with the Revolution were violently opposed to the new frame of government. The oath, however, barred them from voting in the election scheduled for November 5; they could defeat neither the Constitution nor the candidates who supported it. The patriots could. Every newspaper that appeared and every tavern discussion made it clear that many—perhaps even a majority—of those who unquestionably supported the American cause had serious doubts about the wisdom of the Constitution.

They attacked it in published articles and they attacked it in mass meetings. The biggest meeting was a two-day affair held on October 21 and 22, which produced thirty-one resolutions against the Constitution. These scored the illegal assumption of governmental powers, the lack of respect for Christianity, the deviation from Pennsylvania's previous government and from other state governments, the lack of attention to the best political thought, and the oaths. The oath prohibiting all governmental officers from acting to alter the Constitution was the most hated part of the document because it seemed to prohibit all change. Matlack, Cannon, Young, and James Smith defended the Constitution, but Rittenhouse remained aloof from the public debate. With John Dickinson, Robert Morris, John Bayard, George Clymer, and a host of others actively opposing the document, John Adams was restrained in his

[12] *Ibid.*, 747.

comment, "The proceedings of the late convention are not well liked by the best of the Whigs." [13]

The opponents were at no loss in developing their tactics; they would nullify the new government before it ever got established. Nullification had become a fine-edged American weapon. It had brought the repeal of the Stamp Act; it had caused the partial repeal of the Townshend Acts; and it had forced a showdown over the Tea Act. In Pennsylvania, it had destroyed the last assembly to sit under the Charter of Privileges.

The Anti-Constitutionalists demanded a new convention to write a new constitution. To force this requirement they urged voters to defeat the Constitutionalist assembly candidates and to refuse to vote for any candidate for the council. Instead, they should record their votes as "No Counsellor." [14] Without any Supreme Executive Council, the new government would be paralyzed. Then, if the Anti-Constitutionalist assemblymen had refused to take the oath, they could push through a new convention.

Rittenhouse faced this conspiracy when he agreed to run for election to the first assembly to be held under the Constitution with which he was so indelibly identified. He ran at the head of his ticket in the city, but the Constitutionalists were defeated by a 3 to 2 margin, and George Clymer, Robert Morris, John Bayard, Michael Shubert, and Samuel Morris, Jr., were elected. Joseph Parker ran on both tickets, collecting votes from both factions. Matlack, Wharton, Jonathan Bayard Smith, and Jacob Shriner polled still fewer votes than Rittenhouse. The city voted even more decisively against electing any councillor, and most electors cast their ballots without taking the oath required of them. The Anti-Constitutionalists carried the day.[15]

[13] *Pa. Gaz.*, Oct. 23, 30, 1776; Charles F. Adams, ed., *Letters of John Adams......to his Wife* (Boston, 1841), I, 168–69; Marshall, *Diary*, 102; Broadside: At a Meeting Held at the Philosophical Society-Hall, Oct. 17, 1776, LCP; Broadside: At a Meeting of a Number of Citizens, Nov. 2, [1776], HSP.
[14] *Pa. Arch.*, 6th ser., XI, 315.
[15] *Ibid.*

Their victory did not extend to the rest of the state, however, where the Constitutionalists won a clear majority in the Assembly. Everywhere, the vote was remarkably light, less than a third of that of the preceding year, despite the expanded suffrage. The Tories, Quakers, and Moravians were not permitted to vote, and not all of the associators had returned from the New York campaign. Even the deduction of these elements cannot account for the smallness of the turnout; unquestionably numbers of qualified Whigs chose not to vote because of their distaste for the Constitution. In Bucks and Chester Counties, some of them voted instead on the traditional October election day for members of the now defunct colonial assembly.[16]

After the smoke settled, the Anti-Constitutionalists saw that they had won what they sought—the capacity to nullify the new government of Pennsylvania. Philadelphia City and Philadelphia County had refused to elect councillors and, for some months, the Supreme Executive Council was unable to organize. The Constitutionalists had a majority in the Assembly but they did not have a quorum, giving John Dickinson, Philadelphia County assemblyman, the opportunity to issue an ultimatum. The Anti-Constitutionalists would cooperate in organizing the house, electing a speaker, and carrying on urgent business *provided* the Constitutionalists would agree to a new constitutional convention to meet before January 1777. The agreement was not forthcoming, and Dickinson withdrew, followed by enough assemblymen to immobilize the legislature.[17]

Meanwhile, the Council of Safety was the only body in Pennsylvania able to respond to the continuing demands of the war. Rittenhouse devoted his whole energy to the Council and to the war, leaving to other men the problems of accommodation and power within the new government. On the very day of the election, he joined in a committee report urging the

[16] Marshall, *Diary*, 102.

[17] *Pa. House Jours.* (1782), 98; Charles J. Stillé, *The Life and Times of John Dickinson* (Phila., 1891), 208-9.

location of a "Magazine for Military Stores" at a high spot above the Wissahickon Creek. Two days later, he was given primary responsibility for attacking the long-standing problems of currency inflation and salt shortage.[18]

Rittenhouse accepted the popular idea that the value of Continental and state currency should rest upon the virtue of the individual, who must refuse to accept depreciation. The Council had already jailed one man and branded him an "Enemy to his Country" because he refused to accept Continental bills of credit. When Matlack reported that a Continental officer had sold Continental currency at a large discount, Rittenhouse was appointed chairman of a committee to investigate. He consulted the Congressional Board of Treasury, and his committee decided to urge action on the Assembly. Only the Assembly could pass tender acts and provide the penalties required if virtue was to be enforced.[19]

The critical shortage of salt could be met by only two approaches: an increased supply and a more equitable distribution. Rittenhouse took Matlack with him to visit the salt works in an effort to discover means of increasing production, but neither domestic production nor importation could be increased fast enough to ease the need. The Council of Safety had to continue to allot the limited supplies to the counties according to their population in a manner inaugurated under the Convention.[20]

Amidst more general problems, the Council received a request from Rittenhouse's brother, Benjamin, who was superintendent of the state gunlock factory in Philadelphia. Benjamin Rittenhouse had accepted this appointment from the old Committee of Safety before David became a member. He now petitioned for an increase in his contractual salary of £250 to permit him to meet the rising cost of living. Since the Council

[18] *Pa. Col. Recs.*, x, 778–80.
[19] *Pa. Arch.*, 2d ser., 1, 639; *Pa. Gaz.*, Nov. 6, 1776; *Pa. Col. Recs.*, x, 780.
[20] *Ibid.*, 780–81; *Pa. Gaz.*, Nov. 13, 1776.

had already recognized the seriousness of this problem by acceding to a similar request from its *chevaux-de-frise* pilots, it did not hesitate to raise Benjamin's salary too—by £100 a year.[21]

Rumors and alarms received from day to day agitated both the Council and the citizenry; it was never easy to know the truth or to know what to expect next. On November 14, news was received that the enemy had embarked on 500 ships for Philadelphia, and the Council ordered the associator battalions to march to the city "without delay."[22] Almost before it became clear that this intelligence was faulty, news was received of the fall of Fort Washington on the 16th, with the loss of nearly 3,000 men. Four days later, Fort Lee, on the Jersey side of the Hudson, was given up without a struggle. On November 24, Rittenhouse sent a circular letter to the commanders of the Pennsylvania battalions underlining these losses and announcing, "General Howe . . . is now directing his operations against New-Jersey," and in all probability, "his views extend to the City of Philadelphia."[23] The next day, Congress asked the Council of Safety to call up all the associators in the city and in Philadelphia, Bucks, Chester, and Northampton Counties, as well as a portion of those in the western counties.

With the American army defeated, captured, divided, and only a remnant escaping across New Jersey, both the annihilation of Washington's remaining forces and the occupation of Philadelphia seemed more likely than not. Rittenhouse addressed an impassioned plea to the people of Philadelphia on November 27, "It is our duty to inform you that our enemies are advancing upon us, and that the most vigorous measures alone can save this city from falling into their hands. . . .

[21] *Ibid.,* Oct. 9, 1776; *Pa. Arch.,* 2d ser., I, 647.
[22] Broadside: In Council of Safety, Nov. 14, 1776, HSP; *Pa. Col. Recs.,* x, 780.
[23] *Pa. Jour.,* Nov. 27, 1776; Force, *Am. Arch.,* 5th ser., III, 829; *Jours. of Cong.,* II, 444.

There is no time for delay; and by your conduct the Continent will be influenced. We therefore entreat you, by the most sacred of all bonds—the love of virtue, of liberty, and of your country—to forget every distinction, and unite as one man in this time of extreme danger. Let us defend ourselves like men determined to be free." [24]

He invited everyone to a mass meeting called for the following day. At the same time he sent out the Congressional resolution asking for the associators and for the money required to mobilize these troops.[25]

Rittenhouse presided at the meeting held in the State House yard. The Council and the Assembly attended in bodies, and a large number of citizens turned out. He informed them of the intelligence in hand and of the expectation that Howe planned to invade Pennsylvania. He announced that in response to the request of Congress, the city's militia, the militia of some of the counties, and a portion of the militia from the rest would be marched into New Jersey. According to one observer, "The people expressed their cheerful approbation of the measure by the most unanimous acclamations of Joy ever observed on any occasion." The martial spirit of the moment was heightened by the announcement of a militia review for the following afternoon. Thomas Mifflin, now quarter-master general of the Continental army, closed the meeting with a "spirited, animating and affectionate address." [26]

The crisis engendered enough feeling to permit the Assembly finally to command a quorum and to organize that very day. John Jacobs, Rittenhouse's brother-in-law, was elected speaker and Timothy Matlack, secretary. The house was enabled to transact business on three successive days and then it lost its

[24] Broadside: In Council of Safety, Nov. 27, 1776, LCP; *Pa. Col. Recs.*, XI, 17–18.
[25] DR to Peter Rhoads, Nov. 27, 1776, Gratz Coll., HSP; DR to Col. Hart, Nov. 27, 1776, Photocopy, HSP; *Pa. Gaz.*, Nov. 27, 1776.
[26] *Pa. Arch.*, 1st ser., v, 77; Marshall, *Diary*, 119.

quorum. This was a result both of political feeling and of the departure of militia officers.[27]

The house was able to do no more than state its intention of enacting a militia law—the most urgent piece of business referred to it by the Council. The New York campaign had demonstrated the futility of depending upon a voluntary militia; compulsory enrollment was essential. Associators returned from that harrowing experience "disgusted at the Inconveniences, hardships and Losses which they suffered in their late Service, while Non associators were permitted to remain at home in the peaceable Enjoyment of their professions, and many of them increasing their Wealth by grasping the Trade of the absent Associators, whose patriotic Exertions have been Sneered at, and their hardships & fatigues, and the distresses of their families, insultingly made a jest of." [28] Although the present crisis was even greater for Pennsylvania, the Council knew that the associators' response would be feeble.

Individuals reacted in a variety of ways. Some sent their goods out of the city for safe keeping, and some left themselves. Some began to oppress known Tories, while others reached out hopefully to the British. The Council spent most of its time trying to improve the supply of arms and munitions and to raise troops. It took time out to provide for the removal of records from the city—if necessary—and it warned the citizens that they might have to evacuate to escape the "insults and oppressions of a licentious soldiery." [29]

Rittenhouse presided over the Council almost every day in this period, but Wharton was present and in the chair on December 2 when news arrived that the British had reached New Brunswick, hard on Washington's heels. For some reason, the Council's resolution in response to this news was nevertheless

[27] Pa. House Jours. (1782), 98.
[28] Cited by Selsam, Constitution, 233; Pa. Col. Recs., xi, 15.
[29] Ibid., 21; Marshall, Diary, 103; Jours. of Cong., ii, 445.

published over Rittenhouse's signature. The public was advised "That it is the Opinion of this Board, that all the Shops in this City be shut up, that the Schools be broke up, and the Inhabitants engaged solely in providing for the Defence of this City, at this Time of extreme Danger." [30]

According to Christopher Marshall, the advice was followed exactly: "Drums beat: a martial appearance: the shops shut: and all business except preparing to disappoint our enemies laid aside." His own helter-skelter activity reflected the frenzy of the moment, "I went to Coffee House; then to children's; then home; then back to Coffee House and other parts of the City; then home; dined there . . . After dinner, I went to State House; . . . To Coffee House; then Home; drank tea; then down town." [31]

On the 8th, the British were reported at Trenton. Previous orders for the militia to mobilize had produced such a limited response that what could be done was now a question. The Council wrote to all battalion commanders to "entreat" them to march with their troops to the city and authorized them to impress wagons for use in evacuating the city—in case that step should prove necessary. Over Rittenhouse's signature, another emotional appeal was made: "This glorious opportunity of signalizing himself in defense of our Country and Securing the Rights of America forever, will be seized by every man who has a Spark of Patriotic fire in his bosom." [32]

Unfortunately the sparks were burning low. The New Jersey militia had failed to rise during Washington's travail in their state. The enlistments of the New Jersey and Maryland components of the Flying Camp expired near the climax of his troubles, and they decamped in whole brigades. The remaining Continentals faced the end of their enlistments with every indication that they would follow suit. The prospects for aid from

[30] *Pa. Col. Recs.*, xi, 26; *PMHB*, xii, 126.
[31] Marshall, *Diary*, 105.
[32] Broadside: In Council of Safety, Dec. 8, 1776, LCP.

the Pennsylvania militia were not improved when Washington crossed to the west bank of the Delaware. With little effect, Congress tried to strengthen the hand of the Pennsylvania Council in an exhortation "To the PEOPLE in General, and particularly to the Inhabitants of *Pennsylvania*, and the adjacent STATES." [33]

The shocking failure of the back counties to respond was now clear beyond hope. Despite their combativeness, this concentration of Constitutionalists offered little of the single-minded dedication to the larger cause that moved Rittenhouse. The Council even wondered whether some of the lethargy reflected Tory sentiments. It advised Washington to order out the Bucks and Northampton County militias and to disarm all who refused to rise. The brightest spot was Philadelphia; the city provided some 2,000 militiamen who mustered to support the waning war.[34]

Congress was at as much of a loss as the Council of Safety. It voted to stay in the city—and then on December 12 deserted to the comparative safety of Baltimore. At the same time, General Israel Putnam assumed command of the defense forces in the city, and the Council authorized the conscription of all able-bodied men for service in throwing up fortifications.[35]

On December 18, Washington declared, "*The game is pretty near up.*" On the 20th, he wrote, "10 days more will put an end to the existence of our Army." [36]

That was the depth! the absolute nadir of the Revolution. For a moment, reasonable men who were acquainted with the truth could see no probable issue except defeat. At that moment, the quiet passion of David Rittenhouse was conspicuous, elevated as he was on a platform somewhat above the heads of his fellow "mechanics," where he could be seen and could com-

[33] Broadside: The Representatives of the United States, Dec. 10, 1776, NYPL.
[34] *Pa. Col. Recs.*, XI, 54.
[35] *Ibid.*, XI, 46.
[36] Fitzpatrick, ed., *Writings of Washington*, VI, 398, 401–2.

municate his own resolution. The city, at least, saw and responded to his appeals.

The British thrust stopped at the Delaware. With the Pennsylvania associators, the Pennsylvania components of the Flying Camp, and the Pennsylvania Line of the Continental army constituting nearly a half of the forces at his command, Washington struck back in sharp little victories at Trenton and Princeton. He caused the enemy to withdraw to the environs of New York. Not in any strategic sense, but in terms of morale he turned the tide.

Never thereafter would the outlook appear so uniformly black. The country as a whole and Philadelphia especially had plumbed the deepest bottom without falling through. By comparison, subsequent disasters of enormous magnitude were anticlimactic. The loss of the greatest cities, including Philadelphia, the surrender of whole armies, the collapse of the currency, and the mutiny of Continental troops could now be borne. It may be doubted that the British ever again had it in their power to extinguish the Revolution.

CHAPTER XII

The New Government

1776–1777

THE threat of military invasion and collapse only partially obscured the failure of the new Pennsylvania
government under the Constitution to gain the support it needed. Many of those who rallied in the moment of
crisis refused their continued support unless the Constitutionalist leaders agree to call a new convention. Just as the old provincial government had been nullified at its ending, so the new
constitutional government was nullified at its beginning.

The Supreme Executive Council was never able to meet at all,
and the Assembly's quorum, which it enjoyed for a second time
during the height of the British threat, proved fleeting. When
the house was permitted to meet on December 10, 11, and 13, it
made frantic efforts to propitiate the opposition by electing
seven new members to the Council of Safety—most of them
conservatives. The gesture was inadequate. The quorum van-
ished on the 14th, and day after day the Assembly remained
immobilized.[1]

One of the few actions the hapless Assembly took was the
appointment of a committee to recover the state Treasury from
the hands of the former treasurer, then in Baltimore. This was
a matter of the highest priority. Michael Hillegas had not resigned his post as treasurer of Pennsylvania when, on October 4,
he was appointed treasurer of the Continental Congress. This
dual service became impossible when Congress left Philadelphia
and ordered Hillegas to accompany it with the Continental
Treasury. He did not have similar orders from Pennsylvania

---

[1] *Pa. House Jours.* (1782), 101–2.

but, nevertheless, took the state Treasury along as well. On December 13, the Assembly committee met him and arranged for the transfer of all monies and papers belonging to Pennsylvania. For another month, however, the state had no treasurer and found no way of providing for its Treasury.

Finally, perhaps because enough members on military duty returned, the Assembly found itself on January 13 with a quorum and turned immediately to the report of the committee on the Treasury. The following day, it unanimously elected David Rittenhouse treasurer of the Commonwealth. In the interim, Rittenhouse had submitted a letter indicating his willingness to assume this critical post—obviously written after conversations with the Assembly leaders. On the 18th, the Treasury records and money were brought into the city and Rittenhouse posted the required bond. He assumed the third ranking executive position within Pennsylvania—the first two remaining vacant.[2]

As treasurer, Rittenhouse did not neglect the Council of Safety nor did his role in that body diminish. He attended regularly and frequently presided over the Council, which seemed to gain vigor from the newly active Assembly. It remained the executive authority of the government. Although often absorbed with the most serious matters of state, the Council had also to review the sometimes sordid lives of little men.

The case of Captain Gerard Irvine required such an excursion and left an unusual record of Rittenhouse's direct confrontation with wrong-doing. Irvine was a rough, hard-drinking officer of the Continental Line whose own men accused him of cruelty and inhumanity. He was brought before the Council on the charge that a detachment under his command had entered private houses and stolen private property.

His defense was that he had been sent by his colonel to search several bawdy houses for deserters, with instruction to "Pull

[2] *Ibid.*, 104.

down or Burn any dam'nd house that secreted a man of his." [3] Irvine denied stealing or condoning theft but implied that, in any case, such behavior was less violent than his orders directed. He spoke as if he expected the Council to regard these houses of ill-fame as innately evil and beyond the protection of the law. He leveled the foulest accusations at all others involved, and, even today, his protestations of innocence ring false.

Presiding over the initial hearing, Rittenhouse was outraged. "A pretty Officer," he called Irvine, and delivered a stinging reprimand. He refused to accept a coarse joke when the captain asked one of the women appearing against him if she had lost any clothes; Rittenhouse rebuked him with the comment that he was "very Innocent." He expressed the wish that the punishment due the soldiers involved could all be laid on Irvine's back.[4]

Three months later, despite his request for a military trial, Irvine was still in jail and still petitioning. He said he had no money to repay the losses, and he refused to accept the offer of freedom at the price of going to sea on an American frigate.

Even as the Assembly lent strength to the Council of Safety, it took steps to eliminate the need for the Council by buttressing its own position and by establishing the other elements of government under the Constitution. The Assembly provided for elections to replace those who refused to sit in the legislature and to fill the still empty seats on the Supreme Executive Council. The results were encouraging, supporters of the Constitution generally defeating their opponents in these contests. Thomas Wharton, Jr., and George Bryan were elected to the Executive Council, permitting that body to meet for the first time on March 4. The following day, Wharton was inaugurated as president of Pennsylvania and Bryan as vice president. With this ceremony, the new government under the Constitu-

---

[3] *Pa. Arch.*, 2d ser., I, 697; III, 135–36.
[4] *Ibid.*, I, 697, 727–31.

tion was finally proclaimed, amid ringing bells, booming cannon, and long-continued festivities.[5]

Immediately, the Supreme Executive Council became the seat of executive power in the state, superseding the Council of Safety. The transfer of authority was strikingly symbolized by the movement of Wharton to the presidency from the chairmanship of the Council of Safety. For a few days, however, the Council of Safety met as usual and continued to administer routine military matters. During this time, Rittenhouse retained his full importance; he assumed the chair as soon as Wharton departed and continued to play the leading role in the Council.

On March 13, the Supreme Executive Council abolished the Council of Safety but established in its place a new agency which continued some of its functions. The new Board of War was intended to superintend military affairs under the authority of the Supreme Executive Council. Although a Navy Board was appointed at the same time, a variety of factors rendered it distinctly less effective. First named among the nine members of the Board of War was David Rittenhouse.[6]

The establishment of the machinery of government was a major accomplishment, but it did not end or soften the impact of continuing efforts at nullification. Leading citizens still refused to accept either civil or military commissions, and the press reflected intense antagonism toward the government. The organizational focus of this opposition came to rest in a newly established political club called the Republican Society.

As a planned counterpoise, the Whig Society was founded by supporters of the new government. Its membership extended to all who wished to attend. Because their opponents were also Whigs, in the sense that that word was usually used to describe patriots and supporters of independence, members sometimes called themselves "True Whigs." The Republicans in response

[5] *Pa. Eve. Post*, Feb. 11, 15, 22, Mar. 4, 6, 1777; *Pa. Gaz.*, Mar. 12, 1777; *Pa. House Jours.* (1782), 110, 114, 123.
[6] *Pa. Col. Recs.*, XI, 191.

dubbed them "Furious" or "Yellow Whigs." Comprised of mechanics, tradesmen, intellectuals, and men who in origin and in spirit were closer to the mind of the common man than the respectable, mercantile leadership of the Republicans, the Whig Society became a bulwark of the new order. Meetings were frequently held in the hall of the Philosophical Society; a reflection of overlapping membership. When men of greater prominence declined to have their names publicly identified with the club, Charles Willson Peale emerged as the first president.[7]

The society issued a series of letters and memorials marked by their moderate, conciliatory tone. They were signed by Peale alone, but behind him stood a group of like-minded men who were constant in their devotion to the Revolution and determined in their efforts to make the new government work. In addition to Peale, the membership committee consisted of Cannon, Young, Paine, and David Rittenhouse—all strong advocates of the Constitution.[8]

The appeals of the Whig Society grew less restrained as it became evident that the new government was not receiving sufficient support to permit it to function effectively. There was less acceptance of a "Difference of opinion on the best mode of establishing freedom" and more talk of "black and horrid treasons."[9] The return of the Congress to the city brought no tranquility. Even in the face of new threats of British attack, men refused to cooperate with the state government, and desertion notices in the papers multiplied. The Republicans were determined to force through a convention.

Their mounting pressure coincided to an unhappy degree with the renewed activity of the British army. During the first week of April, rumors of enemy troop movements agitated the city. Rising tension was capped by an Executive Council procla-

[7] Sellers, *Peale*, I, 155-57; *Pa. Eve. Post*, Mar. 13, 15, 20, 29, Apr. 5, 10, 1777.
[8] *Ibid.*
[9] *Ibid.*, Mar. 27, 29, May 20, 1777.

mation of April 9 announcing a British movement toward South Amboy and predicting that the enemy would "once more attempt to pass through New Jersey, and endeavour to gain possession of Philadelphia." Every citizen was directed to "hold himself ready to march." On the same day, Congress appointed a committee to confer on defense measures with the executive authority in Pennsylvania, but by the time it turned to look for the Executive Council, it was gone. Despite the admitted peril, the Council drew up orders paying some of its members for their services and followed the Assembly into adjournment —immobilized by nullification. The Council did not meet at all from April 10 to May 6, but, before it adjourned, it sought to transfer to the Board of War its own executive authority so far as it pertained to the conduct of the war.[10]

Although not wholly immobilized, the Board of War was a feeble reliance in such a crisis. Two of the original members refused to sit under any circumstances, and a majority of the rest participated without taking the required oath. Rittenhouse presided at the Board's first two meetings, but after a few days his attendance became irregular. Division so plagued the body that he found his time could be more profitably employed in the Treasury. Some days, only one member appeared, and business usually had to be conducted with two, three, or four. The Board, nevertheless, played a major role in providing for the state's military activities. Before it went into adjournment, the Council had sought to bolster the dubious legality of the Board's actions by declaring that its five active members, including Rittenhouse, constituted the Board. Power was most effectively transferred when the Council turned over to the Board a $100,000 draft placed at the disposal of Pennsylvania by Congress.[11]

This was not at all satisfactory to Congress, which had been growing increasingly restive as Pennsylvania's government

[10] *Pa. Col. Recs.*, XI, 203–5.
[11] *Ibid.*, 181, 199, 201, 202; *Pa. Arch.*, 2d ser., I, 13–17.

ground to a halt. On April 14, it called on President Wharton to convene the executive and legislative authority of the Commonwealth in order to meet the military threat. Wharton did not attempt this for he knew it would be a futile gesture. Instead, he and four members of the Board of War met the following day to discuss the impasse with a committee of Congress. On that occasion, Rittenhouse arrived too late to talk with the committeemen, but he continued with the Board the balance of the day and thereafter attended its sessions with remarkable fidelity.

Painfully all agreed, "the executive authority of Pennsylvania is incapable of any exertion adequate to the present crisis." The Republican nullification was nearly complete. In response to a request from Wharton and the active members of the Board of War, Congress sought to buttress the elements still supporting the government by resolving that the president, any members of the Council who could be found, the Board of War, and, where related, the Navy Board "should in the present critical exigency of affairs, exercise every authority to promote the safety of the state." [12] The people were called upon to submit to the direction of this fractured government.

Even on the face of it, the Congressional resolution was virtually a confession of defeat. One wag was too close to the mark to provoke laughter when he inserted in a newspaper the notice, "Was Lost, a *new invented* Government." [13]

By the time the Assembly reconvened on May 12, the opponents of the Constitution were ready with their terms. Forty-two prominent Pennsylvanians including James Wilson, Benjamin Rush, Robert Morris, John Maxwell Nesbitt, Richard Peters, Charles Thomson, and the two Cadwaladers signed a remarkable "Proposal." At the same time that they deplored the "weakness and Languor" of government in the face of threatened invasion, they tacitly admitted responsibility for it

[12] *Ibid.*, 33; *Jours. Cont. Cong.*, VII, 264, 268.
[13] *Pa. Eve. Post*, May 8, 1777.

by assigning the cause to "differences in sentiment" over Pennsylvania's Constitution.[14] Their ultimatum was sharp: if the Assembly would call a new convention for amending the Constitution, they would, at last, support the authority of Assembly, Council, and the other organs of government. Once the convention met, however, all authority would be transferred to that body.

This was a bitter choice for those who supported the Constitution. From within the undistinguished membership of the Whig Society welled up a determination not to give up their Constitution and not to permit their political opponents to destroy those institutions upon which the state's safety depended. In a published address, the society vigorously attacked the ultimatum of the forty-two, declaring that many of them had been instrumental in causing the very troubles they now deplored. The Whigs outlined a well-devised tactic, announcing that the forty-two were almost all Philadelphians and had no right to prescribe for the entire state. The Assembly, they urged, must discover whether the whole state wanted a new constitution before calling a convention.[15]

The opponents of the Constitution moved quickly into a full-scale political campaign sparked by meetings, pamphlets, newspaper addresses, and petitions. They attacked the Whig Society with invective and satire, accusing it of usurping the functions of government and of seeking to frustrate the will of the people. Individuals declined and resigned commissions in the militia, in county offices, and as justices of the peace. Rittenhouse had seen the beginning of this process while a member of the Council of Safety, and on the Board of War he saw more. Even John Cadwalader and Samuel Miles declined appointments as brigadiers, and Joseph Reed refused the chief justiceship.[16] Nothing, however, was more serious than the nullifica-

[14] *Ibid.*, May 15, 1777.
[15] *Ibid.*, May 20, 1777.
[16] *Ibid.*, May 17, 1777; *Pa. Packet*, May 14, 1777; *Pa. Col. Recs.*, XI, 186.

tion Rittenhouse observed as treasurer of the Commonwealth.

Difficulties in collecting taxes did not begin with the Constitution of 1776, nor end with it, but they were heightened by the widespread refusal to cooperate with the new government. The taxes voted by Assembly did not come in, and Rittenhouse was left with orders to pay far in excess of his resources. At the direction of the Assembly, he inserted notices in both English and German language newspapers calling upon county treasurers to fulfill their tax quotas, but there was no way he could reach the taxpayer directly.[17]

More fundamental than the ineffectiveness of the county treasurer was the attitude of the taxpayer. Obviously, a "considerable number of inhabitants refuse[d] to pay taxes." [18] There were many reasons for this behavior. During the progressing nullification of the Pennsylvania government, men could exercise their latent and recently stimulated distaste for taxes by withholding them. Against this convenient justification for tax violation, notices, resolutions, personal pleas, and threats of legal action had little effect.

Opportunities to avoid paying taxes were multiplied when the men appointed as tax collectors declined or resigned their posts. In some cases, individuals who were ready to pay their taxes could find no collector to receive them. This difficulty was not easily remedied because appointment was in the hands of the Executive Council, which might not learn for several weeks that an appointee had declined. Several more weeks might elapse before a replacement could be appointed and notified. Only a strong executive could have resolved this difficulty, but the Council remained ineffective. Even when it met, it was frequently divided and immobilized by politics.

Without a stronger executive, there was no practicable way to bring in the taxes. On March 20, 1777, the Assembly turned to the only alternative; it authorized the issuance of $200,000 in

[17] Pa. House Jours. (1782), 106.
[18] Pa. Gaz., Feb. 5, 1777.

bills of credit.[19] This move was in no sense designed to create cheap money. Every effort was made to prevent inflation by providing for redemption of the bills of credit through a sinking fund raised from a tax on all real and personal property. The taxes still had to be collected to make this issue good, but in the meantime the treasurer would have money at his disposal.

Unfortunately, it was emitted very slowly, and on June 3 Rittenhouse had to inform the Council that the Treasury was exhausted. He reported that it was completely incapable of meeting the most essential demands upon it, and, in concert with three members of the Board of War, offered two alternatives. Congress might be willing to have the most urgent military expenses transferred to the Continental account; if not, the trustees of the General Loan Office of Pennsylvania had in their hands over £15,000, which could be borrowed. When the money in press was emitted, this loan might easily be repaid. With unusual alacrity, both Council and Assembly agreed to the second suggestion.[20]

Rittenhouse soon found that even the combined legislative and executive authority of the state was insufficient to secure this objective. When he presented a Council order for £20,000 to Dr. Samuel Preston Moore, the only Loan Office trustee who had not left town, he was informed that no monies could be paid except by the concurrence of a majority of the trustees. Moore agreed to send for the approval of the absent trustees, but if he did so he never reported receiving it.

The Assembly responded by setting in motion two simultaneous efforts. A bill was prepared to transfer the Loan Office money to the Treasury, and a committee was appointed to borrow money through commercial channels. On the very day the transfer bill came up for its final reading, the loan committee reported success. The transfer bill was defeated, and the borrowed sum of £15,218..16..3 turned over to Rittenhouse.[21]

---

[19] Dallas, *Laws of Pa.*, II, 735, 39n.
[20] *Pa. Col. Recs.*, XI, 211; *Pa. House Jours.* (1782), 138.
[21] *Ibid.*, 139, 149.

Shortly afterward, the new emission currency began to be received in sufficient volume to relieve the most pressing necessities.

Battered by a succession of crises which would not have become serious had the new government been generally accepted, Rittenhouse emerged with a very different attitude from that of the politicians. His own appointment had been supported by all factions, and he was not concerned about political power. He was very much concerned about the need to support independence and to oppose the British threat with effective civil and military power. In his mind, this had been the purpose of the Constitution of 1776. He approved of most of its characteristics—including those which generated so much antagonism—but he was ready to scrap the instrument if it could not fulfill its fundamental purpose. When he was finally forced to the conclusion that the Constitution imperiled the war effort, he did not hesitate.

He supported on June 12 an earnest entreaty by the Board of War that the Assembly call a constitutional convention. The request was dominated by a deep-felt need "to Harmonize the true Friends of Liberty in every part of this State." Although the members of the Board clashed in their political views, they shared common frustrations; no other body had struggled so ceaselessly to keep the government going. They agreed that the "defects and disorders" pointed out in the remonstrance of the forty-two Republicans were "too apparent." They concluded that vigorous government could be restored only by "calling a Convention for the purpose of revising, altering, amending or confirming the present plan of Government." [22]

Rittenhouse's hopes were certainly reflected in the suggestion that a convention might do no more than confirm the Constitution. Whatever its action, only a popularly elected convention could serve to still the profoundly agitated body politic. But even the decision of Assembly to call a convention should help. If this action were determined, the Board could hope "to

[22] *Pa. Arch.*, 2d ser., I, 54.

185

see the form of Government, as at present established, executed with as much vigor as Possible until such alteration or amendment shall take place." [23] This was Rittenhouse's fundamental objective.

On the same day that the Assembly received the Board of War petition, it voted to hold a referendum on calling a convention. This procedure followed the urging of the Whig Society at the same time that it offered a positive answer to the Republicans and seemed to look toward a new constitution. Yet when the Assembly established procedures for carrying out a referendum to be held in October, it also issued an "Address to the People" designed to influence the vote in favor of the 1776 Constitution. This paper pointed out that much the larger number of memorials received expressed support for that instrument. On the 20th, the Assembly adjourned once again.[24]

Long before the wisdom of the referendum could be tested, the war again intervened. Fears rose sharply in July as rumors began to flood the city. The intentions of Burgoyne in the north were clearer than Howe's next move, which was nervously awaited. His brushes with Washington in New Jersey during June suggested an overland approach on Philadelphia, but when he sailed out of New York harbor with 15,000 troops on July 23, his destination became the guessing game of the hour. Philadelphians were convinced their city was his target. Faced by this new threat, the Executive Council functioned effectively and worked hard to strengthen the defenses of the Delaware. In the Treasury, Rittenhouse was more harried than ever and seldom attended the Board of War which the Council relegated to insignificant tasks. Finally on August 6, the Council thanked the Board and dismissed it—on grounds of economy and efficiency.[25] In fact, however, the political reason was more significant. The Constitutionalists controlled the

[23] Ibid.
[24] Pa. House Jours. (1782), 145.
[25] Pa. Arch., 2d ser., I, 72.

Council, but the Board's petition of June 12—acquiesced in even by Rittenhouse—was ample evidence that they could not control the Board.

Howe was sighted in Delaware Bay on July 29, but when he turned out to sea instead of proceeding up the Bay, almost everyone was confused. Individuals reacted in a variety of ways. An exodus from the city had long been in progress and now took on an added frenzy. Some who remained were charged with scrambling to make their personal peace with the British. Others, especially the Quakers, remained aloof and seemingly unconcerned. Only the steadfast busied themselves in military preparations, but even they scarcely knew what to do.

In this uncertainty of anticipated battle, everyone waited nervously. The humdrum of routine continued on the surface while dreams of better days and nobler pursuits intruded themselves in the mind, trying to obscure a permanent fixation upon the impending assault. In this uneasy state, Rittenhouse thought again of the life of science which now lay so far behind him. Not since his angry letter against Witherspoon, written in another hour of deep frustration, had he produced anything resembling a scientific paper. He had observed an eclipse the preceding January with his old friend William Smith, but he did not take time to write it up or to publish any of the other observations he occasionally made.[26]

Now, he grasped eagerly at an opportunity to escape the momentous uncertainties of war and politics—which he could do nothing to reduce. He was not in a state to pursue a tedious course of studies or to put together a creative synthesis; he chose just the right exercise. He decided to answer, on August 18, a letter he had owed to John Page for four months.

John Page, a Virginia planter who had been a classmate of Thomas Jefferson at the College of William and Mary, was an amateur scientist and president of the Virginia Society for

[26] William Smith, MS Notes in Tobias Mayer, *Tabulae Motuum Solis et Lunae* (London, 1770), flyleaf, APS.

Promoting Useful Knowledge. A pleasant, sociable person, he had been acquainted with Rittenhouse for several years. His letter to the Philadelphian represented an effort to cultivate a correspondence.[27]

Rittenhouse thanked him for his observations of the eclipse of the sun and the transit of Mercury, although he admitted that he had not compared them with his own. He could not now attempt this because, in the face of the British threat, he had sent all his papers out to the Norriton farm. He launched into a lengthy reply to Page's inquiry about the calculation of the angle of a planet's visible way and pointed out errors in handling this concept in the transit of Venus calculations of John Ewing and Hugh Williamson. He quoted both, traced their errors to an English pamphlet which had given faulty rules, and then referred to his own rules, which William Smith used correctly in the *Transactions*. In his usual spare and graphic style, he clearly explained several difficult aspects of the problem of visible way.

He manifestly enjoyed the opportunity to weigh the work of Ewing, Williamson, and Smith in a field where he could neglect their political attitudes with impunity. As he came to the end of his momentary escape, he returned from the planets to the earth with a jolt. The Philosophical Society, he told Page, was not likely to publish anything soon. "Even the meetings of the Society," he complained, "are discontinued, rather through the disputes between whig & Tory than any public necessity." [28] Although he voiced a wish to visit Williamsburg to observe the eclipse predicted for the following June, he knew that he could not. He could return to the peaceful pleasures of science only through the cauldron of war.

Rittenhouse continued to serve as consultant on a variety of defense proposals—some of them fascinating in themselves. For a time, he was absorbed in testing an idea Thomas Paine

[27] Hindle, *Pursuit*, 162–63, 214–15.
[28] DR to Page, Aug. 18, 1777, Photocopy, HSP.

had for coping with the grievous shortage of munitions. No one had taken very seriously Franklin's early suggestion of bows and arrows, but Paine thought that if arrows were tipped with a fire vial, they might be useful. He proposed coupling such arrows with steel crossbows strong enough to hurl them across the Delaware. Together, Rittenhouse and Paine experimented on the project.[29]

At about the same time, Rittenhouse advertised in the newspaper for good pocket telescopes, which he offered to buy.[30] He sought only terrestrial glasses. Whether he planned to recondition them for the direct use of field officers or to apply them to an advanced project, such as telescopic sights, his offer was clearly related to the war crisis.

Four days after Rittenhouse wrote his letter to Page, the tension broke. Howe was reported in the Chesapeake on August 21, and, two days later, Washington marched his army through Philadelphia to intercept him below the city. The threat was no longer distant; the issue would soon be decided. At this point, citizens of uncertain loyalty became an immediate menace and the breadth of opinion previously permitted was sharply contracted. Rittenhouse was called into the unpleasant task of trying to decide who was friend and who potential foe.

The Supreme Executive Council, on August 31, revealed to Rittenhouse, Peale, William Bradford, and Sharp Delaney a confidential resolution of Congress, recommending that eleven named Quakers be seized and their political papers impounded. The Council had no hesitation in arresting them as "persons who have in their General conduct & conversation evidenced a disposition inimical to the Cause of America." It sought advice only on which other potential traitors ought to be apprehended at the same time. Rittenhouse participated in these discussions, which added thirty names to the list submitted by Congress.

[29] Paine to Benjamin Franklin, July 9, 1777, Bache Coll., APS.
[30] *Pa. Eve. Post*, Aug. 30, 1777.

Many were Quakers, but not all. Among them were several leading members of the Philosophical Society of whom none stood out so starkly as, "William Smith, D.D." [31]

William Smith's case was an unhappy one. Long a crusader for American achievement and American liberties within the British fold, he had made it clear from the beginning of the Revolution that his best hope was for reconciliation. His loyalty was challenged at an early date but the charges never stuck. Rittenhouse did not hesitate to make astronomical observations with him or to praise his scientific ability. Ardent patriotism never dimmed the clockmaker's belief that science must remain superior to wars and politics. In addition, he had a deep appreciation of the difficulties of men caught in a world of divided loyalties.

Rittenhouse's own family provided fine schooling in the impossibility of trying to separate mankind into friends and enemies. His brother-in-law, Colonel Caleb Parry, died for the American cause at the Battle of Long Island. Another brother-in-law who was vastly closer to him, Thomas Barton, was even at that moment enmeshed in charges of disloyalty—charges which he ultimately confirmed by fleeing to the enemy. Between these extremes, many of Rittenhouse's relatives professed a pacifism which placed them in John Adams' category of "a kind of neutral tribe, or the race of the insipids." [32]

Yet, accepting a clear and present danger, Rittenhouse cooperated fully with the Council, and Smith had to extricate himself from his own dilemma. As many of the others refused to do, he took an oath of loyalty to Pennsylvania "as a free & independent State," and was released on parole.[33] Those who refused to take the required oath or affirmation were sent to a miserable exile in Winchester, Virginia—twenty-two lonely men, strong in their own convictions.

Shortly after his release, Smith joined Dr. Thomas Bond in

[31] Pa. Col. Recs., xi, 283–84.
[32] Adams, ed., Letters of John Adams, i, 194.
[33] Pa. Col. Recs., xi, 288, 292, 295–96.

an interesting demonstration that he too was anxious to remove from circulation anything that might aid the British. As vice presidents of the Philosophical Society, they directed Rittenhouse, Samuel Duffield, and Pierre du Simitière to collect the various copperplates from which the illustrations of the first volume of the society's *Transactions* had been printed. They feared that the engraving of the canal survey, especially, might prove of service to the enemy since it covered "the Theatre of War." [34]

Meanwhile Howe came on. As the critical hour approached, the Philadelphia press became increasingly frenzied with a growing taste for both British atrocity and patriotic exhortation. News of action taken against Tories was given prominence, and threats were voiced even against Tory women. The Council made plans for defending the city to the end and plans for evacuating. On September 10, the day before the Battle of Brandywine, it issued a proclamation declaring "let us determine, once for all, that we will DIE or be FREE." [35] The battle, however, was lost, and the only force that might have denied Philadelphia to the enemy was routed.

Thereafter, the lines were even more tightly drawn. Those who looked forward to the peace the British would bring had only to wait; those who could not bear to watch the ramparts of freedom crumble jumped into the breach. Congress voted $200,000 to the Council, and the Council turned it over to Rittenhouse; both the Council and the Assembly cooperated in applying it to a variety of defense measures. Four days after Brandywine, the principal elements of both governments still remained in the doomed city. On that day, Rittenhouse, although he had been excused from military service, enrolled in the Fourth Battalion of the Philadelphia militia. [36]

He did not see action as a soldier, but in a civilian capacity

[34] Bond and Smith to DR, Duffield, and du Simitière, Sep. 7, 1777, Arch., APS.
[35] *Pa. Eve. Post*, Sep. 11, 1777; *Pa. Col. Recs.*, XI, 299.
[36] *Ibid.*, 305; *Pa. Arch.*, 6th ser., I, 757.

he was thrown into unwonted service. He arranged and carried through the urgent removal of Continental military stores from French Creek to Bethlehem. With the first thirty-eight wagons, he sent a letter to John Okely informing him of Washington's orders that the town provide for the munitions and supplies.[37] Okely protested but in vain. Before long, tons of sulphur, powder, cartridges, provisions, and whiskey were deposited in a variety of buildings and placed under armed guard.

On September 17, the Assembly instructed Rittenhouse to provide and hold in readiness all the needed wagons for conveying public monies and records to a place of security, "in case the movement of the enemy's army should render it necessary." [38] The Assembly then rose, and the following day Congress abandoned the city. On the 23rd, the Council also left. Between that date and the 27th, when Howe entered Philadelphia, Rittenhouse succeeded in removing his records, his money, and himself. He transferred the Treasury to Lancaster, which became the new capital.

The government of Pennsylvania, driven from its seat in Philadelphia and threatened with capture at any moment, was now assured of existence. The Assembly met early in October and continued to play an effective role. The Council, although often diminished in size, provided genuine leadership. The government became a rallying point, and those who disliked its form or its advocates would never again be able to immobilize it by nullification. Defeat and conquest brought not collapse to the Pennsylvania government, but a new accession of power.

[37] Fitzpatrick, ed., *Writings of Washington,* IX, 214; *PMHB,* XII, 404; XL, 362.
[38] *Pa. House Jours.* (1782), 152.

CHAPTER XIII

Servant of the State

1777–1779

LANCASTER, with its deficiencies magnified both by the insatiable demands of state and Continental governments and by wartime shortages, never became more than a makeshift capital. The state had not succeeded in tapping the credit facilities of the wealthy commercial city of Philadelphia or in realizing the revenue potential of the rich region of which it was the center. Now, the opportunity was withdrawn; the physical possibilities of meeting the war's needs were significantly reduced and the difficulties of the treasurer expanded. Lancaster was a thriving inland town of perhaps four thousand; it was the center of a remarkably prosperous farming county, but it had few of the advantages of Philadelphia.

Rittenhouse was fortunate to be able to make his home with his friend William Henry, who sheltered him against the more unpleasant aspects of exile. He used Henry's library, a second floor, front room, both as a bedroom and an office. Years later, Henry's son, John Joseph, recalled it as a place of calm and refuge. Wounded in the Quebec campaign, John Joseph used to hobble up the stairs to Rittenhouse's room, where he delighted in "affable" conversation or—since Rittenhouse was often busy—in taking a book from the shelves and reading in an atmosphere of peace which became rare in the wartime capital.[1]

Thomas Paine and Colonel Joseph Hart, a member of the Executive Council, shared another room in Henry's house. This

[1] John J. Henry, *Account of the . . . Campaign against Quebec* (Lancaster, 1812), 218–19; Francis Jordan, *The Life of William Henry* (Lancaster, 1910), 34, 71.

crowding strained everyone, but only Paine appeared insensitive to the demands of his situation. Ann, William Henry's wife, was especially disturbed by her guest's argumentative espousal of unorthodox religious views. His ideas were not far removed from Rittenhouse's, but Rittenhouse was careful not to offend his friends. He successfully retained their warmest regard, and remained a friend of the family long after William Henry's death.

Rittenhouse and Henry had shared many experiences even before the Lancaster exile. The two mechanics worked together in the 1773 survey of a canal route between the Lehigh and Susquehanna Rivers. Both had scientific interests, evidenced on Henry's part by his membership in the American Philosophical Society and his invention of a "Sentinel Steam Register," which he described in the society's first volume of *Transactions*.[2] Both vigorously supported the Revolution and the new government in which they were directly associated through Henry's service as treasurer of Lancaster County. Even after Henry accepted appointment as armourer of the state, he remained active in government and politics. His political views were often in harmony with Rittenhouse's; on several levels, the two men spoke the same language.

Rittenhouse did not take Hannah to Lancaster, but left his family at the Norriton farm, where they remained during the occupation. This separation afflicted him much more than it did others who were equally inconvenienced by the dislocations of war. Rittenhouse needed the warmth and stability his home provided, and he worried much about the safety and well-being of his wife and daughters.

After Washington established his encampment at Valley Forge, just a couple of miles from the farm, Hannah was reasonably well protected except from occasional foraging parties. This position also made communication easier and brought to

[2] APS, *Trans.*, 1 (1771), 286–89.

the farm a number of old friends, including Peale, now Captain Peale. He frequently stopped at "Mrs. Rittenhouse's" on his way into or out of camp. Several times, he stayed overnight, once he left his gun there, and on another occasion, he stayed awhile longer to nurse his horse back to health.[3]

At least once during the occupation, Rittenhouse arranged to meet Hannah at an intermediate point—in Chester County —either at her brother Israel's or at her brother John's, depending on the weather. They had to forego plans for a fortnight together and settle on a single night. He wrote Hannah that the risk was too great, "parties of horse are employed to pick up particular persons." [4]

Rittenhouse's life in Lancaster was rendered still more dismal by the darkening clouds surrounding Thomas Barton. As an Anglican priest, Barton was caught in much the same net as William Smith, but he was less capable of compromise. He consistently refused to take the test oath to the new government, regarding it as an abjuration of his oath to the king and his obligations to the Church. His position was that a missionary of the Church of England was an itinerant whose sole business was preaching the gospel and who ought to be exempted from political oaths. He declared, "The proper duties and profession of a minister of the gospel should, in my opinion, never lead him into the field of politics." [5]

Some of his parishioners, however, surely recalled the political role he had played following the Paxton massacres, and others maintained that, despite his denials, he was deeply involved in intrigue against the Revolution. Colonel John Carothers charged him with corresponding with the enemy and with being "at least privy to" a conspiracy to destroy the public magazines at Lancaster, York, and Carlisle.[6] Almost at

[3] Peale, Typed Diary, IV, 26, 34, APS; Barton, *Memoirs*, 267-68.
[4] *Ibid.*, 270-72.
[5] *Ibid.*, 279n.-8on.; *Pa. Arch.*, 2d ser., III, 170.
[6] Jordan, *Henry*, 87, 88.

the moment that Rittenhouse reached Lancaster, William Henry was confronted with the demand that he arrest Barton. Barton, however, was only confined to the limits of his rectory.

At the very least, Barton remained loyal to Britain, both privately and publicly. He insisted on continuing the collects and prayers for the king and the royal family; he felt badly used when this insensitivity drew down upon him the wrath of the populace. He could see in the Revolution nothing but an "unhappy contest." [7] He recognized that America was his children's native country, but it was not his own. He could not come to terms with an independent America; he could only leave.

Fortunately, Esther Rittenhouse Barton had died in 1774 and was spared the tragedy she must otherwise have shared. Barton's second wife, whom he married in 1776, was ready to accompany him out of the country under the interdict "not to return again." The most unhappy part of this voluntary exile was the need to abandon all his children. Esther, his eldest, was the wife of Paul Zantzinger, a leading citizen of Lancaster; William, then a student in England, was old enough to take care of himself; but Matthias was only fifteen, Benjamin eleven, and the four others were younger still. Even under these circumstances, Barton would not bend; he left them under the care of Mary Thornbaugh, who had served as the Bartons' housekeeper for eight or nine years.[8]

In October 1778, he and his wife left Pennsylvania for British New York with the intention of continuing to England or Ireland. His health broke, however, and he was unable to go further, dying there in 1780. Rittenhouse, deeply sensitive to the catastrophe, extended his own protection and assistance to the children. As much as an uncle could, he took the place of their father. He coddled, favored, and recommended the boys, especially William and Benjamin, far beyond their merits. He

---

[7] Barton, *Memoirs*, 280n.
[8] *Ibid.; Pa. Gaz.*, June 29, 1774; *Pa. Arch.*, 2d ser., III, 278–79.

was responsible for lifting both to levels they could not have attained without his patronage—and his nephews never forgot.[9]

Despite this personal travail, Rittenhouse's life followed a course that was determined primarily by public affairs. Less than three weeks after the move to Lancaster, the Assembly reordered the elements of government so that he had to attend to serious matters outside the Treasury. He was appointed, along with all the members of the Supreme Executive Council and eight others, including William Henry, to a newly constituted Council of Safety. This extra-constitutional body was created in fear that the established institutions of government would dissolve or prove incapable of dealing with the disorganization already produced by invasion of the state. Only a few weeks before, the government had been immobilized by politics alone. Now with the terms of the assemblymen about to expire, there was no clear indication that any branch of government could remain effective.[10]

The Council of Safety was an emergency body to which emergency powers were delegated. The Assembly feared that "the preservation of the Commonwealth" might come to rest solely upon this Council. To that end, it was granted "full power . . . to proceed against . . . either capitally or otherwise . . . in a summary mode, either by themselves or others by them to be appointed . . . all persons . . . deemed inimical to the common cause of liberty and the United States of North America." [11] The Council was empowered to seize provisions and other military necessities, to set prices, and to compel sales.

Day after day during the fall, the Council met to grapple with problems of treason and military affairs. It took steps to seize the estates of those who had joined the British army or

---

[9] Barton, *Memoirs*, 281, 329; DR to Thomas Willing, n.d., Etting Papers, HSP; DR to Thomas McKean, Dec. 26, 1795, Provincial Delegates, HSP; *Pa. House Jours.* (1782), 157.
[10] *Pa. Col. Recs.*, XI, 325–28.
[11] *Ibid.*

aided the enemy with intelligence or provisions. It dealt in ordinances with those disobeying militia laws and failing to pay the sums required when substitutes were furnished. It countered the forestalling and engrossing of critical goods by a progressive schedule of penalties, none of which was very harsh. It fixed the price of whiskey; it collected arms, blankets, wagons, and accouterments. It made strenuous efforts to keep the gun factory going and to stimulate the production of such needed items as pans for producing salt by evaporation. It heard John Brown, who bore a third-hand version of Howe's offer of peace, and imprisoned him.

During much of the period for which the records are complete, Rittenhouse attended council meetings with constancy. He was at the same time kept very busy in the Treasury by the Supreme Executive Council, which met regularly from the time its move to Lancaster was completed. The Executive Council handled all the routine business of government, most of it now concerned with the war. It resolved a large proportion of the problems before it by drawing orders to pay upon David Rittenhouse.[12]

After several weeks, men began to breathe a little easier; the governmental collapse most of them had anticipated failed to materialize. Returns from the October elections for Assembly and Council trickled in slowly but by mid-November it appeared that they had been carried off successfully in those parts of the state not occupied by the enemy. After the newly elected Assembly met on the 20th, Rittenhouse practically stopped attending the sessions of the Council of Safety. The legislature confirmed the six ordinances passed by the emergency council, but there was now no justifiable reason for its continuance. On December 6, the Executive Council, following a procedure outlined in the Assembly's act creating the Council of Safety, abolished it.[13]

[12] *Ibid.*, 328–53, 356–81.
[13] *Ibid.*; Pa. *House Jours.* (1782), 158–60, 167.

The demands of the Treasury continued to be more than enough to exhaust Rittenhouse's inventiveness. The revenue system was necessarily less productive than ever with the British in the capital. Increasing numbers of state officers defaulted in their payments of public funds, and no satisfactory means of controlling this abuse was found. Counterfeit money, sometimes blamed on the British, offered an additional hazard. Minor aggravations were more likely in Lancaster, too. For example, the engraver made a serious error in mixing the plates used for printing the new paper money so that the reverse of two denominations showed a conflicting denomination. More fundamental was the continuing stream of orders to pay, issued by the Executive Council. Rittenhouse could do little but complain of his inability to meet the demands.[14]

The new emission money and the sums received from Congress were sufficient only for the most pressing needs. In an effort to utilize every resource, the Assembly turned again to the Loan Office funds. With little ceremony, a committee was appointed to open the Loan Office chest, and on January 6, 1778, Rittenhouse received from them £13,000.[15] Even this modest cache was helpful, but he was left with the constant need to decide which of the demands thrust upon him had the highest priority and which might be deferred. This was the sort of aggravation calculated to produce ulcers even in a previously relaxed man.

In May, the president of Pennsylvania, Thomas Wharton, Jr., died. Rittenhouse walked close to the head of the procession at the funeral, just behind the members of the Executive Council.[16] He had been closely associated with Wharton as his vice chairman on the old Council of Safety, and, since the removal to Lancaster, the two men had been in almost daily contact. Wharton was a man of genuine capacity. In addition, his so-

[14] *Ibid.*, 193; *Pa. Col. Recs.*, XI, 362; *Pa. Packet*, Jan. 28, July 16, 1778.
[15] *Pa. House Jours.* (1782), 178–79, 187.
[16] *Pa. Packet*, May 27, 1778.

cial and economic position had brought to the new government conspicuous support. His death was a loss to the Revolution, to the state, and to the Constitutionalists.

Throughout the period of exile, the government lived on dreams of return. Congress encouraged Pennsylvania projects aimed at forcing British evacuation of Philadelphia, but the withdrawal depended upon other factors altogether. The American victory at Saratoga a year before and the French alliance produced a threat to the British strategic position which was countered by consolidating military commitments. In June, rumors became thick, and, on the 19th, positive word reached Lancaster of the evacuation of Philadelphia which had been completed the day before. Amid much confusion, all of the offices of state government were moved back to the metropolis, Rittenhouse in the midst of the traffic. The Council met in the city on the 26th and the Assembly on July 2.[17]

By June 24, Rittenhouse was not only back in the city but sufficiently at ease to observe the solar eclipse which he had hoped to view from Williamsburg, where it was total. In this enterprise, he was joined by Owen Biddle and John Lukens, who had returned from Lancaster, and by William Smith, who had never left Philadelphia. They may well have gathered at Smith's invitation, for the observations were made from the College. Unfortunately, the day was too cloudy to permit a sight of the beginning of the eclipse, but in the afternoon, the phenomenon became clearly visible.[18] Although the observations had little scientific value, they constituted for Rittenhouse a fine celebration of the recovery of the capital.

Shortly afterward, he heard from Thomas Jefferson, who had come to know Rittenhouse during his service in the Congress. He wrote that the observations in Virginia had not suc-

---

[17] *Ibid.*, July 4, 1778; *Pa. Col. Recs.*, XI, 533.
[18] Barton, *Memoirs*, 275n., 591; Smith, MS Note in Mayer, APS; *Pa. Arch.*, 2d ser., III, 336.

ceeded very well either, because of generally cloudy weather. At Williamsburg, only the beginning was seen. At Monticello, Jefferson saw nothing until the moon had advanced one-third of the way over the face of the sun; thereafter, he caught only intermittent glimpses. He saw the end of the eclipse but to no useful purpose because he did not have a clock sufficiently accurate to establish the time. This provided occasion to ask when Rittenhouse would send the clock he had promised Jefferson much earlier.

So unreasonable a request expressed the Virginian's frustrations with partisan politics and his conviction that Rittenhouse was wasting his talents in the petty problems of governing men. There was, he suggested, "an order of geniusses above that obligation, and therefore exempted from it. No body can conceive that nature ever intended to throw away a Newton upon the occupations of a crown . . . Are those powers then, which being intended for the erudition of the world, like air and light, the world's common property, to be taken from their proper pursuit to do the commonplace drudgery of governing a single state, a work which may be executed by men of an ordinary stature, such as are always and every where to be found?" [19] He urged that Rittenhouse return to the pursuit of science.

To Jefferson, as to other admirers, the risen clockmaker seemed the personification of an ideal nobler than war and party politics. Yet they knew that this was not the time for science. Timothy Matlack apologized when he made an urgent but mundane request of Rittenhouse on July 14. Congress had granted Pennsylvania $100,000 to purchase clothing for the troops, and it was "absolutely necessary" that the treasurer go to York to receive the money. Rittenhouse was at that moment making plans to bring his family back to the city, but Matlack professed to see some good even in the duty he pressed upon his friend. The exercise would "contribute to" his health.

[19] Boyd, ed., *Papers of Jefferson*, II, 203.

By the 17th, Rittenhouse had completed his mission and was back in the city.[20]

There was no long escape for Rittenhouse from the debilitating shortage of funds. The deficiency was fundamental and continuous in Pennsylvania; it was worse, if anything, in the Congress. The inability to mobilize exchange was more the cause of the harrowing character of the Revolution than was the physical shortage of food, clothing, ammunition, or men. Prices fluctuated greatly but not till the end of the year did they take a clear upward course. When foodstuffs needed by the army became scarce, the Executive Council responded by laying embargoes on the critical items, once in August and again in October. Early in 1779, it issued a proclamation against forestalling.[21]

Plagued by the refusal of many who had received public funds to submit their accounts, the Assembly passed an act in September 1778 to compel the settlement of public accounts. It gave additional support to the annually appointed Committee of Accounts, which gave its first attention to the accounts of the treasurer, and it created a special committee of auditors to collect and settle the accounts of the late Committee and Council of Safety.[22] In all of these efforts to reduce Pennsylvania's financial chaos, Rittenhouse was directly involved.

Congress added new urgency to the need to solve these problems when it voted to call in its bills of credit emitted in April and May 1778. The stringency this redemption would cause led the Executive Council to meet early in January with Rittenhouse and with the Pennsylvania delegates to the Congress. They discussed the anticipated effects upon the Pennsylvania Treasury. Just a little earlier, Rittenhouse had stressed the deple-

[20] Pa. Arch., 1st ser., VI, 643.

[21] Ibid., 4th ser., III, 692–93, 694–95, 709; Anne Bezanson, et al., Prices and Inflation during the American Revolution, Pennsylvania, 1770–1790 (Phila., 1951), 336.

[22] W. P. Snyder, Compendium and Brief History of Taxation in Pennsylvania (Harrisburg, 1906), 9; Pa. House Jours. (1782), 243; Pa. Arch., 2d ser., III, 626.

tion of his funds; he reported £20,000 on hand, all of it Continental and half of that allocated. Four days after the conference, and perhaps as a result of it, Congress poured an additional £60,000 into the Pennsylvania Treasury. This, of course, soon melted away too, and Rittenhouse's next report to Council was another comment on the "low state" of the Treasury.[23]

The unresolved problem remained taxes. Enough had been levied to answer the needs, but they could not be collected. As prices rose in earnest at the end of 1778 and early in 1779, tax revenues became more elusive than ever. Few paid their taxes, and often the collectors did not turn them in when they were paid. Northumberland County even petitioned to be excused from paying any taxes at all.[24]

In the midst of these problems, Rittenhouse continued to be regularly returned as a private in the Philadelphia militia. He was mustered in Captain Christian Shaffer's company of the regiment commanded by Colonel John Bayard. Outside the militia organization, Rittenhouse knew Bayard on a plane of equality, but, inside, he was listed on the rolls as a private along with names which—whether fictitious or real—were very caricatures of the citizen soldier: Christian Fight, Henry Stuck, and Daniel Noodle! [25]

Almost as soon as the capital was reoccupied, state political conflict descended to new depths of bitterness, much of the intensity of feeling centering upon economic problems close to the treasurer. The Constitutionalists unquestionably gained strength from the success of government in preserving the state through invasion and exile. They obtained a resounding majority in the October elections, only slightly smaller in magnitude than the support they had received in the invasion election of 1777. On December 1, 1778, Joseph Reed, who had previously refused office, was elected to and accepted the presi-

[23] *Ibid.*, 1st ser., VII, 118, 302; *Pa. Col. Recs.*, XI, 664.
[24] *Pa. Arch.*, 2d ser., III, 218; 4th ser., III, 712.
[25] *Ibid.*, 6th ser., I, 761.

dency of the state. George Bryan became vice president. By contrast, the opponents of the Constitution had been injured through the defection of some of their leaders to the British. To counter these losses, the Republicans mounted an energetic offensive against the Constitution, which again placed the issue in doubt.

The new Assembly voted to hold a referendum, similar to that planned before the invasion, on the question of a new constitutional convention. This decision was followed by a political campaign in which the Republican Society was again opposed by the reformed Whig Society, now known as the Constitutional Society and still under Peale's chairmanship. The Constitutionalists generated so much feeling and so many petitions against the referendum that on February 27 the Assembly canceled plans for holding it, less than a month before the scheduled date.[26]

The Constitutionalists now had ample strength to defeat their political opponents, but they could not similarly master the economic crisis. They preserved a doctrinaire attitude toward depreciating money, rising prices, and scarcity of goods which prevented the best application of available means to the reduction of the difficulties. They took the causes of depreciation to be corruption and the lack of civic virtue, rather than the fundamental dislocations of war, disordered patterns of trade, and inadequate tax income. They did not make sufficient or successful efforts to generate credit. Instead, some of the leaders and many citizens vented their energies in attacking individual merchants who seemed to be causing the trouble as they grew richer and the poor, poorer. In Congress, in Assembly, and throughout the land there was wide support for this view—especially in the militia and in the Constitutional Society.

Popular disaffection came to a head in Philadelphia on May

[26] *Pa. House Jours.* (1782), 249, 324–26; *Pa. Packet,* Jan. 5, Feb. 16, Mar. 16, 25, 30, 1779; *Pa. Gaz.,* Mar. 24, 31, Apr. 28, 1779.

25, 1779, at a town meeting presided over by Daniel Roberdeau, militia general and Constitutionalist politician. He set the stage by calling for the immediate reduction of prices as "The way to make our money good." [27] Combinations which had been formed for the purpose of maintaining prices could be overcome by concerted efforts to drop prices, week by week. The main thing, he emphasized, was to begin. The meeting enthusiastically adopted a set of previously prepared resolutions and appointed two new committees. One, chaired by William Henry, was charged with investigating prices and concerting plans to regulate them. The second, which had a more limited function, included Rittenhouse.

Matlack, Rittenhouse, Paine, Peale, Captain Joseph Blewer, and Colonel Jonathan Bayard Smith constituted a committee to investigate the case of the ship *Victorious*, lately arrived in Philadelphia with a cargo which was said to have been purchased by or consigned to Robert Morris. This appeared to be the most flagrant example of forestalling, monopolizing, and conspiring to raise prices. If evil could be detected and defeated here, many hoped that it would prove only the first step in ending the upward spiral of prices.[28]

So far, no one had been able to get a straight story on the *Victorious*, which served to heighten well-aired suspicions. A French ship, she had arrived at Philadelphia on April 20 with a diversified cargo including dry goods. The cargo was rumored to be the property of Silas Deane, one of the Constitutionalists' most hated whipping boys whom they had already accused of treason—correctly as it later turned out. Morris' earlier connections with Deane fed fears that he was responsible for withholding the imported goods from sale in order to force prices up. In proof of this allegation, some asserted that, since

[27] *Ibid.*, July 2, 1779; Marshall, *Diary*, 217; *Pa. Packet*, May 27, 1779.
[28] *Ibid.*; Robert L. Brunhouse, *The Counter-Revolution in Pennsylvania, 1776–1790* (Harrisburg, 1942), 72.

the ship had made port, "the prices of all kinds of dry goods have been greatly advanced." [29]

The committee, reduced to five by the absence of Blewer, set upon its task immediately. Morris, however, rebuffed their first invitation to meet at the City Tavern on the grounds of an inflammation of his eyes. He did suffer from periodic attacks of this sort, but the evasion tried the patience of the committee. Not to be thus put off, they called the next morning on Morris at his home, where they found the Reverend William White and John Nixon with him. He proved every bit as convinced of his "innocence & integrity" in the matter as the committee was of the justice of their inquiry. Morris, in addition, wore an air of outrage at the personal injury being inflicted upon him. He answered their questions, nevertheless, and promised a fuller statement. As the committee went out the door, Rittenhouse told him that he would hear from them again within a few days.[30]

Morris' facts were accepted as he offered them. A Mr. Sollekoff of Baltimore had obtained, on the day the *Victorious* made port, the right to purchase or not to purchase the cargo as a whole—associating himself with Morris in the transaction. Morris, in turn, agreed to make available to the Commercial Committee of Congress a quarter of the cargo at a price lower than the one called for in his agreement with Sollekoff. Morris had precipitated this contradiction by signing Sollekoff's agreement without understanding the French in which it was written. He was left no recourse but to renegotiate his arrangements with the Congressional committee at a higher price. The merchandise still aboard which was not involved in this misunderstanding was "unsuited to this season and to this Country." [31]

This strange story reflected little credit upon Morris' perspicacity as a merchant, but neither did it reveal a plot or an

[29] Hubertis Cummings, "Robert Morris and the Episode of the Polacre 'Victorious,'" *PMHB*, LXX (1947), 239–57; *Pa. Gaz.*, July 2, 1779.

[30] *Ibid.*, July 21, 1779; *Pa. Packet*, July 8, 1779.

[31] *Pa. Gaz.*, July 21, 1779.

actionable misdemeanor. The committee reported that Mr. Sollekoff had, technically, acted the part of a forestaller. Morris, by getting the whole cargo into his possession, was in fact, "engrossing and monopolizing," although they conceded that the rigorous sense of these terms was abated by his subsequent behavior. They concluded, "though, as a merchant, he may be strictly within the rules, yet when he considers the many public and honorary stations he has filled, and the times he lives in, he must feel himself somewhat out of character." [32]

The statement did nothing to reduce the economic crisis, but it pointed to a wide gulf in attitudes. Morris and most other merchants and traders in paper, land, or goods regarded their economic freedom as fundamental. Rittenhouse and the committee emphasized, instead, the public character of such private transactions which they felt ought to be grounded upon moral principles—upon virtue and patriotism.

Morris continued to be convinced of his own rectitude, while militia members promised armed intervention if effective action could be obtained only by force. At another mammoth town meeting held on July 27, a band of a hundred men armed with clubs and marching to fife and drum prevented General John Cadwalader from speaking because they disagreed with his conservative viewpoint. After the followers of Morris withdrew, the meeting decided to expand the membership of the extra-legal Committee on Prices. Elections for this purpose were held on August 2, when Rittenhouse was among those added to the now gargantuan committee of 120. William Henry continued to give energetic—but largely futile—leadership to this effort.[33]

Somewhat less related to the immediate crisis than the *Victorious* affair but containing still greater destructive potentialities was the case of the sloop *Active*, with which Rittenhouse

[32] *Pa. Packet*, July 24, 1779.
[33] *Ibid.*, Aug. 5, 1779; *Pa. Gaz.*, July 28, Aug. 4, 13, Sep. 1, 15, 1779.

became involved as state treasurer. The *Active* was a war prize whose capture was contested between Gideon Olmstead and three Connecticut fishermen on the one hand and agents of the state of Pennsylvania on the other. Impressed by the British, the Connecticut men had mutinied and gained control of the British sloop *Active* sometime before it was captured by the Pennsylvania ship *Convention* and the privateer *Gerard*. A Pennsylvania court awarded one-quarter of the prize to the Connecticut claimants, one-quarter to each of the two American ships, and one-quarter to the state of Pennsylvania. Immediately, the award was challenged and remained a matter of disruptive dispute for a quarter of a century thereafter.

On May 1, 1779, George Ross, judge of the Pennsylvania admiralty court, delivered to Rittenhouse Loan Office certificates to the amount of £11,496..9..9, representing the state's share in the prize. Rittenhouse, in turn, gave bond for £22,000 to remain in force until the dispute was settled and the money in his hands could be freely applied to the uses of the state. In time, he funded the sum in other interest-bearing securities and regularly deposited the interest. Despite his most strenuous efforts, neither he nor his heirs were able to turn back the *Active* award money to the state. The explosive situation hung fire for many years longer.[34]

In 1779, the affair became a major new ingredient in Pennsylvania's internal politics. Rittenhouse's political friends supported the state position, especially after Olmstead appealed to Congress and secured a reversal. Congress, sitting as an admiralty court, ordered the whole of the prize paid to the Connecticut claimants. The refusal of the Pennsylvania leaders to accept this adjudication was strengthened by the injection of Benedict Arnold into the case. Arnold, by his conduct as mili-

---

[34] Richard Peters, Jun., *The Whole Proceedings in the Case of Olmsted and Others versus Rittenhouse's Executrices* (Phila., 1809), 64–72; Hampton L. Carson, "The Case of the Sloop 'Active,'" *PMHB*, XVI (1892), 393–94; J. D. Sargeant to Samuel Bryan, Jan. 13, 1803, Photocopy, HSP.

tary commandant of Philadelphia, had already brought down upon his head the wrath of the Constitutionalists, who were further irked when they learned that he had bought a share in the Connecticut claim and then used his influence to see it sustained.[35]

The Pennsylvanians refused to compromise the *Active* case and stood behind a series of charges brought against General Arnold, ranging from improper use of public property to undignified treatment of a militiaman (who happened to be Timothy Matlack's son). The bitterness of feeling against Arnold was scarcely assuaged by Washington's mild delivery of the reprimand a military court finally sentenced him to receive.

The Constitutionalists enjoyed so much favor at this time that they won the 1779 elections handily even though Assembly seats, for the first time since the Revolution, were apportioned according to taxables, cutting the strength of the western counties significantly. Although stronger than ever, the government could not always restrain its followers from violent action which broke loose in the Fort Wilson affair, a mob attack on a barricaded group of conservative leaders, and in a street assault on Benedict Arnold. On the constructive side, the Constitutionalists were responsible for pushing through some notable legislation. Most striking was George Bryan's bill for gradual emancipation, but almost equally liberal were the terms of the Divesting Act, which gave the Penns generous compensation for lands the state took over.[36]

The Constitutionalists never developed comparable statesmanship in handling financial affairs, and there is no indication that Rittenhouse offered leadership in formulating such policy. He provided a careful, industrious, and utterly honest administration of state funds. For his day, he was remarkably fastidious

[35] *Pa. Packet*, Nov. 19, 1778; *Pa. Col. Recs.*, xi, 754; Brunhouse, *Counter-Revolution*, 66–67.
[36] Dallas, *Laws of Pa.*, i, 838.

in refusing to buy or speculate in government securities while in office. He did not hesitate to take the responsibility for allotting priorities in disbursing his limited funds. He cooperated fully with Henry's price-fixing committee and with all other efforts to maintain monetary values by governmental or social action. But, he left to the Assembly and to the Council the search for revenues adequate to the needs.[37]

Late in the summer of 1779, Rittenhouse participated in a new approach to the problem known as the "Citizens' Plan." He was appointed to a committee which included also Roberdeau, Bradford, Henry, Paine, Hutchinson, and Biddle and which essayed a house-to-house canvass in the quest of voluntary money subscriptions. The intention was to provide the government with the funds it needed without more issues of paper money that would depreciate as the last one had. The money realized would be paid back by canceling the subscriber's taxes for the ensuing three years. Developed within Henry's price-fixing committee, this plan recognized that, before "the emissions" could be stopped and prices rolled back, more revenues must be obtained.[38]

Although the Council and a town meeting approved the plan, and Congress was invited to stop issuing money in anticipation of good results, it never had a chance of succeeding. People who refused to pay their annual taxes were not ready, effectively, to pay three years' taxes in advance. By waiting, they might be able to discharge their obligations to the government at a very much lower rate. And something more than the patriotism demanded by the leaders of the Constitutionalist party was required to mobilize the resources of the moneyed men. Meanwhile, inflation continued with no end in sight.[39]

Although both state and federal finances were in so critical a condition that collapse seemed but a short distance away, fi-

---

[37] Rush, *Eulogium*, 39.
[38] *Pa. Gaz.*, July 14, Aug. 18, Aug. 25, 1779.
[39] Bezanson, *Prices*, 22, 61.

nancial indices did not accurately mirror the health of the community. The nation had survived its severest threat, the state had emerged from invasion, and the metropolis had thrown off occupation. Energy and a resilient confidence belied the rising price levels. Underneath appearances, a measure of stability had been reestablished.

CHAPTER XIV

Science Ascendant

1779–1781

THE new stability that Philadelphia attained in 1779 was effectively demonstrated in the revival of several aspects of intellectual life. The government was unable to solve its worst problems, but the mere fact that it continued to hold together was enough to awaken one circle after another. Rittenhouse played a central role in three of these: the revival of the American Philosophical Society, the resolution of the Virginia boundary dispute, and the reformation of the College of Philadelphia. At the same time, he diverted more of his tightly rationed time to his own scientific pursuits.

The Philosophical Society had continued a shadowy existence ever since 1776. Rittenhouse resented the discontinuance of meetings, but, although one was occasionally announced, the society seldom got into the news except when its facilities were used by political groups. Rittenhouse was among those responsible for calling a meeting to be held in the College on March 5, 1779. The announced intention was to consider "the present State of the Society" following the "calamities of war, and the invasion of this city by the enemy." [1]

Two weeks later, the election of new officers reflected the circumstances of the war and the feelings of patriotism. Franklin, of course, continued in the presidency—at once the most distinguished American scientist and one of the two most distinguished patriots. Thomas Bond remained a vice president; the other two vice presidents were dropped: William Smith,

[1] APS Mins., 1774–87, 29, 37; *Pa. Jour.*, Mar. 3, 1779.

who was even then combating charges of treason, was demoted to secretary, while the aging Quaker, Samuel Rhoads, was denied all office.[2]

This left more than enough opportunity to raise Rittenhouse to the vice presidential rank. Before the war, he had served as secretary, curator, and librarian. Now, both his scientific reputation and his Revolutionary role demanded this additional recognition.

The patriotism of the other officers was their most obvious qualification. The director of the Continental medical service, William Shippen, was chosen a vice president, and Ewing, Biddle, and the Reverend William White, secretaries. White was unusual among the Anglican clergy for the resoluteness of his attachment to the American cause. Among the others elected were Matthew Clarkson and Lewis Nicola, both of whom held military commissions.

Rittenhouse was almost immediately called upon to introduce one of his Constitutionalist colleagues into office. With Bond and Shippen, he invited Joseph Reed to accept the post of patron of the society, to which Reed readily consented. This was an office of honor always held by the proprietary governor of colonial Pennsylvania and now extended to the president of the Commonwealth.[3]

The society was restored to permanence but not quickly to creative activity. For a long time, it continued to be more marked by the Revolution than by serious scientific work. Until the end of the war, the only foreign members elected were Frenchmen, predominantly soldiers and diplomats who added little of scientific stature. An unsuccessful effort to establish a federal system of scientific societies was a transparent copy of the evolving pattern of Revolutionary government. Similarly a product of the Revolutionary climate was the successful quest for a written charter. This seemed desirable, not primarily as

[2] *Pa. Gaz.*, Mar. 31, 1779; *Freeman's Jour.*, Oct. 13, 20, 1784.
[3] APS Mins., 1774–87, 37, 38; *Pa. Packet*, Apr. 6, 1779.

a legal patent for existence but as a manifesto of principles, in the pattern of the Declaration of Independence and the other great state papers.[4]

Rittenhouse became associated with the charter move only after it ran into a snag in the Assembly. That body upset intentions by adding two clauses to the original draft: one limiting the amount of property that might be owned by the society and the other permitting only citizens of Pennsylvania to serve as officers. The second clause, especially, vitiated the liberal spirit of the document, which sought to place the arts and sciences on a plane above petty boundaries and even above national wars. Fortunately, a committee on which Rittenhouse served was able to persuade enough legislators to have the property restriction lifted entirely and to leave American citizenship as the only limitation upon officeholding.[5]

Organizational activities of this sort were useful, but they did not bring Rittenhouse closer to the world of science as one society commission promised to do. He undertook the duty of replying to the letter from the Mannheim astronomer, Father Christian Mayer, in which Mayer had acknowledged his election to membership and his receipt of the first volume of *Transactions*. Rittenhouse, in turn, thanked Mayer for the observations he had forwarded and, in lieu of another volume of *Transactions*, sent a copy of his own 1775 *Oration*, in which he had predicted the sort of important new information Mayer's study of the fixed stars was yielding. About this, he asked one of the big questions: did the changes in fixed star position discovered by Mayer "agree with any imagined motion of our system?"[6]

Mayer seems not to have replied for there is no trace of further correspondence on either side of the Atlantic.[7] This was

<hr />

[4] Hindle, *Pursuit*, 278.

[5] APS Mins., 1774–87, 21; *Pa. Jour.*, Feb. 23, 1780; *Pa. House Jours.* (1782), 443, 447; Dallas, *Laws of Pa.*, I, 850.

[6] Barton, *Memoirs*, 577–81; APS Mins., 1774–87, 44.

[7] Mayer's instruments and effects are preserved in the Heidelberg Sternwarte.

a disappointment to Rittenhouse, who badly felt the need for such an intercourse and who made continuing, but scattered, efforts to find European correspondents. The foreground of his life, however, continued to be occupied by routine Treasury crises, by violent political conflict, and by the constant expectation that he was available to apply science to useful ends.

Such a demand was placed upon Rittenhouse once again in August 1779 when he was asked to aid in a new attempt to solve the Virginia boundary dispute. Rittenhouse's reputation coupled with his conviction of the justice of Pennsylvania's claims gave the state added strength. Following the abortive negotiations of 1776, the Virginia Convention had surrendered its north and northwest charter claim and had agreed to accept the Pennsylvania charter as the basis of settlement. Thomas Jefferson, now governor of Virginia, opened the door for the first time to promising negotiation.

With rising anticipation, Rittenhouse, George Bryan, and John Ewing met in Baltimore on August 27 with a Virginia commission appointed to work out a boundary agreement. Rittenhouse took with him letters of introduction to some of Maryland's leading citizens, including Charles Carroll and Charles Wallace, but the mission was so brief that there was little time for social activities.[8]

Not only were the conditions of discussion favorable to the Pennsylvanians but the Virginia commissioners were themselves inferior in two respects: they were neither as practiced in politics nor as weighty in prestige as their Pennsylvania counterparts. The Reverend James Madison, president of the College of William and Mary, especially admired Rittenhouse, and he respected Ewing at the same time that he disliked him personally. The Reverend Robert Andrews was subordinate to Madison and, as a graduate of the College of Philadelphia, subtly subordinate to the Pennsylvanians too.

[8] Peale to Wallace, n.d., Peale, Letter Book, I, 64–65, APS; *PMHB*, LVII, 158–59.

At the first meeting, powers were exchanged and the delegates agreed to base initial discussions on the Pennsylvanians' written statement of their case. In this presentation, they had attempted to translate the spirit as well as the letter of Penn's charter, working over once again the old arguments developed in the long controversy between Penn and Baltimore. They even returned to the assertion that "the beginning of the fortieth degree of northern latitude" justified the claim of the thirty-ninth parallel—which lay fifty miles below the compromise Mason-Dixon line. They bolstered this contention by citing Penn's original petition requesting three full degrees of latitude. The case was well knit but, in fact, it had already been bartered away in the Maryland compromise and could hardly be expected to prevail against the Virginians.[9]

Madison and Andrews took two days to put together a reply to the Pennsylvania demand for a southern boundary at the thirty-ninth parallel and a western boundary paralleling the course of the Delaware River at a distance of five degrees. They countered the claim with the obvious suggestion that the Mason-Dixon line be extended to form the boundary.

The trading then began. The Pennsylvanians quickly responded that they would rather submit the whole dispute "to disinterested and impartial judges" than accept the Mason-Dixon line extension—unless Virginia would compensate Pennsylvania for her losses south of the Mason-Dixon parallel by moving her western boundary to a meridian enclosing an equivalent additional acreage in the West.[10] The Virginians rejected any thought of compensation but offered in turn the line 39° 30′ as a compromise. To this the Pennsylvanians agreed—provided the western line were drawn at a meridian five degrees from the Delaware along the 39° 30′ parallel. Such a line would

[9] *Pa. Arch.*, 3d ser., x, 489–90; *Pa. House Jours.* (1782), 399; *Pa. Col. Recs.*, xii, 212–13; Boyd, ed., *Papers of Jefferson*, iii, 77; William W. Hening, ed., *Statutes at Large . . . of Virginia* (Richmond, 1810–23), x, 521, 524.
[10] *Ibid.*, 529.

not only have been vastly easier for surveyors to mark than a line duplicating the course of the river, but it would also have given Pennsylvania distinctly more acreage in the West.

Again the Virginians demurred but offered to accept a meridian line as the western boundary, provided Pennsylvania would agree to the Mason-Dixon parallel as the southern boundary. On August 31, this proposal became the basis of a formal agreement signed by both groups of negotiators. The Pennsylvania commission had done well. In the West, they won more territory than the charter assigned, and they gained in the newly defined southwest corner of the state a population primarily Virginian in origin.

Pennsylvania's satisfaction with the settlement was demonstrated by the Assembly's rapid ratification. Rittenhouse displayed a draft of the projected boundary to the house on November 19, and, on the same day, ratification was voted. Virginia was much more reluctant; several months passed before she could bring herself to confirm the agreement.[11]

Before then, however, the situation deteriorated seriously. President Reed issued a proclamation on December 28 asserting that men who claimed authority under the state of Virginia had proceeded at least thirty miles inside the negotiated boundary to Fort Burd, where they attempted to establish governmental jurisdiction. Settlers long undisturbed in the possession of their Pennsylvania land titles were dispossessed. Reed called on Virginia to disavow the action. At almost the same time, Congress recommended that both states refrain from making further land grants in the disturbed area. In February, fearful inhabitants petitioned Pennsylvania for defense against the Virginia aggression they anticipated during the coming summer.

Large-scale armed conflict was prevented by Governor Jefferson's communication, on July 17, 1779, of a somewhat re-

---

[11] *Ibid.*, 534, 535; *Pa. House Jours.* (1782), 399–400; *Pa. Col. Recs.*, xii, 212–13; *Pa. Arch.*, 4th ser., iii, 751–52.

luctant and conditional ratification of the negotiated line. Among the stipulated conditions, Pennsylvania must agree that land titles would be validated on the basis of prior claim and that no taxes would be collected in her newly defined southwest corner until December 1, 1780. Without argument, Pennsylvania agreed.[12]

The boundary negotiations gave Rittenhouse a chance to think of something other than tax delinquencies and rates of discount, but they hardly represented a return to science. Then, in October 1779, he took a rare excursion into the interior to view the effects of a "freak of Nature" that had occurred near Carlisle on August 19. After a full day of study at the site and after questioning residents of the area, he pieced together the phenomenon. A cataract or "prodigious Torrent" of water seemed to have fallen on the north side of Blue Mountain in a small area no more than ten yards in diameter. As it descended, it tore up trees and rocks to a depth of four to ten feet and to a width of a hundred feet along a course of over a quarter-mile. Originating in sandy and stony soil near the peak of the mountain, it could not have represented a collection of surface water drained from surrounding terrain. Nor did Rittenhouse regard as likely an underground origin of the water. This left only the possibility of a fall of water from the clouds on one spot alone over a period of at least several minutes.

Assuming that the facts had been correctly observed and stated, how could they be explained? The strange event had occurred during a rainstorm but no accompanying lightning or thunder had been reported. Nevertheless, Rittenhouse based his admittedly hesitant "Conjecture" upon a discharge of electricity. Perhaps "a Great Quantity of the Electric fluid, passing silently from the Cloud to the Mountain, carried the forming drops of rain from all quarters of the Cloud to one point, and by uniting them produced this prodigious Cataract." His guess was wrong; rather than a meteorological phenomenon, it was

[12] *Ibid.*, 2d ser., III, 370; *Pa. Col. Recs.*, XII, 444.

undoubtedly an eruption of underground water—but it remains difficult to catalogue precisely.[13]

At the end of that month, Rittenhouse chanced to see another phenomenon in a more familiar realm: in the southwest sector of the evening sky, he observed a bright meteor. It descended in an almost vertical line, leaving behind it a silver trail, which slowly decayed and became distorted in form. After John Page forwarded information on its position and appearance from Williamsburg, Rittenhouse was able to estimate its height at its first appearance and the point of its descent.

His conjecture about the cause of this occurrence was correct. He supposed such meteors "to be Bodies altogether foreign to the Earth, but meeting with it, in its Annual Orbit, are attracted by it, and on entering our Atmosphere take fire and are exploded, something in the manner Steel filings are, on passing thro' the flame of a Candle."[14] The explanation was not novel, but neither was it universally accepted at this time.

The coldness of the winter of 1779–1780, "allowed to be by many people the hardest ever known," presented still another opportunity for study and conjecture. Rittenhouse and William Smith hired a digger, one Isaac Bell, to discover how deep the ground was frozen. His probe placed the frost line seven and one-half inches below the surface, confirming popular impressions of the winter's coldness. Yet, this was an uncomfortably isolated fact.[15]

A larger scale approach to the collection of details of the effects from sustained cold was made through the Philosophical Society. The society inserted notices in the Philadelphia newspapers and requested other papers throughout the country to copy their appeal for recorded temperatures and for reports of effects, including the correlation of weather with the incidence of disease. Thomas Bond, who was especially enthusiastic

[13] Benjamin Guild, Diary, Oct. 19, 1779, MHS; DR to Franklin, Apr. 29, 1780, Bache Coll., APS; Glen N. Cox to Brooke Hindle, Oct. 16, 1963.
[14] APS, Trans., II (1786), 173–76; DR to Franklin, Dec. 29, 1780, APS.
[15] PMHB, XXVII, 50.

about the enterprise, hoped to put together a picture of continental proportions.

The results were disappointing; indeed, most of the reports finally submitted came from or through Rittenhouse. He forwarded one he received from the Reverend James Madison, one from William Charles Houston of the College of New Jersey, and his own. Only two others found their way to the society, and one of these had to be discounted; Herman Husband, the famous regulator, used the opportunity to develop his theory that the earth was a living animal! [16]

In a wholly different direction, Rittenhouse was propelled toward a new opportunity to serve science and the community. The equivocal provost and Tory-spotted Board of Trustees of the College of Philadelphia had aroused strong antagonism among Rittenhouse's political associates. A strange mode of redressing the balance was adopted. The Constitutionalists pushed through the Assembly an act amending the colonial charter of the institution but not abrogating it; on the original charter, they erected the University of the State of Pennsylvania. In terms both of support and control, it was a state university, molded with the same aspirations which brought substantially similar changes in the College of William and Mary and which led before long to the founding of the state universities of Georgia and North Carolina. Support was built up by assigning one confiscated Tory estate after another to the endowment of the University. Control brought Rittenhouse into the picture.

The old Board of Trustees and faculty were dismissed and replaced by a new board and, after a little interval, by a new faculty. Of twenty-four seats on the new board, six were filled by state officers, six by senior city clergymen—including one Roman Catholic priest—and the remaining twelve by outstand-

---

[16] *Pa. Jour.*, Mar. 22, 1780; *Va. Gaz.* (Dixon and Nicholson), Apr. 8, 1780; APS Mins., 1774–87, 21, Feb. 6, Mar. 16, 1781, n.p.; Madison to DR, Nov. [1780], Misc. MSS, APS; Madison to DR, 1780, MS Comm., Mathematics and Astronomy, 1, 9, 17; W. C. Houston to DR, Feb. 22, [1779], MS Comm., Natural Philosophy, 1, 1.

ing citizens designated by name. Most of this latter group turned out to be Constitutionalist officers of the government, including all of Pennsylvania's delegates to the Congress and Timothy Matlack and David Rittenhouse. Almost immediately, Rittenhouse was placed on two board committees; in December he was elected professor of astronomy, and in February 1780, vice-provost.

The board intended that both he and John Ewing, provost-elect of the new University, offer instruction in mathematics and natural philosophy, thus betraying a stronger orientation toward science than even Smith had given to the colonial college. The innovation of two professors in this usually neglected field raised the immediate question of how their work could be divided. The two men, however, had no trouble in reaching an amicable agreement, which the board speedily ratified. As soon as the classes were sufficiently prepared, Ewing would instruct them in "Logic, Metaphysicks and Moral Philosophy, the V. Provost in Geography and practical Astronomy—The business of Geometry and Mathematicks they propose to divide between them, each taking some of the branches.—Natural and Experimental Philosophy they also propose to divide, and not without hopes of Rendering their Lectures in this important Science, by their Joint endeavors, and mutual Assistance as Compleat as Possible.—" [17]

The prospect was exciting—from the viewpoint of Rittenhouse, who would teach only his favorite studies to advanced students, and from the viewpoint of the University, which would inaugurate a hitherto unapproached concentration in science. Unfortunately, it was never fulfilled; the available evidence suggests that the program was never begun. Benjamin Smith Barton, who later became a member of the faculty himself, declared that his uncle did not deliver any of the planned lectures. None of the customary newspaper announcements

[17] Dallas, *Laws of Pa.*, I, 815–21; Trustees Mins., III, 32, 47, 49, 51, 52, 53, Univ. of Pa.

appeared heralding the beginning of the courses. The trustees' minutes reveal that the lectures were not offered in the academic year 1779–1780, and since Rittenhouse resigned his faculty posts in April 1782, he could have taught only through the year 1780–1781. In this period, however, he was increasing rather than reducing his multifold governmental activities. The appointment was defined as a full-time post with the ample salary of £400 plus a housing allowance of £60, none of which Rittenhouse ever collected. The project never got beyond the planning stage.[18]

Whether Rittenhouse finally balked at lecturing or was discouraged by other factors, he was unable to use this means to shake himself loose from the demands of the Treasury. This continued in what Joseph Reed described as a "disgraceful condition." Continual efforts were required to spur tax collection, and continual tight rope walking by Rittenhouse was necessary as he tried to apply feeble resources to satisfy the most essential needs. He complained of being "regularly dunned Six times a week" over a period of three months for a sum of $700,000, which he remained unable to satisfy. "Council," he exploded, "will greatly oblige me by not passing any large orders for payment in our present situation."[19]

In March, at about the same time Ewing and he were deciding how they would divide their lectures, the Assembly gave Rittenhouse a new office and a new responsibility. He was appointed sole trustee of the Pennsylvania Loan Office. This was an effort to bring order to a financial asset which, in the hands of Samuel Preston Moore, had remained out of step with the times.[20]

By September, the financial crisis had so far deepened and previous efforts to increase tax collections had so clearly failed

[18] *Ibid.*, 117; Barton, *Memoirs*, 603; Franklin B. Dexter, ed., *The Literary Diary of Ezra Stiles* (N.Y., 1901), II, 418, 489, 551.
[19] *Pa. Arch.*, 2d ser., III, 343; DR to Reed, Apr. 28, 1780, Reed MSS, NYHS.
[20] *Pa. House Jours.* (1782), 443, 448, 454.

that the Assembly requested Rittenhouse to take part in an unprecedented junket. It commissioned him to go with President Reed and Speaker John Bayard to investigate the failure of the counties to fill their tax quotas and to supply the troops required for war service. Reed wrote in advance to be sure of having the collectors, commissioners, and other officials available with their records when they arrived. Escorted by a horse guard, the three men covered much of the state during the latter part of September and October in this business which their political opponents charged was primarily a matter of campaigning for the fall elections. Political advantage may well have been anticipated, but there was, in any case, far more than ample legitimate justification for the trip.

How to compel the prompt and exact payment of taxes and how to speed the transit of collections to the state Treasury were questions to which no satisfactory answers could be found. Some tax evaders were arrested during the trip, but that was neither a general solution nor a desirable response to individual delinquencies. The commission discovered that collectors often were unable to turn over taxes quickly enough to the county treasurer, and applied them to private purposes. They may genuinely have intended to repay the misapplied funds but were not always able to do so when called upon. Rittenhouse participated in Reed's written report recommending means of improving tax collections and military enlistments; in addition he made his own oral report to the house. The commission was unable to reverse the course of events. Most conspicuously, the trip failed as a political measure, for, in the ensuing October elections, the Constitutionalists lost control of the legislature.[21]

Before the old Assembly retired, Rittenhouse's personal friend, Francis Hopkinson, was engulfed in an impeachment

[21] *Ibid.*, 516–17, 531, 538, 542; *Pa. Arch.*, 2d ser., III, 389, 459; *PMHB*, XIII, 88; XXII, 109; Reed to Commissioners of Taxes, Oct. 14, 1780, Gratz Coll., HSP; Brunhouse, *Counter-Revolution*, 89–90; John F. Roche, *Joseph Reed* (N.Y., 1957), 181.

action and trial on a series of charges ranging from mistaken judgment to bribery and extortionate fee taking in his post as admiralty judge. A heavy political air hung over the whole affair, but the effort of Constitutionalist leaders to bring Hopkinson down failed—without much delay, he was acquitted on all counts. This crisis in no way damaged Hopkinson's friendliness toward Rittenhouse; he continued to regard their conversations as his "chief pleasure," regretting only that public business kept both so occupied that intellectual interchange was infrequent.[22]

The demands of the Treasury upon Rittenhouse increased not only in volume but even more in aggravation, until they became "almost insuperable." The continued depreciation of currency—especially Continental—reduced all plans to shambles. Of the following year's taxes, he estimated, "The sums to be levied are set in the old Continental money, worth at present perhaps about $\frac{1}{20}$ of the nominal Sum, and I shall acknowledge myself greatly mistaken if before the 8 monthly Taxes are collected it does not sink to $\frac{1}{200}$. This would perhaps be of little consequence if we were not under the necessity of reissueing the old money, and could procure and issue the new at full value. But how is this to be done . . . 'Nobody will take it if they cant pay Taxes with it' will be the Cry . . . either you must allow one new Dollar to pay the Tax of 150 or 200, and so the publick revenues dwindle to nothing, or you do not alter the rate, & the new money depreciates as fast as the old—." Rittenhouse was never an economic theorist, but to him the old Continental money was beyond rescue. "Excessive in its nominal Quantity, destitute of any proper support, and with the most unaccountable and Contradictory prejudices tack'd to it," he labeled it "the greatest evil we labour under." [23]

Engulfed in political and public troubles that seemed beyond

---

[22] *Pa. House Jours.* (1782), 539, 546, 547, 558; *Pa. Col. Recs.*, XII, 578–84; Edmund Hogan, *The Pennsylvania State Trials* (Phila., 1794), I, 13–62; Hopkinson to Franklin, Apr. 29, 1780, Bache Coll., APS.
[23] *Pa. Arch.*, 1st ser., VIII, 657, 662.

solution, Rittenhouse had little freedom to pursue science, but he displayed a new determination in seeking to establish contact with the world of science. In April 1780, half a year after his trip to Carlisle, he wrote Franklin in Paris, describing the cataract of water and giving his theory about it. Because his explanation was electrical, it was logical for him to send it to the great electrician, but he had a more fundamental objective. As he had when he wrote Christian Mayer, he sought to open a scientific correspondence. In August, he approached his political friend, James Searle, who was bound for Europe on a mission to borrow money for the state government. He urged him to send back "such new publications as contain anything curious in Philosophy or the Sciences whether in the French, Dutch or English Languages, or any new invented curious Instrument." He told him also that he needed good optical glass to grind into telescope lenses. There is no record that he involved himself equally in Searle's ultimately unsuccessful effort to find financial support for the precarious public finances which afflicted Rittenhouse's daily life.[24]

When neither of these overtures produced any result, Rittenhouse took the opportunity in December of sending another letter to Franklin in the care of Henry Laurens, who was on his way to the peace negotiations in Paris. This time, he forwarded an account of the meteor he and Page had observed over a year previously. More to his purpose, he declared, "you wou'd make me happy by communicating any discovery, of importance or curiosity, in the Philosophical world, on your side of the water," but again, the effort failed.[25] Laurens was captured at sea.

Rittenhouse's Philadelphia friends remained sympathetic with his desire to become a more productive member of the scientific community and continued to seek means of helping him. When the attempt to give him academic status and an opportunity

[24] DR to Franklin, Apr. 29, 1780, Bache Coll., APS; DR to Searle, Aug. 13, 1780, Gilbert Coll., Phila. College of Physicians.
[25] DR to Franklin, Dec. 31, 1780, Bache Coll., APS.

to work in astronomy within the University appeared doomed to failure, another approach was made. Limited aid in support of his observatory came at a critical juncture.

Ever since he left Norriton, Rittenhouse labored under difficulties in attempting to conduct astronomical observations without proper facilities. The Philosophical Society's observatory in the State House yard had fallen into disrepair during the war. The society had approached the problem by appointing Rittenhouse, Biddle, and Lukens to repair and restore the installation, but this directive was never carried out. Some time later, the society reversed its intentions and decided, instead, to demolish the structure. Rittenhouse gave up his expectations of using this observatory and turned to the construction of a private observatory closer to his home.[26]

Early in 1781, these plans attracted the attention of Timothy Matlack, who urged the Assembly to give Rittenhouse some form of encouragement. It responded immediately, appointing George Gray and Henry Hill to confer with the astronomer to discover what sort of assistance might be in order. The ensuing report led the legislature to vote "unanimously" the sum of £250 in encouragement of the project.[27] This was a far more modest form of public support than the prewar effort to appoint him public astronomer with a fixed salary, but one was attained and the other was not. In due time, Rittenhouse erected an octagonal brick observatory on the corner of Seventh and Mulberry Streets.

Before he completed his observatory and even before he received the Assembly's money, Rittenhouse registered an important scientific achievement in an unexpected quarter. Unsuccessful in developing a European scientific correspondence, he made the most of the "curious" queries he received from John Page, who had speculated briefly about magnetism in the same

[26] APS Mins., 1774-87, 40-41, Sep. 26, 1783, n.p.
[27] Pa. House Jours. (1782), 599, 611, 614; State of the Account of David Rittenhouse, Treasurer . . . from January 1786 till January 1787 (Phila., 1790), 14.

letter that led to Rittenhouse's calculations on the course of the meteor. On February 6, 1781, a year and a quarter after the Page letter, Rittenhouse read to the Philosophical Society "An Account of Some Experiments on Magnetism." [28]

Page was attracted by the often observed similarities between magnetism and electricity, but the focus of his interest was the "matter" or the material cause of observed magnetic phenomena. Rittenhouse turned his attention to this question.

At this point of time, magnetism was a mystery which had refused to yield to any of the various theories advanced to account for it. Cartesian vortices underlay many explanations, and corpuscles or particles were a frequently introduced ingredient. Leonhard Euler had suggested a corpuscular fluid which flowed through the earth, through the ether, and through the internal pores of magnetizable bodies, aligning them in the direction of its flow. Probably most popular in the English-speaking world was the theory of Æpinus, who used the analogy with Franklinian electricity to support a single magnetic fluid, the particles of which repelled each other but were attracted by iron particles. He accounted for the magnetizing of iron by a process of accumulating magnetic particles at one pole and iron particles at the other.[29]

As early as 1737, Joseph Privat de Molières elaborated a theory based upon the assumption that magnetized iron was composed of little magnets whose poles were aligned in the same direction. The process of alignment he attributed to the action of vortices, and he was refuted largely on the ground of the vortices rather than the magnetic dipoles which were an incidental part of his scheme.[30]

There is no clue to the extent of Rittenhouse's knowledge

---

[28] APS, *Trans.*, II (1786), 180.

[29] Franz M. U. T. Æpinus, *Tentamen Theoriae Electricitatis et Magnetismi* (Petropoli, [1759]), *passim*.

[30] Joseph Privat de Molières, *Leçons de Phisique* (Paris, 1734), III, *passim*; Jean Daujat, *Origines et Formation de la Théorie des Phénomènes Electriques et Magnetiques* (Paris, 1945), 457.

of previous writers on magnetism, but his conceptions were well within the context of the thought of his time. His governing assumption was that iron was composed, in part, of very small permanent magnets, of which he wrote: "These magnetical particles I suppose have each a north and a south pole, and that they retain their polarity, however the metal may be fused or otherwise wrought. In a piece of iron which shows no signs of magnetism these magnetical particles lie irregularly, with their poles pointing in all possible directions, they therefore mutually destroy each other's effects. By giving magnetism to a piece of iron we do nothing more than arrange these particles, and when this is done it depends on the temper and situation of the iron whether the piece of metal shall remain for a long time magnetical or not." [31]

He then described a series of familiar experiments, not because he found in them new information but because they illustrated phenomena which could be accounted for by the concept of magnetic dipoles. Most of them were performed by John Mitchell back in 1750, and the publicist Benjamin Martin made them widely known in his *Philosophia Britannica*.[32] Rittenhouse produced magnetism in a steel rod by rubbing it with a magnet and by hammering it when held in alignment with the direction of a dipping needle—that is in alignment with the earth's magnetic field. He destroyed magnetism by heating, twisting, and hammering the rod. The mechanical arrangement or disarrangement of elementary magnetic particles seemed to explain all of these phenomena. Even the fact that "hard" steel was more difficult than "soft" steel to magnetize but retained its magnetism longer strengthened the picture by suggesting a differing resistance to the realignment of magnetic particles.

Rittenhouse's explanation was harmonious with the general philosophy of an ardent Newtonian who was predisposed against

[31] APS, *Trans.*, II (1786), 180.
[32] John Mitchell, *A Treatise of Artificial Magnets* (Cambridge, 1750), 13, 17; Benjamin Martin, *Philosophia Britannica* (London, 1771), I, 43n.

vortices, fluids, and pores at all levels. He could accept a particle theory with enthusiasm, but he could not follow Privat de Molières or any others when they moved on to explain corpuscular behavior by introducing vortices. He could not accept Æpinus' Franklinian fluid because this seemed even less Newtonian and less congenial than a purely corpuscular explanation.

As a consequence, Rittenhouse left the cause of the behavior of his magnetic dipoles unexplained. Few men could live with so frugal a theory although, again, he found warrant for such an approach in Newton's refusal to offer an account of the cause of gravitation in the *Principia*. When the Irish chemist, Richard Kirwan, published his "Thoughts on Magnetism" a few years later, he too abandoned vortices, fluids, valves, and pores in favor of magnetic particles, but he supplied another organizing principle, suggesting that crystalization might account for the alignment of particles.[33]

Of the cause of alignment, Rittenhouse would only say, "There is some power, whencesoever derived, diffused through every part of space which we have access to, which acts on these magnetical particles, impelling one of their poles in a certain direction with respect to the earth and the other pole in the opposite direction." The spareness of his picture is the very thing that has suggested comparison with the clean, mechanical theory of molecular magnetism advanced by Wilhelm Weber in the mid-nineteenth century, but there was no immediate reaction to Rittenhouse's work.[34]

There is no record that this paper stimulated correspondence or scientific thought. When it was finally published in the Philosophical Society's *Transactions* after the war, the London reviews were critical, as they were at that time of anything American. The *Monthly Review* branded the paper "Conjecture and hypothesis," while the *Critical Review* offered faint encourage-

[33] Royal Irish Academy, *Trans.*, vi (1797), 177–83.
[34] APS, *Trans.*, ii (1786), 179; *Poggendorf Annalen*, 87 (1854), 154; J. A. Ewing, *Magnetic Induction* (N.Y., 1892), 339.

ment that it might "afford light for future travellers in the hitherto little known regions of magnetism." [35]

Unfortunately, it was not the source of later theories of molecular magnetism. Advance to quantitative knowledge came through Coulomb's rickety two-fluid theory, and a better theoretical picture was achieved through Poisson, Ampère, and Faraday. Only after a different level of understanding had been attained was there room for Rittenhouse's mechanical picture of magnetic dipoles—and then it was put together from different materials.

But Rittenhouse's theory can stand on its own as the respectable production of a disciplined mind. It was consistent both with the knowledge of his day and with his ideals in science. It was evidence that those who wished to free him to devote all his energies to science did not overrate his capacities.

[35] *Monthly Review*, 76 (1787), 142–43; *Critical Review*, 64 (1787), 247.

CHAPTER XV

Business before Science
1781–1784

E VEN as Rittenhouse squeezed out the time to accomplish effective work in science, shadows cast by the stalemated war increasingly darkened the Treasury. Philadelphians were less alert to the needs of the southern campaign than to the mutiny of the Pennsylvania Line on New Year's Day, 1781. That frightening event was compounded from many sources of unhappiness but from none more directly than the deepening financial crisis which transfixed both the state and the Congress and which held the Pennsylvania Treasury in especial bondage.

Rittenhouse was powerless to deal with the fundamental problem of inadequate revenue, but each day he suffered from its continuing effects. His temperament did not permit him to cast off problems he could not solve; he worried about them, and the sharpness which crept into his letters on financial matters mirrored his tension.

For long months, he had lived with the necessity of conducting business in a variety of state and Continental emissions, each passing at a different and generally worsening rate. During 1780, the Continental currency seemed to be holding fairly well, but toward the end of the year it began slipping again. In 1781, it entered on a disastrous decline that dragged the state money with it.

Joseph Reed commented that the most exasperating aspect of the crisis was the evident capacity of the state to supply the physical needs of the army but the inability of government to find the credit and purchasing power required to tap the sources of commodities. As president, he pushed through in January a £15,000 to £20,000 subscription loan designed to provide some of the money required for essentials. Rittenhouse was instructed to give his signed note for all monies received, promising repayment with interest "as soon as circumstances will admit." [1] The expedient failed, even under pressure of Reed's ill-advised embargo intended to force the merchants into subscribing.

Soon it became virtually impossible to collect taxes, everyone hesitating lest they pay more than they might have to pay if they waited just a little longer. In March, Rittenhouse had no money to finance the recruiting service and was directed to draw orders for £500 on each of six county treasurers. This desperate move had no better success than previous efforts. The county treasurers had no money either, and Reed's follow-up letters expressing "great surprise" at their failure to make collections were insensitive to the realities.[2] Also lacking in understanding was the Assembly's action specifically authorizing the Council to draw directly on the county treasurers.

How to stimulate tax payments and stabilize the money were questions no one could answer with certainty, but gradually some light began to appear. The Assembly took a large step in authorizing a new £500,000 issue of state money based on tax arrearages. Whether Robert Morris was behind this or not, he made continuing efforts to bring some order to state finances even after his appointment as Superintendent of Finance by Congress. One of his most significant successes was in getting the state to eliminate the legal tender quality of state money.[3]

An arrest of a sort was put to the currency decline on May 2, when the Pennsylvania Assembly established the ratio between Continentals and the new state money at 175 to 1. That virtually ended the circulation of Continentals in the city. On

---

[1] *Pa. Col. Recs.*, XII, 594.
[2] *Ibid.*, 655; *Pa. Arch.*, 2d ser., III, 409.
[3] *Pa. House Jours.* (1782), 609, 658, 664; Brunhouse, *Counter-Revolution*, 97.

the same day, Rittenhouse wrote out his views on the crisis in a letter he sent to Vice President William Moore. Five months before, he had declared his opinion of the relationship of tax collection to currency depreciation. If new money is rated high with respect to the old, he said, the taxes paid are worth very little; if it is rated low, it depreciates as fast as the old money. Now, he feared that the 175 to 1 ratio would discourage the payment of taxes and also reduce the value of any payments made to a negligible sum.

To prevent this, he urged a middle course between the ruinous 175 to 1 ratio and a ratio that would discredit the new money. He suggested that taxes paid in the new currency or in specie be received at no easier rate than one for each £75 of assessed taxation—instead of one for £175. He reasoned that when the current series of eight monthly taxes began to be collected, the exchange rate was no worse than 75 to 1. In the name of justice, he asked that those who had paid immediately not now be penalized by permitting others to pay back taxes at an easier rate. The only drawback he could see to this approach was that taxes would be paid fast in Continentals, "which," he wrote, "is the very thing we have wished for." Two days later, he reported that he had instructed county collectors to receive taxes in Continentals at face value but in new state money at the 75 to 1 ratio.[4]

The Council, however, decided against accepting Rittenhouse's moderate ratio for tax payment and, on May 15, established a different mode of procedure. After June 1, taxes were to be received only in specie or in new state money. Taxpayers were required to exchange old state money and Continentals for the money emitted in April, a large part of which was put to this service, and Rittenhouse was directed to supply the county treasurers with the new money. The exchange rate

[4] *Pa. Arch.*, 1st ser., IX, 117; DR to Reed, [May 4, 1781], Dreer Coll., HSP.

varied for the different state issues but for Continentals it remained fixed at 175 to 1. Rittenhouse's ratio of 75 to 1 was perpetuated only for the payment of military fines.[5]

Over many months, Rittenhouse struggled in another effort to win justice against the ravages of currency depreciation. He was responsible for carrying out the Assembly's decision to compensate the troops of the Continental Line for their losses in pay suffered as a consequence of the depreciation of Continental currency. The state issued depreciation certificates, varying in value according to a scale established by appointed auditors. Rittenhouse had to untangle cases which did not precisely fit the adopted formula, and he had to administer the records and payments.[6]

The insuperable problems of the treasurer's office were heightened by occasional harassments, most dramatic of which was a series of robberies of collectors and county treasurers. The newspapers charged that not all of these losses were occasioned by the assaults reported, but the suggested remedy of making collectors responsible for all their losses was never adopted. Robberies as well as embezzlement continued to be charged against anticipated revenue. Counterfeiting constituted an additional loss which was not eliminated by either executive proclamation or by the vigilance of the treasurer.[7]

Almost inevitably, the Treasury became a political target. In the elections of 1781, Rittenhouse's friends, the Constitutionalists, lost some of their support. On the face of things, the new Assembly seemed more or less balanced between Constitutionalists and Republicans, but its actions increasingly inclined it toward the Republican position. Rittenhouse could not help noticing that he moved in a less friendly atmosphere—sometimes it was even hostile.

His office was in no jeopardy—he was reelected treasurer

[5] *Pa. Gaz.*, May 16, 1781.
[6] *Pa. House Jours.* (1782), 675; *Pa. Arch.*, 3d ser., III, 761–71.
[7] *Pa. Col. Recs.*, XIII, 4, 129; *Freeman's Jour.*, Feb. 6, 1782, Apr. 2, 1783.

without any question—but occasional incidents revealed antagonism. In November, the Assembly was officially satisfied with his report that "a severe fit of sickness" would prevent his rendering his accounts promptly at the end of the year.[8] Outside the house, there were murmurs; Rittenhouse's friends had to defend him against charges that he was keeping the accounts out of sight for dark reasons. Another charge vented in the newspapers held that the treasurer had paid some politicians in specie while the army never received anything but depreciating paper. Rittenhouse was among those assaulted by hints that funds derived from forfeited estates and from the sale of city lots had been misapplied. He made no specific response and in a short while the charges withered; his reputation for integrity stood unscratched.[9]

Unexpectedly, Robert Morris approached Rittenhouse at this juncture with an offer to bring him within Morris' plan for re-ordering the administration of congressional finances as receiver of taxes and monies for Pennsylvania. Morris made a series of appointments of this character, in which he sought to engage men of influence in their own states without much regard for their politics. Each was intended to be more than a local receiver of Continental funds; he would serve as a Congressional fiscal officer with general responsibilities for his state. When Rittenhouse declined the post, Morris gave it to John Swanwick, whom he already employed in the Office of Finance.[10]

Throughout his planning, Morris remained alert to Pennsylvania's own need of financial reform. In March 1782, the Assembly followed his lead by approving the charter of the Bank of North America, one of the keystones of his policy. The bank by then had received a charter from Congress, but Morris' friends in Pennsylvania sought state incorporation as well. In this fight, they were able to ride down Constitutionalist oppo-

[8] *Pa. House Mins.*, 1st sess., 6th assem., 526.
[9] *Freeman's Jour.*, Jan. 30, Mar. 6, 27, 1782.
[10] Clarence L. Ver Steeg, *Robert Morris, Revolutionary Financier* (Phila., 1954), 102.

sition including charges of Toryism against Thomas Willing, the bank's president. They also defeated attempts to introduce a measure of public control over the bank and to limit its private powers.[11]

In April, the Assembly passed a far-reaching "Act for Methodizing the Department of Accounts of this Commonwealth," a reform which touched Rittenhouse directly and which casts some doubt on Morris' motives in offering him the post of Continental collector. If he had sought to remove the treasurer to permit the easier reform of state finances, his timing could not have been improved. Rittenhouse never recorded his reactions, but he was aware that his office would never be the same again.

Fundamental to the reform was the creation of the new position of comptroller general with almost unlimited authority over the fiscal affairs of the state. He was empowered to settle and collect all accounts due the state and to settle all claims against it. He could issue subpoenas and writs of attachment. He could commit delinquents to jail. The treasurer was specifically instructed to pay no public monies without a warrant signed by the president and vice president of the Council and recorded in the comptroller general's office. The accounts of all officers of the state were subject to the comptroller general's jurisdiction and were not to be deemed settled until he had audited them.[12]

In the act establishing this post, the Assembly appointed to it John Nicholson, who once served as a commissioner of accounts of Pennsylvania and who had been a business associate of Robert Morris. Upon him the effective meaning of the office depended. His opportunities for improving the efficiency of Pennsylvania's fiscal administration were vast. His opportunities for the political use of his office were almost equally great,

[11] Pa. Gaz., Mar. 6, 1782; Pa. House Mins., 2d sess., 6th assem., 605, 606.
[12] Ibid., 632, 635; Joseph B. Anthony, Report on Liens of the Commonwealth upon the Lands of John Nicholson and Peter Baynton (Harrisburg, 1839), 6; Dallas, Laws of Pa., II, 19–24.

and the direction in which Nicholson would turn his power was for some time uncertain.

For several months, he poured over his accounts. Only occasionally did he report the result of an audit, in nearly every case revealing an error or a debt owed by some individual. Most of the audits related to the treasurer's office, but the early ones revealed little error on Rittenhouse's part. The initial indication that Nicholson did not find himself in conflict with Rittenhouse was strengthened in June when General James Potter, now Constitutionalist vice president of the state, appealed to both men for help. He defended himself against a newspaper charge of financial peculation by publishing two certificates, one signed by Rittenhouse and the other by Nicholson.[13]

Nicholson's fiscal success remained for some time as unclear as his political effect. He certainly offered no immediate relief to the financial crisis which had now become endemic but which deepened so frighteningly in March that Rittenhouse was given authority to raise money by private 6 per cent loans. This produced such a "trifling sum" that the president called the Assembly into special session for the sole purpose of dealing with the depressed "state of the treasury." The legislature borrowed £5,000 from the Bank of North America and dumped the problem back in Rittenhouse's lap by directing him to repay the loan with funds to be squeezed out of the Loan Office.[14]

Even £5,000 was not readily available from this source, but Rittenhouse made valiant efforts. He moved the office to his own home and tightened up the entire operation. In newspaper advertisements, he called sternly for the sums due. When repeated appeals failed, he proceeded against the delinquents; their mortgages were foreclosed and their properties sold.[15]

[13] Pa. Arch., 6th ser., xii, 18; Freeman's Jour., June 19, 1782; Pa. House Mins., 3d sess., 6th assem., 710, 799, 801, 803.
[14] Ibid., 654, 685; Pa. Gaz., Aug. 21, 1782.
[15] Ibid., Aug. 21, Sep. 25, 1782, July 16, 1783; Freeman's Jour., Apr. 16, 23, 1782.

Pressure from the Council led Rittenhouse, as treasurer, to take similar action to compel payment by purchasers of city lots. In this effort, he not only advertised but visited many of the debtors at their homes. He used the threat of publishing the names of delinquents as long as he possibly could, hoping that he would not have to carry it through. Although the badgering of debtors and the institution of legal action remained distasteful to him, he sought to complete the depressing business with dispatch.[16]

The coming elections of 1782 finally threw the comptroller general squarely into the political ring. The Assembly, now under the leadership of Republicans who sensed a useful scandal, directed Nicholson to investigate charges that Timothy Matlack was deficient in turning over public monies to the treasurer. Nicholson made a careful study of the accounts, called on Matlack several times, and finally reported that the Constitutionalist secretary of Council was still in debt to the state. With delight, the house directed Nicholson to resort to law to compel payment and passed a resolution censuring Matlack as "unworthy of public trust or confidence." [17] The secretary resigned his office.

If Nicholson's report was politically motivated, Rittenhouse was logically next in line for his attention. The treasurer was closely associated with Matlack and intrinsically more vulnerable because of the numerous tangled and tortuous accounts under his responsibility. Deficiencies reported by the comptroller general in the accounts of Owen Jones, provincial treasurer, and Michael Hillegas, first state treasurer, revealed the likelihood of errors in the later, more complicated days of the Treasury. Strikingly, Nicholson failed to produce evidence damaging to Rittenhouse. From account to account, he located

[16] DR to the president, Apr. 27, 1784, Pa. Miscellaneous, LC; Barton, *Memoirs*, 325.

[17] *Freeman's Jour.*, Oct. 1, 1783; *Pa. House Mins.*, 1st sess., 7th assem., 758, 776, 880.

occasional errors, but they were minor in character and as often in one direction as the other.[18]

On January 29, 1783, John Nicholson returned a report that finally made it clear he was no hatchet man for the Republicans. He revealed errors in the account of Samuel Miles, a leading Republican who held a seat on the newly elected Council of Censors. When Miles, in consequence, decided to resign from the Council, control of that critical body passed to the Constitutionalists, who made the most of their slim majority. The Council of Censors was required by the Constitution of 1776 to review governmental actions during the preceding seven years, but its report became a party document rather than a judicial inquest. It tended to exonerate Constitutionalist measures and to condemn as unconstitutional many of the actions taken under Republican leadership. Among the legislative acts so branded was the very one which created the office of comptroller general and appointed Nicholson as its first incumbent. The Council took occasion, too, to attack the resolution passed against Timothy Matlack, declaring that the secretary had been "condemned unheard." [19]

Nicholson's report on Miles had such sweeping political repercussions that a committee of the house proposed removing the comptroller general from office. Such action would have been so patently political, however, that it failed.[20]

Thereafter, no one could imagine that John Nicholson was in the pocket of Robert Morris. At what point Rittenhouse arrived at his friendship with Nicholson is not clear but the two men developed a warm feeling for each other which was reflected even in their official correspondence. Whatever his political inclination when he assumed office, Nicholson emerged a Constitutionalist.

[18] *Ibid.*, 799, 801, 812, 826, 913.
[19] *Ibid.*, 801; Brunhouse, *Counter-Revolution*, 161; "Report of the Committee . . . adopted by the Council of Censors," in *The Constitution of the Commonwealth* (Phila., 1784), 43.
[20] Pa. *House Mins.*, 2d sess., 8th assem., 207-8.

In the ensuing years, Nicholson's financial abilities effectively improved Pennsylvania's fiscal administration, but he was no more able to cope with inadequate revenues than others had been. Neither the president's armistice proclamation nor the final treaty of peace ending the war eliminated the inadequacies of the Pennsylvania Treasury. Indeed, only the opportunity for patriotic appeals to tax delinquents was lost with the return of peace; the fiscal crisis remained. Rittenhouse complained again in April 1784 of "the exhausted State of the Treasury," urging the Council to find means of stimulating returns from the several revenue officers. He informed it that there had been "almost a Total Stop to the Collecting of Taxes." For his part, he took refuge in the "little authority" he possessed, but he had also another escape shared by few of his friends in government.[21]

Throughout the years of crisis in the Treasury, Rittenhouse continued to find pleasure in the moments he snatched for the pursuit of science. Sometimes quietly in his own study or in a lonely astronomical observation, sometimes in the company of others, he sought answers no one had yet been able to find. He looked forward to participating in 1784 in some surveys—although here public service rather than science was the major objective. To the extent that he had been able to channel his work in science and relate it to the larger world of inquiry, it usually revolved about the American Philosophical Society.

Unfortunately, the Philosophical Society offered little sustenance in these years to a man who needed a haven of encouragement where scientific projects could be stimulated, developed, and tested. It never again suspended activities altogether as it had during the depth of the war, but it stumbled along with irregular meetings, lightly attended. Its relationship to science was peripheral.

Rittenhouse's attention to the failing institution declined through 1781 and 1782 even more rapidly than the society it-

[21] DR to the president, Apr. 27, 1784, Pa. Miscellaneous, LC.

self, despite his continued election as vice president. This was only partially due to his absorption in Treasury business; he was not attracted by the society's engagement with organizational change or by its penchant for drawing up elaborate memorials, one issued on the occasion of the Yorktown victory and another upon the end of the war. He was first named on a committee to plan the publication of a second volume of *Transactions*, but for several years this led nowhere.[22]

In 1783, Rittenhouse was elected to the newly established council of the society instead of to the vice presidency. This twelve-man body, which followed closely the pattern of the Royal Society, represented the principal organizational change. As a member, Rittenhouse joined a number of distinguished gentlemen, including Jefferson, Stiles, McKean, Bryan, and Witherspoon, few of whom contributed either to science or to the society. Yet for whatever reason, his interest in the society now rose; he attended more frequently, and, at the end of the year, he joined Francis Hopkinson and Samuel Vaughan in an attempt to infuse some life into the institution.

Hopkinson provided the leadership and the verbal lash. He conceded that the Americans till recently had been absorbed with politics and with war. But, he complained, "If it shall be perceived, that year after year elapses, and nothing interesting is produced, no discoveries made, or even attempted to be made: when it shall be perceived that our barrenness must be occasioned, either by a want of abilities, or which is, indeed the truth, by a shameful want of attention, we must unavoidably sink into contempt." [23]

When Hopkinson went on to stress the availability of the "open book of nature," he antagonized members of the University faculty who disagreed with his idea that science depended more upon right method than upon learning. They

[22] APS Mins., 1774-87, Jan. 5, Dec. 27, 1781, Jan. 3, Dec. 12, 1783, n.p.
[23] *Ibid.*, Jan. 16, 1784; Francis Hopkinson, "An Address to the American Philosophical Society," *Miscellaneous Essays and Occasional Writings* (Phila., 1792), I, 360–65.

constituted the largest pool of members with the capacity for making scientific contributions and would have brought his effort to a speedy end except for the authority lent it by Rittenhouse and for the energy poured into it by the mercurial Englishman, Samuel Vaughan.

Among several reforms projected by Hopkinson, the most concrete was his demand that the society build a hall to house its activities—the repetition of a suggestion made earlier and more quietly by Rittenhouse when he had become concerned about the disposal and proper use of the society's library. Now, as a site for the hall, Hopkinson turned over to the society a lot he owned in return for some cash and a rather dubious mortgage. Rittenhouse, Vaughan, and he formed a committee to plan a suitable building, but after talking with the directors of the Library Company of Philadelphia, they were deflected to another approach. In concert with the Library Company, they decided to seek from the Pennsylvania Assembly matching lots on the east and west sides of State House Square on which the two institutions would erect separate buildings. Meanwhile the Hopkinson lot lay unused while it accumulated taxes and mortgage interest. To cover these charges, Rittenhouse rented it from the society; conveniently, it lay across the street from his home and next to the lot on which he was building his observatory.[24]

Rittenhouse's contributions to such efforts defined his relationship to the society better than the office he held, for the council never became an effective organ. The post of librarian, which he held before the war, was not revived in 1779 although he continued to serve in that capacity. He collected the books belonging to the society which had been scattered and in 1783, was asked to make room in his home for the whole of the

---

[24] *Pa. House Mins.*, 2d sess., 8th assem., 178, 212; Mins. of the Directors of the Library Company, 1768–85, 206, LCP; APS Mins., 1774–87, Mar. 6, Apr. 18, 1783, Feb. 20, Mar. 5, 19, 1784, n.p.

library which did not total more than one hundred fifty volumes. When Vaughan donated a telescope, a microscope, and other instruments to the society, he put them in Rittenhouse's hands as a matter of course. Rittenhouse constituted the most tangible connection the society had with the world of science; he offered more in these years than he received, a fact underlined by the dismantling of the society observatory.[25]

Rittenhouse's observatory probably did not become functional at any precise moment of time; rather, it appears to have grown in permanence and completeness over several years. Ever since he moved to Philadelphia, he had made occasional observations of stars and weather in the vicinity of his home. He began recording data about the weather years before 1788 when his known daily journals begin. "The ingenious Mr. Rittenhouse" was cited by the press for the assertion that on July 24, 1783, the mercury reached 94½° Fahrenheit, two degrees above any temperature recorded in the city since 1769. Privately, he acknowledged that William Henry's Lancaster readings were higher than any taken in his own "observatory."[26] Then and thereafter, Rittenhouse was regarded as the leading authority on Philadelphia's weather.

The most spectacular astronomical achievement of this period was William Herschel's discovery, in March 1781, of the planet Uranus—called by him Georgium Sidus. Rittenhouse told Ashbel Green that, as soon as he received news of the discovery, he pointed his telescope at the spot in the sky where he estimated it to be and found the planet in the field of his instrument without searching further. The first news Ezra Stiles had of Uranus was much less accurate; he appealed to Rittenhouse in high excitement to know whether a planet had been discovered circling one of the fixed stars! Rittenhouse followed

[25] *Ibid.*, Sep. 26, Nov. 21, Dec. 5, 1783, n.p.; *MHS Colls.*, 7th ser., I, 336; Vaughan to DR, Feb. 14, 1784, APS; *Pa. Jour.*, Mar. 3, 1784.
[26] *Pa. Gaz.*, July 30, 1783; *Freeman's Jour.*, July 30, 1783; cited by Jordan, *Henry*, 163.

through with several series of observations of the successive positions of Uranus the first of which he reported in 1783; the only set he published began in 1784.[27]

Later, too, he published his observations of the transit of Mercury of November 12, 1782, and of a comet he discovered on January 21, 1784. In one of his papers, Andrew Ellicott printed some of Rittenhouse's observations of the immersions of Jupiter's satellites.[28] None of this work was carried beyond the observational stage, however; Rittenhouse placed the bodies in position and in time; he did not calculate the elements of any of the orbits. He nowhere demonstrated the imagination or insights of which he was capable—a result, perhaps, of the demands of the Treasury which hemmed in his thoughts as they did his movements.

Limited as this work was, his reputation glowed ever more brightly, especially in the opinion of Thomas Jefferson, who unfolded a scheme to put it to the use of the new nation. He proposed that Rittenhouse build an orrery to be presented to the King of France—a means of honoring an ally at the same time that he was honored himself. The Philosophical Society accepted the idea enthusiastically, Rittenhouse agreed to build the machine, the king let it be known that he was pleased by the thought, and Jefferson expanded his design to embrace sending Rittenhouse with his orrery to Europe.[29]

The idea was a chimera; whether Rittenhouse realized it or not, there was never any possibility that he would build another complete orrery. He could not even bring himself to undertake the tedious business of repairing the Philadelphia and Princeton orreries when they sorely needed attention. It may be doubted that, even if he had been wholly free of political

[27] Ashbel Green, *Life* (N.Y., 1849), 41n.; APS, *Trans.*, II (1786), 260–63; Stiles to DR, Nov. 16, 1781, APS; APS Mins., 1774–87, Nov. 21, 1784.
[28] *Ibid.*, Mar. 19, 1784; APS, *Trans.*, II (1786), 195, 260; IV (1799), 32–34.
[29] APS Mins., 1774–87, Jan. 18, Mar. 6, Sep. 26, 1783; Boyd, ed., *Papers of Jefferson*, VI, 418, 508; La Luzerne to White, Sep. 1783, APS.

office, he could have undergone the drudgery of repeating a great many intricate and now pointless operations. Despite his agreement, he never built an orrery for the king—or even a lunarium, which was later suggested as an attenuated form of the project.

Occasionally, Rittenhouse resumed his role as scientific expert on practical matters. The Assembly appealed to him and to Thomas Hutchins on the merit of John Harris' proposal to erect a town on the Susquehanna River. Although the two men had five months to visit the proposed town site—and intended to do so—they wrote their enthusiastic report without having made the trip. In fact, previous visits had given them detailed familiarity with the area and they were fully competent to comment on the project. Their judgment proved sound; the town became Harrisburg.[30]

As a trustee of the University, Rittenhouse continued to respond to duties placed upon him—some of them rather unpleasant. He served, for example, on a committee to examine William Smith's claims for compensation from the institution he had once headed. He also served on several committees appointed to grapple with one of Smith's less successful investments of College funds. Early in the war, the then provost had paid £6,000 to acquire the lands and mills that once had constituted the estate of Charles Norris at Norriton, not far from Rittenhouse's farm. A variety of troubles continued to plague this property, and efforts to sell or lease it proved difficult. Commissions more to Rittenhouse's taste were those involving the University's scientific apparatus, which were always assigned to him.[31]

Rittenhouse also aided his friends Owen Biddle and Timothy Matlack, who were among the leaders of the Free Quakers and who sought to provide more satisfactory and more permanent

[30] *Pa. Arch.*, 1st ser., x, 129; *Pa. House Mins.*, 2d sess., 8th assem., 176.
[31] Trustees Mins., ii, 99, 100; iii, 73, 150, 156, 169, 174, 216; iv, 54; v, 91, Univ. of Pa.

quarters for their war-born group. He studied the plans for the vaulting under their proposed Free Quaker Meeting House and on July 24, 1782, approved the design.[32]

On several occasions, Rittenhouse employed his craftsmanship to honor George Washington, whom he esteemed as the leader who carried the American cause to victory. His most satisfactorily documented gift was a pair of eyeglasses, the lenses of which he ground himself to the required specifications. In 1783 also, he probably repaired a misaligned theodolite which Washington sent him earlier but which for some time could not be located. He may also have presented to the general a vernier compass of his own manufacture, although the evidence linking Washington with the instrument is indirect.[33]

The compass, however, possesses an intrinsic importance which far transcends its association with Washington. The vernier had been used on a variety of instruments, but there is no clear record of an earlier American compass equipped with a vernier. Whether because he made the very first one or because of the prestige of his instruments, the vernier compass was sometimes called "the Rittenhouse compass."

In the Washington instrument, the compass ring was not fixed in permanent alignment with the sights as it was in the plain compasses previously made by Rittenhouse and by his fellow instrument makers. Instead, the ring, graduated in degrees, could be rotated with respect to the line of sight and the divergence between the two could be read with heightened accuracy because of the vernier scale against which the compass ring rotated. In both of the vernier compasses made by Rittenhouse, the compass ring could be set at any given angle with respect to the sights. However, when the major advantage of this improvement proved to be in laying off the magnetic declination, later vernier compasses were restricted in

[32] Plan of Vaulting, Free Quaker Meeting House, 1783, HSP (through the courtesy of Mrs. Joseph Carson).
[33] Fitzpatrick, ed., *Writings of Washington*, xxvi, 27, 136, xxvii, 6.

their adjustment to a small arc, sufficient only to accept the few degrees variation between true and magnetic north.[34]

Sometime in these years, the "Rittenhouse stove" also appeared; the first known reference to it was made in 1784. Like the "Rittenhouse compass," it was a significant and widely adopted innovation which left behind it very little written record. A modification of the Franklin stove, the "Rittenhouse stove" rose in popularity in the 1780's and, in the 1790's, carried Rittenhouse's name into many households. Robert Leslie included it in the museum he planned in 1789, "A new invented open stove. By David Rittenhouse." Peale reported that he heated his parlor with the device, "one of the best constructed open stoves, being an improvement of Mr. Rittenhouse on Dr. Franklin's stove." [35]

It was a cast iron, open fireplace of much simpler construction than Franklin's. It appears to have boasted "Z" shaped side plates and a three-piece back plate, the large central portion of which was inclined downward from the vertical at an angle of 10° to reflect and radiate more heat into the room. The inclination was not new, but the simplicity of the stove, as a unit, made for its success and not only celebrated Rittenhouse's name but linked him significantly with Franklin.[36]

Franklin himself became more ready than ever to celebrate his ties with Rittenhouse during his extended mission to France. From Paris, he sent the Philadelphian a letter speculating on the nature of light, which he inscribed with a new warmth, "For the Consideration of my Dear Friend David Rittenhouse."

[34] See compasses owned by the New York State Library and the Gurley Museum; Charles E. Smart, *The Makers of Surveying Instruments . . . Manufactured by W. & L. E. Gurley* (Troy, 1855), 5-7; Penrose R. Hoopes to Brooke Hindle, Dec. 31, 1961.
Penrose R. Hoopes to Brooke Hindle, Dec. 31, 1961.
[35] Broadside: A Catalogue of Plans and Machines [Phila., c. 1789], Collection of Penrose R. Hoopes; *Weekly Magazine of Original Essays*, Mar. 31, 1798, 268.
[36] Most of this information including the Peale reference is based on a manuscript on stoves by Mr. Samuel Y. Edgerton, Jr., of Wheaton College.

More jocularly, he inserted in the newspaper a fictitious account of a balloon ascension in Philadelphia of which Rittenhouse—tagged "Ritnose"—was one of the projectors. When Jefferson reached Paris to succeed Franklin, his admiration of Rittenhouse suffered no diminution. He wrote back a delighted, but delicate, approval of his daughter Martha's plans for taking drawing lessons from du Simitière in the Rittenhouse home. He regarded the exposure as a special privilege.[37]

Thomas Paine, another admirer, took a problem in the combustion of gases to his old acquaintance on one of his visits to Philadelphia. Paine had an idea that any combustible substance, when heated without access to air, produced a gas which was similarly combustible. Rittenhouse evidently shared this view, and the two proceeded to experiments which seemed to confirm it. They heated a sealed gun barrel containing sawdust and found that the gas contained was flammable. Years later, Paine read into these results lessons that might be useful in preventing yellow fever—using Rittenhouse's participation as authority for their scientific reliability.[38]

Few admired Rittenhouse more unrestrainedly than Francis Hopkinson, and none sought as eagerly to place the man on a pedestal where he would be celebrated and free for creative scientific work. Early in 1784, Hopkinson set on foot a petition for "appointing *David Rittenhouse*, Esquire, Astronomer to this commonwealth, and annexing an adequate salary, to enable him to prosecute his philosophical enquiries." Much support was generated. Rittenhouse admitted to a committee of the Assembly that he would be more useful in such a station than in any of his present offices, and he asserted his readiness to accept such an appointment. Hopkinson became very optimistic, reporting on February 23 that he expected a salary of £600 or

[37] Franklin to DR, June 25, 1784, Franklin Papers, LC; Sparks, ed., *Works of Franklin*, vi, 451; *PMHB*, xxxv, 53; Boyd, ed., *Papers of Jefferson*, vi, 465.

[38] Philip S. Foner, ed., *Complete Writings of Thomas Paine* (N.Y., 1945), ii, 1063–64.

perhaps £750 to be attached to the post. By March 12, he reduced this estimate to £500, and shortly afterward he realized that the bill would never get past its second reading.[39]

The project was not defeated for any lack of regard or good will on the part of the Assembly. Few men have been so universally admired, and, in a peculiarly effective manner, Rittenhouse both accepted and cultivated the image assigned him. The French minister reported that the American's habitual modesty made more believable his occasional admission of unusual powers. According to La Luzerne, Rittenhouse told a friend, "If I were independent in my fortune and free to devote myself to my passion for astronomy and science, I would produce a work which would fill Europe with astonishment."[40]

No one would have disputed the assertion, but the provision of public funds for the continuing support of basic science was altogether unprecedented in America. As Jefferson commented, it would have been "a singular instance of a republic's encouragement of science."[41] Yet no one knew better than Rittenhouse that there were many more usual and seemingly more imperative demands for the skimpy financial resources of the state. In any case, he became so engaged in a variety of surveys which removed him for long intervals from the woes of the Treasury, that he had little opportunity to bemoan still another failure to provide public patronage free of mundane duties.

[39] Pa. House Mins., 1st sess., 8th assem., 120, 136, 166; Boyd, ed., Papers of Jefferson, VI, 556; VII, 20.

[40] La Luzerne to Vergennes, Dec. 25, 1783, Archives de Ministère des Affaires Etrangères, Correspondance Politique, Etats-Unis, XXVI, fols. 252–53 (through the courtesy of Dr. Howard C. Rice, Jr.).

[41] Ibid., 41.

CHAPTER XVI

The Great Surveys
1784–1785

WITH the end of the war, the state called Rittenhouse to service in several major surveys designed to improve internal transportation and to define long unsettled interstate boundaries. He was appointed on September 20, 1783, with Thomas Hutchins and Nathan Sellers, to study the feasibility of establishing a "Water Communication" between the Susquehanna River and the Schuylkill River. On the 26th, he joined Thomas Hutchins in a commission to survey the ascent over Vanderen's Hill in Roxbury Township, Philadelphia County, preliminary to planning a road there. The following March, he was first named on a commission of twenty-one charged with clearing the Schuylkill to make it navigable.[1]

Of these three efforts, the most far-reaching in its influence was the Susquehanna-Schuylkill survey conducted during May 1784. Rittenhouse, Hutchins, and Sellers carefully traversed the ground between the Tulpehocken Creek, a tributary of the Schuylkill, and the Swatara Creek, a tributary of the Susquehanna. They navigated about thirty miles of the Tulpehocken in a small boat, and they examined carefully springs and water sources above the level of any canals that might be constructed along this route. They returned to the Assembly an enthusiastic report urging the practicability of river improvement and canal construction to provide water communication from Philadelphia to the West. Alternatively, they suggested that, if the two river systems were made navigable, land carriage be-

[1] Pa. Arch., 1st ser., x, 334; 9th ser., I, 367; Dallas, Laws of Pa., II, 90–91.

tween them might be provided "at a very reasonable expence." [2]

This report was one of the fountainheads from which the great canal enterprises of the 1790's arose, but, for the moment, it led to no further demands upon Rittenhouse. Instead, he was called on to devote the balance of the summer of 1784 and most of the succeeding summer to a piece of unfinished business—the determination of the boundary between Pennsylvania and Virginia.

The line had never been drawn; year after year followed the agreement of 1779, and plan after plan was formulated for defining the boundary, but the exigencies of war always gave priority to measures which might contribute to victory. The war, however, did not stop the westward movement or serve to decrease unrest in Pennsylvania's southwest corner. Continuing conflict and violence led in 1782 to a temporary line based on an exclusively terrestrial survey conducted by Alexander McClean for Pennsylvania and Joseph Nevil for Virginia. This solution was in some respects worse than none at all for it satisfied no one while it called visible attention to the need for a definitive survey. [3]

Governor Benjamin Harrison of Virginia brought the matter to a head on July 23, 1783, when he urged Pennsylvania to appoint commissioners for running the "astronomical" line. The Assembly responded with alacrity, and, on September 11, the Supreme Executive Council issued commissions to Lukens, Rittenhouse, Ewing, and Hutchins. They were empowered to open a correspondence with the commissioners appointed by Virginia, to obtain the needed astronomical instruments, and to make plans for the accurate completion of the boundary between the two states. Congress was informed of the plans because Pennsylvania intended to run its western boundary throughout its entire length, including the portion north of the

[2] DR, Notebook, 1785–92, n.p.; Draft of Report by DR, Hutchins, and Sellers, 1784, APS; *Pa. Col. Recs.*, xiv, 442.
[3] *Ibid.*, xiii, 253; *Pa. House Mins.*, 1st sess., 7th assem., 844.

Ohio River where it bordered territory the individual states were ceding to the United States.[4]

Meanwhile, Virginia appointed Madison, Andrews, John Page, and Andrew Ellicott; Ellicott was attached to the group because his surveying skills were needed even though he was not a resident of Virginia. The Pennsylvanians experienced no difficulty in assembling all the equipment required to outfit the observatory planned for the eastern extension of the Mason-Dixon line on the Delaware, but the Virginians ran into trouble when they undertook to supply the items required at the western end of the line. They made timely plans for borrowing some of the instruments from the College of William and Mary and importing others along with the necessary astronomical tables from abroad. Unfortunately, the importations were delayed by the severity of the winter, and, in April, Madison made frantic efforts to acquire the tables, at least, both through mercantile channels in Virginia and through Jefferson in Paris.[5]

The Pennsylvania commissioners assumed, correctly, that they could leave most of the work of readying their instruments to Rittenhouse, and they devoted their joint energies to the question of remuneration. On March 30, 1784, the four men signed a note addressed to President John Dickinson declaring that the proffered allowance of forty-five shillings per diem was inadequate if they were expected to deduct from it the costs of their provisions. Indeed, they urged that provisioning be left entirely in the hands of a commissary in order to free them to conduct the observations. To strengthen their case, they cited their understanding that the Virginians would receive six dollars a day —plus expenses. This memorial clarified the role of the commissary, who was allowed a separate budget; the commissioners' allowance was not changed. Madison later admitted, however, that the Virginia commissioners obtained a satisfactory

---

[4] *Pa. Arch.*, 1st ser., x, 95, 175; *Pa. Col. Recs.*, xiii, 678, 685; H. R. McIlwaine, ed., *Journals of the Council of State of Va.* (Richmond, 1931—), iii, 295.

[5] Boyd, ed., *Papers of Jefferson*, vii, 133.

allowance only after they had reported the arrangements Pennsylvania adopted![6]

The first step of the planned survey called for half of the commissioners to proceed to the western end of the extended Mason-Dixon line while the other half established an observatory in Wilmington, as close as they could get to the eastern extension of the line at the Delaware River. Each group would then make simultaneous observations of the eclipses of Jupiter's satellites. The difference in local time recorded at the two stations for the same event would be a function of the difference in longitude alone. The hope was to place the two stations reasonably close to the required five degree distance between the Delaware River and the western border. The necessary adjustment could then be easily made as soon as the eastern commissioners joined the western group with the data they had obtained.

Accordingly, Ewing, Madison, Ellicott, and Hutchins—two men from each of the state commissions—went out to the western end of the line in late June, where they set up an observatory on a mountain top near the spot marked by McClean and Nevil as the southwest corner of Pennsylvania. Ewing considered himself the senior commissioner at the western end of the line and regarded Rittenhouse as the senior of the eastern group. Madison did not accept Ewing's assumptions easily. Ewing placed himself at the presumed corner while Madison urged that everyone meet initially at the last point on the line marked by Mason and Dixon—ultimately Ewing had his way. Madison frequently bridled at Ewing's "obstinacy" and resented his petty criticisms. Ewing, for example, found fault with the clock Madison had brought over the mountains, while the Virginian maintained that it was a fine timepiece, excelling "even Mr. Rittenhouses."[7]

---

[6] *Pa. Arch.*, 1st ser., x, 230, 233; *Pa. Col. Recs.*, xiv, 69, 74; Madison to Ellicott, Apr. 20, 1785, LC.

[7] *Ibid.*, June 23, 1784; *Pa. Arch.*, 6th ser., xiv, 3, 18; Boyd, ed., *Papers of Jefferson*, viii, 74.

Madison complained to Ellicott that the Presbyterian clergyman was too thoroughly an advocate of Pennsylvania to be able to confront the boundary determination judiciously. "The old Gentleman," he growled, "had always too much the Idea of a *good Bargain* about him, to agree readily to any Decision which threw him one Inch East of our Observatory." Ellicott, on the other hand, regarded this personality clash with equanimity, reporting, "my Companions are very agreeable Men and I think we enjoy all the Happiness that people in our Situation could expect." [8]

At the eastern end of the line, there was no evidence of discord. Rittenhouse had none of the magisterial air affected by Ewing, nor did he seek to place himself ahead of his fellow commissioners. He maintained the "modesty" which was an integral part of his personality, but the others appealed to his judgment, inevitably, because of the unquestioned superiority of his knowledge and of his skills. John Page chose the eastern station solely because this would put him in association with Rittenhouse. His expectations were not disappointed.

Page had "heard much of that Great Man," and he had corresponded with him, but the more he saw of Rittenhouse, the more unrestrained his praise became. Almost in ecstasy, he reported to Jefferson, "I must confess, that I found him greatly superior to any Idea I had of him . . . His Genius had penetrated as deep into the Secrets of the moral and political World, as into those of the natural." [9]

When he commented on Rittenhouse's astronomy, he revealed his own sophomoric understanding of science, coupled with an adulation of the Philadelphian which Madison privately ridiculed. Page glowed, "As an Astronomer I doubt when the World can produce another for, if every Instrument and Book upon Earth which Astronomers use were destroyed, I am cer-

[8] Madison to Ellicott, Jan. 16, 1784 [85]; Ellicott to Sarah Ellicott, July 30, 1784, Ellicott Papers, LC.
[9] Boyd, ed., *Papers of Jefferson*, VIII, 117–18.

tain, from the Instruments which he made and the manner in which I saw him use them, that he himself without any Assistance could replace Astronomy in the present State of its Perfection." [10]

From July 1 until September 25, whenever the temperamental summer would permit, the Wilmington group conducted a regular series of observations. In addition to the primary data on the eclipses of Jupiter's satellites, they made other observations required for establishing local time and for verifying their meridian. Nearly sixty satellite eclipses were recorded. Each commissioner contributed to this sum, for each was equipped with a telescope of his own—although Page recalled that Rittenhouse and Lukens had the best ones.[11]

On September 9, Page went home; on the 25th, the instruments were packed up and sent to Philadelphia; about that time, Lukens also returned to his home. Only Rittenhouse and Andrews undertook the overland trip to join the western commissioners, where they could compare observations and run the line. Page said that he and Lukens withdrew to save public money, but others laid it to their inability "to endure the Fatigues of so long a Journey," and "the Subsequent labour of running and marking the Boundary Line." [12]

Rittenhouse, in any event, went on. With Robert Andrews, he reached the camp site of the western observers about October 14 and found them waiting with the records of some forty or fifty satellite observations. Enough simultaneous observations were discovered among the two sets that the commissioners decided to base their longitude determination upon them alone. As soon as this decision was made and before the boundary marking began, Madison withdrew, averring that "the affairs of his family and public station obliged him" to return home.[13]

Calculations revealed that the two observatories were sepa-

---

[10] *Ibid.;* cf. Madison to Ellicott, Jan. 16, 1784 [85], Ellicott Papers, LC.
[11] DR, Observations made at Wilmington, n.p., APS.
[12] Page to ?, Jan. 27, 1803, APS; *Pa. Arch.*, 1st ser., x, 375.
[13] *Ibid.*, 375–76; APS, *Trans.*, iv (1799), 32–34.

rated by twenty minutes, one and one-eighth seconds of time. The twenty minutes was equivalent to the desired five degrees, and therefore the corner mark had to be placed eastward from the site of the observatory by a distance equivalent to one and one-eighth seconds, or nineteen chains and thirteen links—plus the distance of the eastern observatory from the Delaware River. This additional distance amounted to one hundred fourteen chains, thirteen links. When the whole correction was measured off by chain, the southwest corner was permanently marked by a square, white oak post around the base of which a pile of stones was raised. Recent longitude determinations place the post twenty-three feet too far to the west—an error equivalent to a time difference of less than one-fifth of a second.[14]

The next step was the extension of the Mason-Dixon line a distance of a little more than twenty miles to the corner post. The biggest impediment proved to be the weather, which prevented astronomical observations for nearly a week. As soon as it cleared, the commissioners began extending the line along the last bearing given it by Mason and Dixon. The work was easy and fast because McClean and Nevil had already opened the course of the line and the western commissioners had done additional work on it before Rittenhouse and Andrews arrived. The laborers hired for the purpose had a relatively easy time cutting vistas of twenty to thirty feet over all the ridges crossed by the line. At three intermediate points, the boundary was corrected on the basis of astronomical observations. Throughout, it was marked by posts with a "P" on one side and a "V" on the other.

The commissioners sometimes had trouble getting about the rugged country; on one occasion Rittenhouse and Colonel Andrew Porter, the commissary, wandered too far into the woods and got lost. Their plight was worsened by a downpour of rain accompanied by occasional snow flurries, but the

[14] APS, *Proc.*, XCIII (1949), 132; *Pa. Arch.*, 1st ser., x, 376–77.

two men were brought in when their companions fired off guns to guide them to the camp.[15]

As an additional guarantee that the corner mark would not be lost, the commissioners recorded its distance and bearing from two large trees in the vicinity. Then on November 18, they agreed to discontinue their labors until the following spring when they would return to run the north-south line marking Pennsylvania's western border. Porter stabled five of his horses with a nearby settler and stored two of his wagons. Two other wagons, he loaded with the instruments, books, and papers to be sent back to Philadelphia, but before they were ready the commissioners rode on ahead, anxious to get home.[16]

Back in the city, the Pennsylvania commissioners wrote into their report more than a detailed account of what they had accomplished. They included a strong plea that economic aid be extended to the western inhabitants of the state, who might otherwise turn over their trade to Maryland and Virginia when those states completed their road building plans. The commissioners estimated that a satisfactory road might be put through for less than £1,000. They further urged that terms for the purchase of western lands be eased, especially by foregoing interest due on purchase money during the periods owners had fled their farms in the face of Indian attack.[17]

Rittenhouse's political friends, the Constitutionalists, were generally favorable to the western interest, and, after the October elections, they were in a stronger position than ever. One demonstration of this strength lay in their extension to seven years of the term of Comptroller General Nicholson, who was now recognized as an adherent of their party.[18] The political maelstrom became so turbulent, however, that many desirable objects were lost from view, including the commissioners'

[15] Ibid., 373; Mathews, Ellicott, 21.
[16] Pa. Arch., 1st ser., X, 372.
[17] Ibid., 377.
[18] Pa. House Mins., 2d sess., 9th assem., 280.

recommendations on western policy. Rittenhouse was caught
up in the current as soon as he returned and caught especially in the crises of the Treasury with which Hannah had been
trying to contend almost alone.

Perhaps the largest political issue of the moment which
related closely to the Treasury was the Constitutionalist plan
for the assumption and funding of debts due Pennsylvania citizens from both Congress and the state. The program called for
paying off the obligations through the sale of public lands, a
general tax, and an issue of paper money. It was vigorously
opposed by many merchants, by the Republican leadership, and
by the conservative president, John Dickinson, who was anxious instead to concentrate upon speeding taxes into the Treasury
rapidly by passing them through as few hands as possible. Before the funding act was passed—and afterward—leading Constitutionalist politicians, such as Charles Pettit and Jonathan
Dickinson Sergeant, were charged with speculating in the depressed securities and designing the legislation to enrich themselves. Rittenhouse did not commit to writing his reactions to
the funding plan, and neither at this time nor later was his name
linked with the speculators. There is no evidence to contra-
dict the prevailing belief that he meticulously refused to purchase public securities while he held public office.[19]

The demands of the Treasury and of the Loan Office continued to be heavy, but Rittenhouse applied a larger proportion of his free time to science—although with little result.
Toward the end of the year, he was granted a master's degree
by the College of William and Mary at the initiative of President James Madison. In the Philosophical Society, he returned
to a close cooperation with Hopkinson and Vaughan; together,
they carried through to fulfillment the plans to secure a lot on
State House Square and set in motion a building fund to raise
the money to erect there a suitable hall. Less successful were

[19] *Ibid.*, 217–18; *Pa. Col. Recs.*, XIV, 335, 348; *Pa. Arch.*, 4th ser., III,
1004; *Pa. Gaz.*, Feb. 16, 23, Mar. 23, 1785; Rush, *Eulogium*, 39.

efforts to convert Hopkinson's lot into a botanical garden and to bring out the next volume of *Transactions*. Meanwhile, many of the communications and donations made to the society continued to pass through Rittenhouse.[20]

One wit suggested to the society that Rittenhouse equip a set of carved wooden figures with sufficient "anatomical powers" to permit them to give an affirmative vote and to replace the present wooden-headed assemblymen at a great public saving in salaries! Despite this exercise of imagination, Hopkinson labeled the society "as dull as ever." [21]

Hopkinson's own imagination continued to run on many tracks, from sketching to music. The harpsichord even awakened interests which led him to call in Rittenhouse because his ideas proved as much mechanical as musical. One evening, he invited "several philosophical Gentlemen," including the astronomer, to witness the effects of his new method of quilling a harpsichord. He reported to Jefferson, "They declared in Favour of the Experiment." [22]

Jefferson attempted to keep his American friends, especially Rittenhouse, informed of scientific developments in Paris. He sent him a copy of the report condemning animal magnetism, an account of a balloon ascension, and the current *Connaissance des Temps*. He reported the recently noted refracting properties of Iceland spar and the method of constructing a newly invented windmill. He wrote Charles Thomson that he would have sent over examples of the new "phosphoretic" matches but that he heard Rittenhouse already had some. To Hopkinson, who responded more regularly, Jefferson sent similar collections of news—always requesting that they be communicated to "Mr. Rittenhouse." [23]

---

[20] Barton, *Memoirs*, 302; APS Mins., June 19, 1784, Nov. 12, 1785; *Pa. House Mins.*, 1st sess., 9th assem., 256; *Indep. Gaz.*, Mar. 19, 1785.
[21] MS Comm., Natural Philosophy, I, 11, APS; Boyd, ed., *Papers of Jefferson*, VIII, 51.
[22] *Ibid.*, VIII, 50.
[23] *Ibid.*, VII, 516–17, 518, 602; VIII, 50, 98.

Most of his solitary hours, Rittenhouse spent with his telescope and in the improvement of his observatory. He continued recording the weather, observing Uranus, and observing occasional astronomical phenomena, but he accomplished nothing of permanent scientific significance in this brief interval between the summer surveys. The interval was, in fact, briefer than the number of months between the western trips suggests, because plans for the 1785 observations were made and remade several times between the writing of the 1784 report and the dispatch of the 1785 expedition. The project remained in the forefront of his mind.

He had originally intended to leave the drawing of the western boundary to other men but, during the winter and spring, one after another of the former commissioners withdrew. Among the Virginians, Andrews and Page early indicated that they could not attend, and Madison reported in January that he would be wholly engaged in other business until August. That left only Ellicott who was joined in the Virginia appointment for 1785 with Colonel Joseph Nevil.[24]

Lukens was absorbed in the routine demands of his office as surveyor general, and Ewing from the beginning had maintained that there was no need for both Rittenhouse and him to participate. When it became clear that Rittenhouse preferred not to be included, the Council, on April 11, appointed Ewing and Hutchins as the commissioners for 1785. Ewing, however, immediately withdrew, protesting that the welfare of the University demanded his presence and that he doubted whether the trustees would consent to his absence for even a single month. A few days later, Congress dispatched Hutchins to New York, and, as geographer general of the United States, he had no choice but to go.[25]

Plans had to be reformed completely with the result that

[24] Madison to Ellicott, Jan. 16, 1784 [85], Apr. 20, 1785, Ellicott Papers, LC.

[25] *Pa. Arch.*, 1st ser., x, 443; Barton, *Memoirs*, 305; *Pa. Col. Recs.*, xiv, 402.

Rittenhouse and Andrew Porter were appointed commissioners and Captain Stephen Porter engaged as commissary. Rittenhouse succeeded in limiting his association with the enterprise by pressing the Council to appoint Andrew Ellicott as commissioner for Pennsylvania north of the Ohio, where his Virginia commission would run out.[26]

The wagons and supplies were sent westward late in April, but before the commissioners could begin their trek one more complication arose. New York was pressing that very spring to arrange with Pennsylvania for the determination of the boundary between those two states. Under the impression that nothing could be done to execute this design until the summer of 1786, the Council had appointed Rittenhouse and Porter to the New York service on April 6, 1785—even before appointing them commissioners on the western line. Early in May, however, Dickinson received a letter from Governor Clinton of New York reporting that the commissioners appointed by his state were ready to proceed and urging that the plans be concerted. Simeon De Witt, one of the New York commissioners, wrote Rittenhouse at the same time requesting a meeting in Philadelphia.[27]

This placed Rittenhouse and Porter in an impossible position. If the New Yorkers proved adamant and if the Pennsylvania Council refused to defer the project, Rittenhouse saw no alternative but that he should move from the western line to the northern line in June and carry on both simultaneously. In even mentioning so distasteful a suggestion, he reminded Dickinson, "how little my Constitution is adapted to so much fatigue."[28] He was, however, ready to face the prospect, for the major responsibility in the determination of Pennsylvania's boundaries had somehow devolved upon him. Fortunately, he was able to convince the Council and the New York commis-

---

[26] *Ibid.*, 454; Ellicott to Dickinson, May 4, 1785, Dreer Coll., HSP.
[27] *Pa. Col. Recs.*, XIV, 399, 454, 457; Dickinson to DR and Porter, May 8, 1785, Pa. Misc. Papers, HSP; *Pa. Arch.*, 1st ser., X, 454.
[28] *Ibid.*

sioners to forego the northern boundary expedition for another season.

Rittenhouse at last turned to his preparations for the western trip. He put his own instruments in order, got permission to take several owned by the state, and bought one new telescope. He spent the two nights immediately prior to his departure making astronomical observations—undoubtedly to test some of his equipment. He turned over the affairs of the Treasury to Hannah as he had done the preceding year, and, on May 17, set out with Andrew Porter and his nineteen-year-old nephew, Benjamin Smith Barton, who went along for the experience.[29]

The trip west began on a road that had been well-traveled even before the Revolution and that now carried numbers of families moving out, most of them to Kentucky. The roadbed was poor, of course: stony and rutty or muddy and sometimes impassable. Under the best of circumstances, overland travel offered "many a weary Jolt," as Rittenhouse put it, but this aspect of the journey affected the travelers less than the inspiring view of a fresh and "fertile" countryside. Mile by mile, Rittenhouse's cares slid off his shoulders. He was conscious of a new peace, of freedom from "that eternal din for money," and of release from the wearing politics in which he had become inextricably entangled. On the third day out, he was met in York by John Hay, who turned over £270 of tax money; thereafter the business of the Treasury lay behind him. Whenever he thought of it, he experienced an exquisite sense of delight in escaping "the plagues of that office," but at the same time he carried with him some sense of guilt at Hannah's having to bear them in his place.[30]

They followed a course from York through Abbotstown, across South Mountain at Black Gap, along a branch of the

[29] Ibid., DR to James Irvine, May 12, 1785, Gratz Coll., HSP; DR, Notebook, 1785–92, May 14, 1785, APS.
[30] Ibid., May 19, 1785; DR to Samuel Williams, Sep. 17, 1787, Gratz Coll., HSP; Barton, Memoirs, 309.

Conococheague, and over the Mason-Dixon line on roads often "much out of repair." On the night of the 20th, they lodged on the bank of the Potomac, just four miles below the Pennsylvania line. Thereafter, the road deviated but slightly from the course of the river, bringing the party to a "Beautiful Situation" just before Old Town, where the rock bottom of the river stretched over a width of at least a half-mile. On the same day, Monday the 23rd, a wagon axle-tree broke and there was nothing to do but wait at Old Town until a wheelwright and a smith could set things right. This gave Rittenhouse and Barton a welcome opportunity to poke about the area, examining rocks with close attention and breaking them open in search of fossil shells which they found in abundance. Soon however, they had too much of a good thing when they found they could not proceed anyway until the creeks, swollen by three consecutive days of rain, subsided.[31]

Finally on Wednesday, they were able to resume the trip amid continuing showers. The rain made the pass beyond Fort Cumberland, known as "the narrows," frighteningly difficult. At Wills Creek, they found the current so swift that they had to cross in a small canoe and float the dismantled wagon over after them. Pounded by roads now "bad beyond description," another axle-tree gave way very close to the meadow where Washington had capitulated to the French in 1753, already known as a historic site. This time, the wagon and baggage had to be loaded on a sledge and dragged about a mile to the next habitation, where repairs were made. Rittenhouse and his nephew searched the rocks for fossil shells during the delay but this time could find none.[32]

Saturday, they recrossed the Pennsylvania line, and Sunday they forded the large branch of the Youghiogheny River, or "the Yock" as it was popularly known. Young Barton was

[31] DR, Notebook, 1785–92, *passim*, APS; *PMHB*, IV, 268; Benjamin Smith Barton, Journal, n.p., HSP.
[32] *Ibid.*; *PMHB*, IV, 269; DR, Notebook, 1785–92, n.p., APS.

much impressed with this "beautiful and considerable stream of water . . . nearly as large as the Potomack at Old-Town," but for some reason he did not ride the ten miles down stream with his uncle to see the already celebrated Ohiopyle Falls. With his customary precision, Rittenhouse observed the scenic attraction, sketched the course of the river freehand, and estimated the height of each of the two tiers of falls at about ten feet, while he placed the width of the river at that point at some eighty feet. Sometime later, he wrote a brief but enthusiastic description of the falls, which he considered "by far the most magnificent, of any thing of this kind in the state of Pennsylvania." After his return, he published his description in the *Columbian Magazine* beside a truly remarkable engraving.[33]

The striking fact about the published view is that it was executed by an engraver who had never seen the falls, copying a drawing by Benjamin Smith Barton, who had never seen the falls either! Barton said that his drawing was based upon a "rude sketch which Mr. Rittenhouse made on the spot"—possibly nothing more than his plan view of the river's course which still survives. At any rate, the engraving was incredibly accurate; even today it is a satisfying rendition. The individual rocks are not exact, stone by stone, but the impression is precise. The curve of the banks and even the tree line is accurate. It is a tribute to Rittenhouse's powers of recall and communication that he was able to convey to his nephew so clear an impression of the appearance of the falls.[34]

Just before noon on Saturday, May 31, the expedition drew into Beesontown, now known as Uniontown, where they were greeted with enthusiasm by the Virginia commissioners—by Andrew Ellicott with particular joy. For days, he had been restive under enforced inactivity as he and Nevil waited impatiently for the Pennsylvanians. This disagreeable situation had

[33] *Ibid.;* Barton, Journal, n.p., HSP; *Columbian Mag.,* 1 (1786–87), 284.
[34] *Ibid.,* opp. 284; DR, Notebook, 1785–92, n.p., APS; Barton, Journal, n.p., HSP.

been made worse by Ellicott's feeling that he had no one with whom he could talk about plans for running the boundary or about anything else of significance. He was not so anxious about the days lost from work on the boundary line as he was for the arrival of his "good and Wise Friend David Rittenhouse." The event fulfilled the anticipation; he recorded, "the Afternoon was spent in much good Humour and mirth and philosophick enquiry." [35]

When the two groups left Beesontown, they could no longer travel by recognized roads and their precise route to the previously marked corner of Pennsylvania can only be conjectured. The Pennsylvanians reached the spot first, pitched their camp, "reconnoitered the Woods to the corner and returned to Camp." The next day, June 6, the Virginians appeared and set up their equipment near by.[36]

Almost immediately, they began the serious business of making astronomical observations to determine the true course of the meridian running north from the corner. This required, first, the discovery of the correct local time and the maintenance of accurate knowledge of it by a clock whose rate of gain or loss was precisely known. Then, they compared the meridian transit times of several stars with the times of meridian transit predicted by astronomical tables for the longitude of Greenwich. This time difference yielded the difference in longitude, directly.

Moving slowly northward along the meridian, they repeated this process at one station after another. Between stations, they ran the line for several miles by the use of a transit instrument; then at the next station, they corrected it. Before long, the surveyors experienced the satisfaction of looking backward along the path of their progress, where vistas were cut over each ridge and trees girdled, but not felled, in the valleys. Sometimes they

[35] Ellicott to Sarah Ellicott, May 25, 1785, Ellicott Papers, LC; Mathews, *Ellicott*, 38, 39.
[36] *Report of the Secretary of Internal Affairs of . . . Pennsylvania containing Reports of the Surveys and Resurveys* (n.p., 1887), 435.

could follow the clearings with their eyes as far as fifteen or twenty miles, and they could see the marker stones defining successive ridges for a shorter distance.

After a time, the operation became tedious. There was nothing intellectually stimulating in repeating the same observations night after night. There was little chance that they would discover anything new except the course of the line. The slowness of their progress was an additional source of frustration; Rittenhouse reported in June that they had not advanced faster than a mile a day. He laid the trouble to the roughness of the ground and the idleness of the "people of the country" of whom some thirty were employed to open the vistas.[37]

He wrote Hannah that he had considered complaining to the vice president of the Supreme Executive Council but had thought better of it. He told her that an official letter from the Council was needed, urging them "to proceed with all the dispatch consistent with the accuracy they expect." Just about a month later, Rittenhouse and Porter received an official letter from John Dickinson, encouraging them to prosecute the survey "with the utmost Diligence, & with all the Dispatch that is compatible with Accuracy in your Proceedings." They were Rittenhouse's words precisely! [38]

Other complaints were not so easily answered, and Rittenhouse found much to complain of even though he slept better now than at home, his pain was reduced, and he never failed to acknowledge his sense of release from Treasury woes. His food was reasonably well prepared by a woman they employed as a cook, and he even had access to a good ulcer diet, for each of them kept a cow to furnish fresh milk which was used, after a custom established the year before, in a wine syllabub they shared every afternoon. Despite such trappings of luxury and ease, this life seemed deficient. He wrote, "If I were to view only the dark side of my situation, I should complain that I am

[37] Barton, *Memoirs*, 309.
[38] *Ibid.*; Pa. Arch., 1st ser., x, 489.

here secluded from the society of those I love, deprived of books and every other of my most favourite amusements; confined to homely fare by day, and a hard bed at night; and obliged, by our business, to take rather too much exercise." [39]

He was even annoyed by the continuous proximity of his fellow commissioners and by occasional visits from residents of the region. "They hindered me from enjoying a lonely walk," he went on, "or some passage in Milton,—or, perhaps, a loll on my bed. Nay, even our fellow-commissioners, the Virginians, I mean; I sometimes wish their wine was better, and flowed more plentifully: not that I might enjoy it with them; but that I might enjoy myself the more, alone." [40]

Yet, he was not at all a misanthrope. Of those with whom he was thrown most closely, he reported, "Colonel Porter is attentive, and cousin Benjamin has recommended himself as an agreeable companion to all of us; and I could almost call Mr. Ellicott a congenial soul." Ellicott's comment on their relationships was, like the man, less restrained. He wrote, "the greatest Harmony possible subsists among us, Mr. Rittenhouse in perticular has frequently complimented me, which I confess has somewhat raised my Vanity, because he is commonly sparing, but where he conceives there is real Merit." Rittenhouse's greatest pleasures were found in company with these men—usually in exploring the country or examining its natural history.[41]

Indeed, only in the contemplation of nature did Rittenhouse's deep and throbbing emotion escape his disciplined restraint. He found undiminished delight in riding or walking with his friends about the "wild uncultivated country." He enjoyed the untouched woodlands, and he enjoyed the inhabited countryside. After one long immersion in the forest was relieved when Rittenhouse's party came upon cultivated farmland, he even enjoyed the barking of dogs and the crowing of cocks. To his

---

[39] Ellicott to Sarah Ellicott, July 30, 1784, July 29, 1785, Ellicott Papers, LC; Barton, *Memoirs*, 313-15.
[40] *Ibid.*
[41] *Ibid.*; Ellicott to Sarah Ellicott, June 20, 1785, Ellicott Papers, LC.

wife he admitted, "This is truly romantic, and, at this season of the year, beautiful and luxuriant in the highest degree." To his friend, Jefferson, he declared that the western boundary, "being one Straight Meridian Line is certainly the most grand and beautiful Vista in the World." [42]

Once, he caught a fawn and kept it as a pet with the thought of taking it back as a present for Hetty, but when their cows ran away his little deer starved to death. He then tried to salvage something of the plan by having the skin prepared so it could be given to his younger daughter.

The little excursions he took with his friends revealed to each a different side of the man. With Porter, who was less interested in nature than in politics, he went some distance out of his way to visit the Ohio Court House, which turned out to be a log cabin and a matching jail. With Barton, he examined and collected mineral and botanical specimens. A plant he called the "Wheeling Star," which he afterward cultivated in his garden, he probably found on this trip. With Ellicott he shared the most, including one moment of fantasy during a walk up a rivulet bounded by steep hills and paved with large flagstones which rose in steps to produce frequent cascades. At last, Rittenhouse suggested, "we should proceed no further for if we did, we should in all probability find some of the water-godesses, —perhaps stark naked and fast asleep." After telling that story, Rittenhouse recalled that they had been accompanied by a third man, but commented, "neither the nymphs nor their shady bowers had any charms for him." [43]

Yet the fragments of interest he shared with his companions were surface evidences of a deeper quest of which he spoke but little. How did all the pieces of knowledge he picked up about the character of the rocks, fossils, metallic ores, river courses, terrain, and vegetation fit together? Why did he observe more coal to the west of the Appalachian divide and more iron to

---

[42] Boyd, ed., *Papers of Jefferson*, VIII, 566; Barton, *Memoirs*, 310–11.
[43] *Ibid.*, 310–11, 606; *PMHB*, IV, 273.

the east? What had caused the sedimentary layers to be up-ended in the mountainous regions? How had the whole been formed and how had it been altered? The big questions—not the details—bothered him, and, after his return, he wrote his perceptive and sometimes brilliant answers for publication.[44]

These interests and his petty discomforts occupied his mind to the exclusion of such justifiable fears as Hannah suffered—fears especially of Indian attack. He reassured her accurately by admitting reports of hostile activity, but pointed out that it had all taken place in the Ohio region, which they did not plan to enter. Shortly after he left the area, however, reports were received of Indian killings along Fish Creek which at one point runs within two miles of the Pennsylvania line. If he heard of such events, he kept the facts to himself.[45]

On August 23, having reached the Ohio River, the four commissioners signed a joint certificate declaring that they had completed the line to that point and had marked it with in-scribed stones on the tops of all the hills and at the bank of the Ohio. Nevil left at once, his job completed; but Ellicott re-mained, for on the other side of the river he became a Penn-sylvania commissioner. As Rittenhouse had planned it, he was then free to go too, but for some reason he remained another two weeks. Perhaps, as he said, he wanted to avoid travel in the heat of the summer; perhaps he enjoyed his companions and their life together more than he admitted; perhaps he sought to keep clear of the cares of the Treasury as long as possible.[46]

At any event, his friends were downcast when he announced that he could delay no longer but must leave on September 12. Their comments reflected the feelings of men who had shared a closeness in the wilderness yet felt they had to elevate their eyes a little to see him. Ellicott wrote on the day before, "To-

[44] "Some Observations on . . . the Western Countries," *Columbian Mag.,* I (1786–87), 49–53.
[45] Richard Butler, "Journal," *The Olden Time,* II (1847), 436; Barton, *Memoirs,* 313.
[46] *Ibid.,* 311; *Pa. Arch.,* 1st ser., X, 506.

morrow my Dear Friend the Great Mr Rittenhouse leaves us, and proceeds for Philadelphia, his absence will be greatly felt by our little Band, but by none more than myself, he has been my constant companion in all our little Excursions." Barton expressed similarly heartfelt praise of "one of the best of men: a man who was to me the friend, a patron, and a father." [47]

Rittenhouse began his trip home with Colonel Harmen and Major Doughty but completed most of it attended only by one James Otley. By way of Fort Pitt, Ligonier, and Bedford he made his way back to the road they had taken out, which he rejoined in the vicinity of the present town of Greencastle. On the 25th, after a two-week trip and after four months of absence, he reached home with his collections of "curiosities" and with a certain refreshment of spirit.[48]

In the green woods behind him, he left a piece of his legend. When General Richard Butler visited the boundary commissioners at the end of September, he found them some thirty miles north of the Ohio. The work he inspected was not in his mind the product of equal commissioners but, "the line, which Mr. Rittenhouse and his assistants have run." Respectfully, he noted, "It bears all the marks of correct judgement, wisdom, and care in the execution, and will be a lasting monument of his excellence in this kind of business." Precision was nothing more than he had expected, but he recorded with manifest pleasure the fantastic assertion, "it is open, well marked, and I am told so correct as to vary but 1-10 of an inch in forty miles." [49]

[47] Mathews, *Ellicott*, 48; Barton, Journal, Sep. 12, 1785, HSP.
[48] *Ibid.*; DR, Notebook, 1785–92, n.p., APS.
[49] Butler, "Journal," 436.

CHAPTER XVII

Sunshine in Philadelphia

1785–1787

R ITTENHOUSE found Philadelphia preoccupied with the return of her greatest citizen, Benjamin Franklin, who had arrived the week before amid pealing bells, shouts, and exultation. The festive mood remained and the celebrating continued; the Philosophical Society was planning for September 27 a reception and a special meeting in honor of its distinguished president.

Rittenhouse was caught up in the enthusiasm too, but he could not avoid a concomitant depression. Although he would not have admitted it, he was now dethroned as reigning scientist, and he brought in his curiosities and tales from the West at a devalued rate. Inevitably, he had been left out of the planning because of his absence, and, as a result, he felt less a part of the activities than he might have in other circumstances. The Philosophical Society's welcoming address, wordy and full of platitudes, was delivered by one of the political members, Chief Justice McKean. Hopkinson vented his annoyance at this choice in a satire contrasting McKean's pomposity with the brevity of Franklin's reply; Rittenhouse kept his peace. His silence was, however, more eloquent than Hopkinson's wit, for the very next day he wrote Thomas Jefferson, Franklin's successor in Paris, without including a single word about Franklin or the meeting.[1]

Before long, it became clear that Franklin's presence would be a source of pleasure to Rittenhouse and a significant ad-

[1] APS Mins., 1774–87, Sep. 27, 1785; Hopkinson, *Miscellaneous Essays*, II, 69–75; Boyd, ed., *Papers of Jefferson*, VIII, 565–66.

vantage in both his science and his political life. The politicians sensed Franklin's value immediately, and both factions hastened to attach his name to their cause. The Constitutionalists assumed that since Franklin had sat in the 1776 Constitutional Convention, he would adhere to the political group which still favored the Constitution. He was also expected to feel friendly toward the Mechanical Society, often allied with the Constitutionalists, because in some respects he never ceased thinking of himself as a mechanic. On the other hand, the Republicans knew that Franklin was favorably inclined to some of their tenets—notably the abolition of the test laws—and they hoped for his support. Franklin agreed, finally, to run for the Council under Constitutionalist sponsorship but, when he was elected, all factions united in supporting his elevation to the presidency in the anticipation that he could reduce partisan antagonisms.

In some measure, this hope was fulfilled. There seemed to be more attention to social legislation and less absorption with the most divisive issues. State politics became a shade less virulent—partly because of Franklin's influence, partly because of the rising attention given to the problems of national government, and partly because the political balance in the Assembly was close—although tipped slightly in favor of the Constitutionalists.

Franklin served three terms as president and during all of them Rittenhouse prospered, despite the slowly declining strength of the Constitutionalists. He prospered most obviously in his personal income, which benefited markedly from an increase in commissions voted in 1785. In money that was now very stable, his income from the Treasury alone was over £1,100 in 1786 and over £1,400 in 1787—almost as much as the president's salary. In addition, he received £150 from the Loan Office and generous compensation from the surveys in which he participated. He demonstrated his respectable financial position in November 1786 by purchasing the lot on the northwest corner of Seventh and Mulberry Streets. There, he constructed a large and well-designed house, sixty-eight feet in width and three stories in height. Known thereafter as the Rittenhouse mansion, it provided a comfortable and gracious home for the balance of his life and for his family after him.[2]

The declining fortunes of Rittenhouse's political friends had little immediate effect upon his life in the Treasury. Finances continued to be perplexed by a multiplicity of monies which passed at changing rates; he had to keep in mind at least twelve different Pennsylvania and Congressional issues—to say nothing of the paper of other states which passed through his hands. If revenues flowed somewhat more freely, the collection of taxes remained an unsolved problem and there was still not enough money to answer demands based on legal appropriations. Rittenhouse was sometimes pressed so hard that he wrote out orders on the county treasurers, thus putting into circulation still another species of money which itself passed at discounted rates. This practice drew so much political fire that in July 1787, the Assembly ordered it stopped. The legislature continued to prod Rittenhouse to proceed against Loan Office delinquents and to use all his powers to stimulate tax collection. He never accommodated himself to the burdens of the office or its harassments, and he never ceased to complain. To Jefferson, he lamented, "The business of my Office, continually increasing, not only occupies my time intirely at present, but is become almost insupportable." [3]

Yet, except for the volume of work, his office was less harrowing than it had been and certainly less than it would become because he was insulated from hostile criticism by Hannah at home, Franklin in the presidency, Nicholson in the comptroller general's office, and Hopkinson wherever he alighted. Rittenhouse could never doubt that his work was applauded and that he was valued. This warmth in his environment was reflected in his letters and in the general pace of his life.

Moreover, both the state and the nation were economically

[2] *State of the Account of David Rittenhouse . . . 1786*, 37, 38, 39, 46; Pa. *House Mins.*, 1st sess., 11th assem., 62; Barton, *Memoirs*, 331.
[3] Pa. *Col. Recs.*, xv, 253; Boyd, ed., *Papers of Jefferson*, IX, 293; Pa. *Gaz.*, Sep. 6, 1786, July 18, 1787.

prosperous. The funding plan pushed through earlier by the Constitutionalists and extended in 1787 continued to be a matter of violent difference, but only an economically healthy state could have sustained the shock of such an effort. One index of stability was Rittenhouse's success in collecting over £300,000 of various emissions for retirement and destruction in 1786 and his recurring accumulation each year thereafter of £20,000 of the 1785 emission which the law required be burned. This was never easy because there were so many citizens with legal warrants who felt their needs should have priority over the burning of money. Rittenhouse collected the money, nevertheless, and turned it over for disposal with a regularity that would have been utterly impossible during the dark days of the war.[4]

Then and later, men wrote of American distress and depression, but in April 1786 Charles Thomson told Jefferson, "I will venture to assert that there is not upon the face of the earth a body of people more happy or rising into consequence with more rapid stride, than the Inhabitants of the United States of America. Population is encreasing, new houses building, new lands clearing, new settlements forming and new manufactures establishing with a rapidity beyond conception. And what is more, the people are well fed, well clad and well housed." [5]

This mood influenced Rittenhouse too. His personal health remained precarious, he was usually "neither absolutely well nor absolutely ill." Franklin's return, however, introduced him to a new fellowship. On Wednesday evenings, Rittenhouse and Hopkinson developed the custom of calling on Franklin for "a little, pleasing philosophical Party." When Jefferson heard of these weekly conversations, he confessed that he would rather sit in on one of them than spend a whole week in Paris.[6]

[4] Ibid., Sep. 6, 1786, Nov. 21, 1787; Pa. House Mins., 1st sess., 10th assem., 152; 3d sess., 10th assem., 296, 331; 1st sess., 12th assem., 60; [John Nicholson], A View of the Debts and Expences of the Commonwealth [Phila., 1786], 23.

[5] Boyd, ed., Papers of Jefferson, IX, 350.

[6] Ibid., IX, 322, 440; X, 249.

Andrew Ellicott drank in the optimism and the warmth of Rittenhouse's surroundings during a two-week visit at the end of 1785. Most of the time, he luxuriated in his host's "Philosophy and agreeable Manners his Ladies good sence and uncommon good Nature added to the lively conversation and wise observations of the Daughters." Once during this period, he attended lectures at the University, once he went to a Philosophical Society meeting, and twice he visited the home of Benjamin Franklin—the first time escorted by Rittenhouse.[7]

Rittenhouse was probably associated socially with Franklin on many occasions, for men often thought of them in the same context. Rush reported one dinner he attended at which Franklin, Rittenhouse, David Ramsay, and Lewis Littlepage were also present. On this occasion, they discussed the roots of the Revolution, and Franklin's observations were, of course, the ones Rush recorded carefully.[8]

Hopkinson credited Franklin's return with a genuine revival of the Philosophical Society; by his presence alone, he gave members a new sense of importance. Sometimes they met at his home when he was too uncomfortable to leave it, and at one such meeting he intervened to save their projected Philosophical Hall from abandonment. When Rush read to the society his significant *Enquiry into the Influence of Physical Causes upon the Moral Faculty*, he dedicated it to Franklin. He included in his oral presentation a paragraph of full-flowered praise which had the prior and enthusiastic approval of Rittenhouse but which he deleted from the printed version at Franklin's emphatic request.[9]

There is no evidence that Franklin played any direct part in the publication of the second volume of *Transactions*, but the journal did finally appear in 1786 after years of unsuccessful efforts to get it in print. Rittenhouse had been associated

[7] Mathews, *Ellicott*, 53.
[8] Benjamin Rush, Notes, 1785, Rush Papers, LCP.
[9] Rush to Franklin, Mar. 3, 11, 1786, Franklin Papers, APS.

with the earlier plans, and he took pride in its final appearance at the same time that he felt he had to apologize for not contributing more to it. This feeling was an index of the preeminent role he thought he was expected to play. The volume contained the most important scientific work Rittenhouse ever did. Although he thought of himself primarily as an astronomer, not even his transit of Venus work matched the originality of three significant experimental papers: his fundamental "Experiments on Magnetism," his pioneering examination of the illusion of reversible relief, and a third paper he had just finished.[10]

If anything, this last paper was still more valuable than the others; in it he described his invention and study of the diffraction grating. Here, Rittenhouse scored a first-rate achievement, designing a plane transmission grating and observing with it six orders of spectra. At every point, he displayed imagination and experimental dexterity.

He was set on this work by the "man of a Thousand whims," Francis Hopkinson, who sent his friend a deceptively simple question. Why, he wanted to know, when he looked through a fine silk handkerchief at a light source, did he see a grid of dark lines which did not move at all, even though he moved the handkerchief back and forth? Rittenhouse did not know but he set out to examine the phenomenon.

First, by repeating Hopkinson's experiment he disposed of the possibility that the visible lines might represent images of the silk threads. He accurately identified the phenomenon as diffraction, or, in the terminology of his day, "the *inflection* of light in passing near the surfaces of bodies, as described by Newton." Newton's *Opticks* provided the framework of Rittenhouse's understanding, but, curiously, Newton had conspicuously failed to identify these "Fraunhofer lines." [11]

Next, Rittenhouse made a finer grating of 106 lines to the

[10] Boyd, ed., *Papers of Jefferson*, x, 73.
[11] APS, *Trans.*, 11 (1786), 202; Thomas D. Cope, "The Rittenhouse Diffraction Grating," *Jour. of the Franklin Inst.*, 214 (1932), 99–104.

inch, constructed of hairs placed parallel to each other. Finding the resultant lines too faint and indistinct, however, he increased the size of the hairs until the slits between were about $\frac{1}{250}$ of an inch. Now he was able to see six lines of light on either side of the middle line and to find that beyond the first or second line, the prismatic colors could be clearly distinguished. At the fifth or sixth line, the spectra nearly touched each other.

Borrowing a small prismatic telescope and micrometer from Franklin, he measured the angular displacement of the various orders of spectra. These measurements were accurately made in terms of the now known wave lengths of the colors he observed. He further found that the angular displacement of the nth order was always n times the displacement he found for the first order. This is a corollary of a better known law discovered by Fresnel some thirty years later.

To this point Rittenhouse proceeded and no further. His published experiments were commented upon favorably by at least one English review, despite the antagonistic national feelings. They were discussed by the Royal Society and repeated by Henry Cavendish, but they were not extended. If Rittenhouse had constructed a second grating with a different period, he would have been confronted with phenomena which only the wave theory of light could explain. Indeed, when rediscovered by Fraunhofer and Fresnel, the diffraction grating provided significant support for the wave theory.[12]

As it was, Rittenhouse rested comfortably in the corpuscular theory and was content to close his paper with a quotation from Newton, who had also encountered the surprising result of red rays being more diffracted than blue. Once again his pioneering work fell dead for lack of attention, not because it was unknown but because no one, including Rittenhouse, had the need for it that would in time arise.

Rittenhouse undervalued this and his other experimental pa-

[12] *Critical Review*, LXIV (1787), 439; *Monthly Review*, LXXVI (1787), 144; Boyd, ed., *Papers of Jefferson*, XI, 288.

pers because they seemed only curious fragments rather than elements of a rising edifice. Besides, he always weighed his accomplishments in terms of astronomy and here his contributions to the *Transactions* were limited. His observations of the 1779 meteor, the 1782 transit of Mercury, the 1784 comet, and Uranus were competent and reliable, but offered nothing of challenging significance. His data were unique in the sense that no similar observations had been made in his part of the world, but the position of his observatory did not give the same advantage it had in the case of the transit of Venus. His information was primarily useful for calculating the orbits of the bodies involved—which he did for the comet. Except for the meteor, however, more complete sets of observations were available from European observatories.[13]

The observational techniques Rittenhouse reported were more exciting than the data he obtained; he solved two mechanical problems with a brilliance which has been justly recognized. When faced with the obscuring of a distant mark by which he had lined up his meridian telescope, he installed a collimating lens system that permitted him to use a much closer mark on his own property. Without this method of arranging lenses so that the rays of light from the mark were rendered parallel, a close mark was useless because it was subject to so much parallax. Such a lens system was not new, so Rittenhouse cannot be called the inventor of the collimating telescope, but his inventiveness is beyond question.

Of similar character was his introduction of a spider web, "with no small difficulty," to serve as a cross hair in his telescope.[14] Far finer than the silk filament he had been using, the spider web was an improvement in every way. He never knew that this technique had been used earlier by the Abbé Fontana.

Rittenhouse had distinct reservations about the weight of his

[13] APS, *Trans.*, II (1786), 195, 260–63.
[14] *Ibid.*, 183; Fr. von Zach, *Monatliche Correspondenz* (Gotha, 1800), II, 215.

contributions to the second volume of *Transactions*, but, in fact, they offer the best demonstration of his subtlety as an experimental scientist, his mastery of instrumental techniques, and even his role in astronomy. The volume sustained and extended his reputation wherever it reached. So too, did his concurrent activities in which he still sought to fulfill the ideal of the abstract scientist who applied his knowledge to practical affairs. Indeed, Rittenhouse was off drawing another boundary line when the volume came from the printers.

Again, in the summer of 1786, two boundary-drawing commissions competed for his attention. Congress had appointed him in December 1785, with Ewing and Hutchins, to determine the recently resolved boundary between New York and Massachusetts; at the same time, Pennsylvania and New York were anxious to begin work on their common boundary which had already been deferred for one year. Rittenhouse was ready to attend to both commissions, but this proved impossible. Ewing could not serve until July, at which time Hutchins had an unavoidable commitment to begin surveys in the West. Congress was not willing to appoint Robert Patterson in place of Hutchins, as the three commissioners suggested, and there was nothing to do but defer the New York–Massachusetts survey until the following year.[15]

This freed Rittenhouse to devote his full attention to the Pennsylvania–New York boundary. He began the planning as early as February when he wrote Simeon De Witt to request that the New York commissioners meet him and Ellicott, the other Pennsylvania commissioner, in Philadelphia that spring. When they agreed, Andrew Ellicott happily made the trip from Baltimore on April 18, settled down at Rittenhouse's home again, and called the following day, "incognito," at the lodgings of the New York commissioners. In this guise, he evaluated De Witt and General James Clinton without their knowing

[15] *Jours. of Cong.*, IV, 607; *Documents of the Senate of the State of N.Y.* (n.p., 1877), 100th sess., vol. 5, no. 61, p. 200.

who he was. He found the general "a thoughtful old gentleman" and De Witt a young man of capacity; these impressions
were strengthened during the two ensuing days of formal discussions by all the commissioners.[16]

Andrew Porter came to town at the same time to talk over
plans for completing the western line, which was to be en-
trusted to him. Rittenhouse continued as a commissioner on
the western boundary, but he participated only in the planning;
he did not intend to take further part in the actual survey. The
two expeditions were mapped out at separate meetings in an
atmosphere of great friendliness and harmony.

Ellicott enjoyed these planning sessions enormously, but most
of all he enjoyed having another opportunity to share Rittenhouse's company. He never ceased to marvel at the strength of
his friend's genius; a man who without "even the common advantages has raised himself a Monument of Fame more durable
than all the glittering pomp attendant on Wealth and Power."
Ellicott asserted, he "is now justly esteemed the first Astronomer in this New World and perhaps inferior to none in the
Old." And all this he had attained, "without creating one Enemy
or exciting Envy." [17]

The northern expedition did not get off until June, Ellicott
leaving Philadelphia on the 17th with the stores and instruments and Rittenhouse following ten days later. At Easton, they
met and proceeded together through Wind Gap and along a
road that held to an unusually straight northerly course.[18] They
followed existing roads, although often bad ones, to reach the
vicinity of the border. They reconnoitered the country through
which the boundary would run, crossing its probable course at
several points.

By July 9, they were at Tioga on the Susquehanna River,
about ninety miles from the Delaware. Here they stayed a few

[16] DR to De Witt, Feb. 7, 1786, Photocopy, HSP; Mathews, *Ellicott*,
57.
[17] *Ibid.*, 58.
[18] DR, Notebook, 1785–92, June 27, 28, [1786], APS.

days, much surprised to find whites and Indians "liveing together in great Harmony." The two men explored the natural curiosities of the region and were impressed especially by a giant tooth they found on the banks of the Susquehanna. The grinding surface of the tooth was about six inches by three and was regarded as distinctly more smooth than the rough, carniverous teeth of the "mammoth" or mastadon which had been previously found. Ellicott took it to be the tooth of a sea monster, and Rittenhouse carried it back to Philadelphia where Charles Willson Peale sketched it and published an engraving from his drawing in the *Columbian Magazine*.[19]

Less than a week after leaving Tioga, they pitched camp with the New York commissioners and together established two observing stations: one on the west bank of the Delaware where Rittenhouse and Samuel Holland had marked the forty-second parallel back in 1774 and the other twenty miles to the west. Favored by good weather, they made observations to fix their latitude on several nights in late July. It turned out that they were two miles too far south, so they moved their location north and a bit west to the bank of the Susquehanna. After two more weeks of observations, they were satisfied with their determination of the forty-second parallel—eleven chains and nineteen links to the north of the relocated station. They quickly laid off this distance by terrestrial measurement.[20]

The lack of occupation during the daytime and during cloudy nights did not bother Rittenhouse; he enjoyed his enforced leisure. He and the other commissioners became acquainted with some of the members of the little Onondaga Indian community at Chenango, about twelve miles from their camp site. This relationship began when an Onondaga sachem drew up below the camp with his family in three canoes and stayed there for the night. The next day, he sent a message, translated by an in-

[19] Ellicott to Sarah Ellicott, July 11, 1786, Ellicott Letters, LC; *Columbian Mag.*, 1 (1786–87), 655.
[20] DR, Notebook, 1785–92, July 18 to Aug. 4, 1786, APS.

terpreter Clinton had prudently brought along, in which he requested an audience for two young ladies of the family.

In due course, the girls appeared, drank punch, and requested that flour and other provisions be made available to them because they were in great need. The commissioners readily gave them salt meat and bread, encouraging the Indians to bring fish and other fresh provisions in return. Thereafter, Jacowe and Sally, the neice and daughter of the sachem, returned each day for tea and to play cards and checkers with the white men.

Sally, attractive and about twenty years old, captured the imagination of all the commissioners. Rittenhouse described her as "a fine girl . . . and extremely well dressed." De Witt made a drawing of her which Rittenhouse hoped to be able to show Hannah and Ellicott planned to have "Coppied Large." They were surprised to learn that she and her people had been converted by the Anglicans and were practiced at singing hymns and praying. Sally could read and write in Mohawk. She was undoubtedly the source of the Onondaga words for the ordinal numbers which Rittenhouse copied down in the same journal where he recorded his astronomical observations.[21]

When they began the final process of running the boundary line, the commissioners introduced a somewhat different technique from that used on the southern border of Pennsylvania. There, the arc of a great circle had been traced by following a fixed bearing, and then corrected into a parallel of latitude. Here, a compass direction was used to run a line to the west as true as possible and this corrected at intervals by reestablishing the latitude through the measurement of the zenith angles of several stars. This proved faster and more economical than the southern border method which had been introduced by Mason and Dixon and continued in the extension of their line as a matter of course.

Each time the latitude was adjusted, the commissioners moved on about twenty miles to establish a new station where they

[21] *Ibid.*, n.d.; Mathews, *Ellicott*, 59–69; Barton, *Memoirs*, 241–46.

made zenith observations again. On August 25, they were observing within two or three miles of the point where the Susquehanna is joined by the Chemung River and crossed by the forty-second parallel for the third and last time. By October 12, they reached the South Branch of the Tioga River—the objective for which they had been aiming ever since Rittenhouse and Ellicott visited it in July. They had carried the line across the ninety miles from the Delaware and, with the fall season advancing rapidly, everyone was ready to start for home.[22]

Even before this, Rittenhouse's boredom returned. The new surveying technique interested him for a time, but it was soon proven superior to the old, and he never enjoyed the tedious repetition of any operation. He could not get away from the unpleasantness of being "cooped up in a little tent, night and day, for weeks together."[23] As he took the road south, he was determined not to return the following season.

At least, the summer surveys removed him from another project which threatened to engulf him both before and after his northern expedition. With Hopkinson, Ewing, and two other Pennsylvanians, he had been appointed in April to treat with Maryland and Delaware commissioners on improving the navigation of the Susquehanna River. When they found a summer meeting was impossible, they delayed until late in the fall, but even then nothing useful was accomplished.[24]

The Treasury reached out as soon as Rittenhouse got back to the city from Tioga, but this time he did not permit it to monopolize him. He put time into his office but not much of his heart—that was engaged by a series of opportunities, some old and some new. Among his new interests was the first general magazine to come out in Philadelphia since the war; the initial number of the *Columbian Magazine* had appeared dur-

[22] *Ibid.*, 24on.–41n.; DR, Notebook, 1785–92, Aug. 25 to 27, 1786, APS; *Pa. Arch.*, 1st ser., XI, 522.

[23] Barton, *Memoirs*, 246.

[24] *Pa. Arch.*, 1st ser., X, 755; *Pa. Col. Recs.*, XV, 2; Boyd, ed., *Papers of Jefferson*, X, 512.

ing his northern sojourn. It offered a vehicle for those of his papers which he regarded as useful or amusing but not of sufficient scientific significance to be placed in the *Transactions* of the Philosophical Society. All of his material on natural history he placed in this category.

He began by giving the magazine his description of Ohiopyle Falls, with Benjamin Smith Barton's drawing of it, and a little later he turned over his description of the tooth found at Tioga with Peale's drawing of that. A more ambitious piece was an article on the phenomenon of cloud formation as he had observed it in the Wyoming Valley.[25]

In the form of a letter to Hopkinson which was read to the Philosophical Society, this essay demonstrated again Rittenhouse's capacity for crisp, precise description. He wrote of watching a cloud that lay low above the mountain range northwest of the Susquehanna River and ran parallel to it. The cloud remained apparently stationary for a long time, but from it clouds continuously moved off to the northwest—away from the valley and from the mountain. He then noticed small clouds forming above the mountain and moving up to attach themselves to the large cloud. This was a striking visual representation of the classic picture of warm air picking up water by evaporation over the river valley and dropping it in the form of clouds as it cooled in its passage over the mountain. Rittenhouse focused on the condensation phase of this cycle, which he explained very clearly.

He also published in the *Columbian Magazine*, anonymously as he had the other articles, "Some Observations on the Structure of the Surface of the Earth in Pennsylvania and the adjoining Countries." Primarily descriptive, this paper was concerned with the terrain, the strata which underlay it and accounted for much of its character, and the other agents which had contributed to the appearances he found. He wrote in the same context as some of the earlier commentators on these topics,

[25] *Columbian Mag.*, 1 (1786–87), 284, 655, 301–3.

although he gave no indication whether he had read Buffon, Lehmann, or Pallas. He made no effort to present a general theory of geological formation, but underlying his descriptions was a rejection of the deluge and an acceptance of both the gradual processes of erosion and sedimentation and a form of catastrophism. He accounted for the formation of mountains by "a supposition, that the former shell, or outward crust of the earth, has been broken to pieces, and its fragments thrown confusedly in every direction." [26]

Although the location of iron ores and the discovery of coal beds in different stages of formation interested Rittenhouse more, his comments on sea shells provoked the greater reaction. As he had already done privately, he contradicted Jefferson's explanation in his *Notes on Virginia* of the origin of sea shells found on inland mountains.[27] Jefferson accepted the crystalline explanation—that the apparent shells were not real sea shells but had grown there as crystals grow to assume the form and appearance of sea shells. This, Rittenhouse denied.

Characteristically, he struck vigorously at the heart of Jefferson's doctrine rather than debating the theories of how the shells had gotten so far inland. He commented, "Besides the arguments against this hypothesis, which will occur to every one who examines such petrifactions, there is one which to me appears perfectly conclusive—Pieces of these petrified shells, lightly calcined, have precisely the same taste with fresh shells heated," and, he implied, the same odor.[28]

Rittenhouse was right but he never succeeded in convincing Jefferson, who responded in a manner not unusual for him. He announced first, "It will not be difficult to induce me to give up the theory of the growth of shells without their being the nidus of animals. It's only an idea and not an opinion with me." Then he proceeded to show he had no intention of giving up the

[26] *Ibid.*, 49–53.
[27] [Jefferson], *Notes on the State of Virginia* ([Paris], 1782 [85]), 52–54; Boyd, ed., *Papers of Jefferson*, VIII, 566.
[28] *Columbian Mag.*, I (1786–87), 53.

idea by debating the question of how the shells could have gotten so far from the sea—forgetting altogether Rittenhouse's insistence that the fundamental question was what they were rather than how they got there.[29]

In the Philosophical Society, Rittenhouse hoped that the second volume of *Transactions* might soon be followed by a third, but the organization was not yet that vigorous. Although it continued to meet and to display various evidences of activity, its strength was sapped at this time by serious personality clashes.

Francis Hopkinson was at the center of this. He had long felt the resentment of members who believed his efforts to invigorate the society disguised an attempt to inflate his own prestige. He stopped attending meetings after September 15, 1786, when the bills of the engraver he had hired to do the illustrations for the *Transactions* were protested. Samuel Vaughan asserted that the charges were too high and succeeded in having £9 deducted from the bills. On October 20, the building committee for Philosophical Hall, consisting of Vaughan, Hopkinson, and Rittenhouse, was discharged and only Vaughan appointed to the new committee. On November 17, Hopkinson resigned his office as treasurer—a month and a half before his term was due to expire.[30]

The balance then began to shift. Rittenhouse, a known friend of Hopkinson, was appointed with Robert Patterson to audit the treasurer's accounts. In the 1787 elections, Hopkinson was elected treasurer again and Rittenhouse chosen vice president in the place of Vaughan, who was making plans to return to England. Hopkinson seemed mollified and Rittenhouse was back in a post more suitable than the wholly ornamental position of councillor which he had filled for several years.

A new departure for the society in 1787 was the Magellanic Premium, offered for the best discovery or improvement in navigation or natural philosophy. Both Rittenhouse and Hop-

[29] Boyd, ed., *Papers of Jefferson*, IX, 215.
[30] APS Mins., 1774–87, Sep. 15, Oct. 6, 20, Nov. 17, 1786.

kinson turned with enthusiasm to this opportunity. Rittenhouse wrote Jefferson that he was laboring with all his "might" to improve astronomical timekeepers, and Hopkinson added that his friend's entry for the prize would be an improvement in the pendulum. Hopkinson's project was a "spring block" for improving the sailing quality of ships. In the end, however, his did not win because it was too theoretical, and Rittenhouse's appears not to have been completed or submitted.[31]

Inside and outside the society, the air was electric with inventions, discoveries, and proposals. As Rittenhouse put it, "We have abundance of projectors and pretendors to new Discoveries, and many applications to the Legislature for exclusive priviledges, some of them ridiculous enough. The self-moving boat, the Mechanical Miller, the improved Ring Dial for finding the Variations of the Needle. The Surveying Compass to serve 20 other purposes, And a project for finding the Longitude by the Variation of the Magnetical Needle." Hopkinson frankly classified himself among these "semi-lunatic projecters."[32]

Many of them came to Rittenhouse for evaluation or for support. As a Philosophical Society referee, he abruptly dismissed Temple Henry Croker's paper on the compass and dipping needle: "all the reasoning on the subject is founded on a Mistake of the Laws of Composition & Resolution of forces." Besides, he commented, his ideas had been published long ago. On the other hand, he was willing to give George Wall, Jr., a boost by signing a joint endorsement of his "trigonometer," a device which permitted the measurement of both vertical and horizontal angles and offered the instrumental solution of right angle problems.[33]

The most haunting fantasy was suggested by John Churchman, a surveyor and mapmaker who had earlier invented one

[31] *Ibid.*, Jan. 5, 1787; Boyd, ed., *Papers of Jefferson*, IX, 321; X, 73.
[32] *Ibid.*, XI, 293–94, 563.
[33] MS Comm., Natural Philosophy, I, 14, APS; George Wall, Jr., *A Description . . . of . . . the Trigonometer* (Phila., 1788), [ii].

of the many perpetual motion machines. Playing on the old desire to use the earth's magnetic field for obtaining precise navigational fixes, Churchman offered a new theoretical base. He credited the magnetic field to the effect of two iron satellites, each orbiting close to the earth, one around the north pole and the other around the south pole, in periods so extended that it would require hundreds of years to complete a single revolution. A Philosophical Society committee on which Rittenhouse served properly branded the idea, "groundless . . . whimsical . . . and impossible in the nature of things." [34]

Churchman continued to attract lay interest on both sides of the Atlantic and several respectable institutions considered his ideas after he had amended them. When Nevil Maskelyne's opinion was finally solicited, he remarked, "Mr. Churchman might have been well satisfied with the judgments of such able men and good philosophers as Mr. Ewing and Mr. Rittenhouse." [35]

Most important of all the projects was the first realization of a practical steamboat, which—to the extent that any date is meaningful—can best be dated to this time and place. In this episode, which developed in the form of a duel between John Fitch and James Rumsey, Rittenhouse found himself separated from Franklin and Hopkinson. Fitch had failed in 1785 to win the support of the Philosophical Society, where Rumsey was more successful. A few members, including Vaughan, aided Fitch's enterprises privately, but Franklin, Hopkinson, Rush, and many more gave their support to Rumsey.

Rittenhouse never joined either group to the extent of contributing money, despite an impassioned plea by Fitch in which he offered primacy in his list of backers. Rittenhouse did offer a testimonial after the inventor got a boat running on the Delaware, which turned even Franklin to a somewhat more favorable view. In the name of promoting useful arts in America,

[34] MS Comm., Natural Philosophy, I, 12, APS; Hindle, *Pursuit*, 350–51.
[35] *Pa. Packet*, July 31, 1788.

he urged the generous encouragement he felt that Fitch "justly deserves." [36] Rittenhouse's support probably owed nothing to politics—although some have suggested that it did—but it may have owed much to Henry Voight, who had worked for Rittenhouse on his orreries and was now a partner of Fitch. Voight unquestionably supplied much of the mechanical ingenuity which made Fitch's boats so much more successful than Rumsey's. Both Fitch, an itinerant silversmith, watchmaker, and surveyor, and Voight were mechanics, as was Rittenhouse.

This almost constant activity made Philadelphia more stimulating than ever, and Rittenhouse left reluctantly on the New York–Massachusetts boundary commission in the summer of 1787. Again, Ewing asserted that the University could not spare him until July, so the Congressional commissioners did not start north from New York City until July 11. Ewing was also, in all probability, the chief author of a joint letter in which the three commissioners protested that the line the New York–Massachusetts agreement called upon them to draw was "impracticable," because founded upon an old magnetic bearing. In elementary terms, the letter impatiently explained that no principle in astronomy or natural philosophy made it possible to reconstruct the magnetic variation which had prevailed at any given time in the past. This serious problem was somehow adjusted, and the commissioners determined and marked the required line—fifty miles long—in a little less than a month's time. They were attended throughout by delegates from the two states directly concerned, most congenial of whom were Simeon De Witt of New York and Samuel Williams, who had succeeded to Winthrop's chair of mathematics and natural philosophy at Harvard.[37]

When Rittenhouse returned to the city, he realized that he

[36] DR, Certificate, Dec. 12, 1787, Franklin Papers, APS; Fitch, Autobiography, II, 307–8, LCP.
[37] Ewing, DR, and Hutchins to Delegates of N.Y. and Mass., June 7, 1787, NYHS; Documents of the Senate of N.Y., 100th sess., vol. 5, no. 61, pp. 197–98, 205–13.

had spent a large part of four successive summers in boundary surveys. They had benefited him greatly by removing him from the harassments of the Treasury and by offering a kind of recreation he would not otherwise have accepted. Now, however, he decided that the disadvantages, the exertion and the absence from home, far outweighed the advantages. He announced that with this expedition, he would "bid adieu, forever, to all running of lines," a resolution he kept.[38]

During Rittenhouse's absence, the Pennsylvania Society for the Encouragement of Manufactures and the Useful Arts was launched, following a large meeting at the University and a series of emotional appeals. Tench Coxe, the leading publicist behind the movement, pointed to Rittenhouse in justification of the most sanguine expectations. He declaimed, "Every combination of machinery may be expected from a country, a NATIVE SON of which, reaching this inestimable object, at its highest point has epitomized the motions of the spheres that roll throughout the universe." [39]

Coxe was a Republican, but his admiration for Rittenhouse was not limited by party feelings, and his enthusiasm was shared by many of the fifteen hundred subscribers to the stock of the manufacturing society. Effortlessly and without apparent opposition, Rittenhouse was nominated for the presidency.

Before the election, however, a second and secret ticket was put together in which Rittenhouse was replaced as the presidential candidate by Thomas Mifflin. The rest of the slate was somewhat reshuffled with the elimination of such notable Constitutionalists as Charles Pettit and Peter Stephen Duponceau and the addition of men of wealth who were active in the Bank of North America. This lent credence to the charge that the secret slate was put together by the bank; so did the presence of busy bank clerks and runners at an otherwise quiet election.

[38] Barton, *Memoirs*, 239n.
[39] *American Museum*, II (1787), 250; *Plan of the Pennsylvania Society, for the Encouragement of Manufactures* [Phila., 1787], 3; *Pa. Jour.*, Aug. 15, 1787.

Only about a fifth of the subscribers turned out, since a perfunctory election on the basis of the publicly announced nominations was anticipated. In consequence, the secret ticket won. Rittenhouse emerged as first vice president of the society—the office allotted him in the secret ticket. His friends lamented this demotion of "a man who may perhaps be justly called the first mechanical genius in the known world, and who is in this respect the glory of his age and of his country." He was left, of course, with a post of honor which seemed tarnished only because he had first been proposed for the highest office. Under the circumstances, Rittenhouse regarded it as an empty honor; he apparently refused to take any further part in the society and he did not stand for reelection the following year.[40]

This defeat was an unpleasant reminder that Rittenhouse's reputation could not prevail when powerful political and economic interests ran in a contrary direction. This was a harbinger of greater troubles to come, but, for the moment, the setback was overshadowed by continuing recognition which came even from England.

Charles Dilly, the London bookseller, published in 1787 a collection of writings he called, *The Philosophical Papers of David Rittenhouse*. Friendly with many Americans, Dilly handled the English sale of the second volume of the Philosophical Society's *Transactions*, and he was anxious to have the first volume reprinted because he found that buyers of the second wanted both to make a set.

His Rittenhouse volume was related to these activities. Consisting entirely of papers from the second volume of *Transactions*, complete with the illustrations which had appeared in the original, it made up to forty pages of relatively large type. Still, it was a respectable collection, containing as it did Rittenhouse's most important contributions to science. Dilly wrote

[40] *Pa. Gaz.*, Sep. 12, 1787; *Freeman's Jour.*, Sep. 12, 1787; Minutes of the Pennsylvania Society for the Encouragement of Manufactures and the Useful Arts, I, *passim*, HSP.

a preface which was not the less sincere because designed to aid sales. Certainly few of the Americans who saw it would quarrel with the assertion that Rittenhouse's accomplishments *"justly entitled him to one of the first places among the most distinguished* Astronomers of *the present Age."* [41]

Rittenhouse never came closer than he did in these years to attaining a modicum of contentment and satisfaction with his role in life. His health was little better, but his letters were less weighed down with consciousness of ill health; his Treasury job was heavier than ever but it did not seem to matter so much. He was surrounded by warm and friendly men who not only admired his work but who were sufficiently alert themselves to stimulate him to some of his best efforts. Unsolicited, Cassini sent him astronomical observations from Paris, and from various states and nations distinguished visitors were as a matter of course introduced to him whenever they visited Philadelphia.[42] The skies were full of sunshine.

[41] DR, *Philosophical Papers* (London, 1787), [ii].
[42] *MHS Colls.*, 7th ser., I, 35.

CHAPTER XVIII

The House Comes Tumbling Down
1787–1790

RITTENHOUSE's reputation was sufficiently secure that he no longer felt so driven by the need to justify men's anticipations. He was able to enjoy the position assigned him as an ornament of society and to pursue some of that work in science which most interested him. His condition was far from ideal because the bulk of his time had to be turned over to the harrowing and boring job in the Treasury, which returned few enough satisfactions. Nevertheless, he had attained a reasonably happy adjustment which he was quite willing to continue so long as no better arrangement could be achieved. The choice was not his. Beginning in November 1787, he was absorbed in a revolution which shook his political world to its foundations and finally left him outside the doors of state preferment.

The crisis had been long building. Rittenhouse's political friends, the Pennsylvania Constitutionalists, began to lose strength in the Assembly elections of 1786, and in 1787 they slipped still further. Meanwhile, the Federal Convention meeting in Philadelphia through the summer of 1787 came to dominate the political scene. The Republicans tended to tie their fortunes to this effort to alter the form of the national government while the Constitutionalists opposed. The fall air was heated with party controversy over the ratification of the Federal Constitution which had been completed and submitted to the states in September.[1]

On November 6, 1787, Rittenhouse ran on a Constitutionalist

[1] Brunhouse, *Counter-Revolution*, 191–211.

293

ticket for the state ratifying convention. The city slate was headed by Franklin, despite his attendance at the Federal Constitutional Convention and his somewhat equivocal position on the document it produced. Both he and Rittenhouse were put forward in the hope that their names would strengthen a losing cause. The opposing ticket, headed by Thomas McKean, favored the Constitution much more openly and vigorously than the Constitutionalists were willing to argue against it. The electorate proved very nearly of one mind; they buried the entire Constitutionalist slate under an avalanche of votes for the opposition, the least of whom was given 1,157 while Franklin got only 235 and Rittenhouse a mere 148. Never had he been so far out of step with prevailing public opinion.[2]

The Constitutionalists fared better in the outlying counties but they were unable to delay Pennsylvania's speedy ratification of the Constitution. After some hesitation, enough other states followed suit to guarantee the institution of the new government and to bring to Philadelphia a new mood of excitement and celebration. Francis Hopkinson directed the highly successful "Grand Federal Procession," held in the city on July 4, 1788. In units, the trade groups and institutions, to several of which Rittenhouse belonged, marched in a new spirit of unity and national accomplishment.[3] He stood aloof.

No record remains of Rittenhouse's specific ideas about the Constitution; it is not unlikely that his words were suppressed by those who cherished his memory, for he certainly did not favor it. John Nicholson, his closest associate in government, wrote a pamphlet against the Constitution which, point by point, he compared with the Articles of Confederation. He was not willing to admit that the financial inadequacies of the Confederation resulted from insufficient powers; he laid them instead to mismanagement. Almost as a matter of course, the

[2] *Pa. Jour.*, Nov. 3, 10, 1787.
[3] *Pa. Gaz.*, July 9, 23, 1788; [Francis Hopkinson], *Account of the Grand Federal Procession* [Phila., 1788].

Constitutionalist leaders reprobated the Constitution for its failure to include a bill of rights and this libertarian emphasis ran through their other objections. They asserted that so large a territory required a confederation of republics, that the power given Congress under the Constitution would annihilate the states, and that despotism rather than liberty would follow.[4] They clearly understood that, on a more selfish plane, the foundations of their own power were at stake.

In losing the struggle against the Federal Constitution, they lost their long-challenged control of the state as well. The period from 1787 to 1790 was a mournful decline from power for the Constitutionalists although many individuals altered their ties and allegiances, and all of the more adroit politicians worked out compromises with the new order. In retrospect, the end seems forecast in the beginning, but that was not clear to the participants. Rittenhouse, in particular, went down a long road of trials and aggravations. His creative accomplishments in these years were fewer and less significant than during any period, except for the depth of the war, since he had emerged from obscurity at Norriton.

The Constitutionalists did not admit immediately that even their struggle against the Federal Constitution was irretrievably lost. They met at Harrisburg in September, where they urged support of the new government but stressed the need for an immediate general convention of the states to amend its form. This gesture called forth only a few echoes of support, and the elections of that fall and winter ran with overwhelming decisiveness against their candidates for both state and national office. Again Rittenhouse stood beside his routed friends, without wavering, running on their ticket this time as a presidential elector. Again, he was crushed by the opposing candidates, now described as the "Lancaster Ticket" or the "Federalist Ticket."

---

[4] [Nicholson], *A View of the Proposed Constitution of the United States, as Agreed to by the Convention* (Phila., 1787), [2]; *Freeman's Jour.*, Oct. 24, 1787.

He must have known that his name was put forward so often in these days of defeat because it had an appeal that was above party and might succeed where no ordinary Constitutionalist could hope to win. It was not enough.[5]

The Treasury was as unpleasant as ever. Demands for payment multiplied and revenues were, if anything, less able than ever to keep pace. Rittenhouse filled the newspapers with advertisements calling for the payment of back taxes and announcements of sheriff sales of tax defaulters' properties. The accumulation of the £20,000 for currency retirement posed increasing difficulties, but he had come to terms with all these worries.[6] The new and frightening aspect of his situation was the rise of personal attacks upon close associates and finally upon Rittenhouse himself.

John Nicholson was the target of a carefully developed attack by Richard Wells which was fully aired early in 1788. Wells, an interested merchant, charged that, when the ship *Anna* was seized for smuggling, the state's full share of its auction price was never paid into the Treasury. Instead, he asserted, Nicholson deposited only a part of the sum due, and that part in depreciated currency and other paper instead of the specie and more valuable currency paid by the purchaser. Further, the original auction price of £2,200 was never collected because Nicholson resold the ship privately for £1,500. Wells then hedged somewhat, adding that even if the sum deposited by Nicholson were the correct one, he had nevertheless made a 10 per cent profit on the case by his currency manipulation.

Before he was finished, Wells had Rittenhouse and Nicholson presenting different versions of what sort of money was actually deposited. He further charged Nicholson with using this occasion to obtain cash payment of his own salary and with receiving money from the treasurer on the basis of orders *"to be procured"*—that is without any written warrant in hand.

[5] *Ibid.*, Sep. 17, 1788; *Pa. Packet*, Jan. 7, 9, 1789; *Pa. Gaz.*, Sep. 3, 17, 1788.
[6] *Ibid.*, Jan. 2, June 18, 1788; *Pa. Col. Recs.*, xv, 493; *Freeman's Jour.*, Jan. 16, June 18, 1788.

The case dragged on for over a year and opened many questions that were never satisfactorily answered.[7]

Wells took pains not to attack Rittenhouse's honesty. He protested high respect for the man, commenting, "If the comptroller, by the almost ungovernable authority he has assumed has led the treasurer into any mistake, he alone, not the treasurer is reasonably answerable for it."[8] The suggestion of honest incompetence, however, was almost equally damning, and the Federalists, now riding high, remained content to acknowledge Rittenhouse's integrity.

In March, the Assembly began to display a lack of sympathy with Rittenhouse's difficulties, something new in his experience. A friendly assemblyman told an unresponsive house that if Rittenhouse could not begin early to lay up the money needed, he could not accumulate the sum required to be sunk. On the other hand, whenever he began early, he was continuously pressed by public creditors, some of whom complained of injustice to their claims. To strengthen his hand, the treasurer needed a specific order from the house calling upon him to set aside the money early each year.

The Assembly declined thus to favor him. Its attitude was punctuated by Richard Peters, who opposed the request: "unless gentlemen think our shoulders better able to bear the burthen of the complaints and chagrin of the people, who are disappointed by this means of the demands which they have at that office, than those of M. Rittenhouse, for surely when he is applied to for money he can give this short answer: 'I am appropriating the money I receive every day to other purposes, by a late directive of the legislature.'" Perhaps it even sounded easy to Peters, but to a man of Rittenhouse's temperament it was not; the hardening attitude of the Assembly made him still more uncomfortable.[9]

Soon, a battery of complaints surrounded him: both the treas-

[7] *Ibid.*, Dec. 26, 1787, Jan. 9, 1788.
[8] *Ibid.*
[9] Thomas Lloyd, *Proceedings and Debates of the General Assembly* (Phila., 1787–88), III, 103, 106, 107.

urer and the comptroller general were slow in submitting information to the legislature, the treasurer's accounts did not sufficiently identify the sources of his revenue, he did not always apply the receipts from one fund to the specific purposes designated, and he was more responsive to the Congress than to the state. One resolution, quickly passed, called for more prompt and more precise accounts and for strict adherence to legislative appropriations.

The most specific charge was hurled by the house Ways and Means Committee, which reported that Rittenhouse had worsened the state's financial crisis by paying into the United States Treasury $128,506 beyond her proper share. Outside the legislature, estimates of the overpayment ran as high as $1,446,368. The Assembly sharply demanded "That the Treasurer inform this House, at their next session, upon what authority he has made payments to the United States to the amount charged in his accounts." [10]

John Nicholson quickly came to Rittenhouse's defense. Far from having paid Congress more than authorized by legislature, his accounts showed the treasurer to be short in his payments by upwards of $30,000.[11] Unfortunately, Nicholson was sitting on the same bull's eye as Rittenhouse and his testimony lacked force in the legislature where their friends were too few to be able to help either of them.

Rittenhouse hung on. He submitted detailed financial reports and careful responses to the Assembly's resolutions. He complained vigorously of the slowness with which taxes were coming in and dwelt upon the pattern of these deficiencies. By the middle of July, the city and county of Philadelphia had not yet turned in a shilling of their current taxes. This was significant in the present political contest because the now heavily Anti-Constitutionalist city usually complained that it was the back counties which never paid their taxes. Rittenhouse sug-

[10] Pa. Gaz., Mar. 26, 1788; Pa. House Mins., 2d sess., 12th assem., 182–83.
[11] Freeman's Jour., Apr. 23, 1788.

gested to Vice President Peter Muhlenberg, one Constitutionalist who because of German support still enjoyed a strong position, that the difficulties opposing his accumulation of that year's £ 20,000 were suspicious. "One can scarcely forbear," he said, "suspecting a combination to prevent it." He urged a letter to the collector of imposts to speed returns from that quarter and the Supreme Executive Council, still under Constitutionalist domination, readily complied.[12]

The Assembly, however, remained obdurate. Rather than use its powers to spur tax collection, it focused increased responsibility for collection upon Rittenhouse. In October, it gave him direct authority to issue a warrant for seizure of both real and personal property in cases of non-payment of taxes and to have the property sold if taxes were not forthcoming within twenty days.[13]

Lest any observers had missed the meaning of the 1787 elections and the votes on the Federal Constitution, the state elections of 1788 confirmed the coming demise of the Constitutionalists. The 2-to-1 Republican control of the Assembly was not drastically altered, but now executive leadership was tailored to suit. Franklin, no longer eligible after three terms in office, was succeeded in the presidency by Thomas Mifflin, who had been speaker of the house. Mifflin was an adaptable and popular politician who was now in the good graces of the Republicans and effectively a member of that group. Into the speakership moved Richard Peters, who had already demonstrated his lack of responsiveness to Rittenhouse's problems. George Ross, a conservative Republican, became vice president. As the next ranking executive officer, Rittenhouse had never been so isolated politically, but again he requested reappointment and again he was unanimously reelected.[14]

[12] Pa. House Mins., 1st sess., 13th assem., 12, 13; Pa. Arch., 1st ser., XI, 337; Pa. Col. Recs., xv, 493.
[13] Dallas, Laws of Pa., II, 33n.
[14] Freeman's Jour., Nov. 5, 1788; Pa. House Mins., 1st sess., 13th assem., 37, 44.

During the following year, conditions worsened until they finally became intolerable. In March, the new Assembly scrapped the last remnant of the test oaths which had been one of the bulwarks of Constitutionalist power. The legislature next turned its guns on that bête noire of Pennsylvania Republicanism—the Constitution of 1776. By a vote of 41 to 16, it adopted resolutions declaring alterations and amendments "immediately necessary." The governing mood was a popular determination "to conform our State Constitution to the government of the United States." [15] Against the tide, Rittenhouse stood gauntly—the only prominent governmental officer remaining who had participated in writing the instrument and in its early establishment. Many former supporters decided now that they had never thought much of the Constitution, but Rittenhouse remained unapologetically associated with it.

The intention of reforming the fiscal administration of the state was inextricably tied to the demand for a new state constitution. Indeed, the Assembly prefaced its final statement calling for a constitutional convention by the assertion that "the burthen and expences of the present form of government are with difficulty borne." By a single vote, the Constitutionalists in the Supreme Executive Council had enough strength to defeat the effort to associate that body with the demand for a new constitution, but they could not prevent legislation aimed at reforming state finances.[16]

With rising indignation, the Assembly listened to a committee report which detailed the immense powers exercised by the comptroller general. The report concluded with the recommendation that an officer be appointed to methodize, state, and keep the accounts of Pennsylvania. As soon as a bill to this end could be prepared, it was rushed through three readings in a single day to establish the office of "Register General." Henceforth, before he could finally settle any adjusted account, the

[15] Pa. Gaz., Mar. 18, 25, Apr. 29, 1789.
[16] Ibid., Mar. 25, 1789; Pa. Col. Recs., XVI, 41.

comptroller general was required to submit it "to the inspection and examination of the Register General, and take his advice and assistance." In addition, that part of the act of the Constitutionalist Assembly of 1785 which had given Nicholson a seven-year term was repealed. Bypassing the Constitutionalist-dominated Executive Council as usual, the Assembly appointed John Donnaldson, register general of the Commonwealth.[17]

Donnaldson carried out his duties in the spirit of the act which had created his position. Established in State House offices, he went to work immediately, conscious that he had behind him the full power of the legislature and the principal executive officers and only the attenuated force of the comptroller general, the treasurer, and the Executive Council opposing. From the beginning, he and Rittenhouse clashed.

The Constitutionalists were able to win only rear-guard actions now, as they did when Richard Wells's case against Nicholson finally came before the Executive Council in April 1789. Voting separately on four distinct counts, the Council failed to support Wells on any one. The vote, however, was strictly on party lines, Mifflin, Ross, and the Republicans opposing the comptroller general consistently. Only because the western counties were so overrepresented in the Council were the Constitutionalists able to hold the precarious balance there. No one could doubt that even this citadel of power would soon be lost.[18]

In this time of deepening trouble, Rittenhouse turned for comfort to other phases of his life. Since 1787, he had been attending Philosophical Society meetings much more regularly, and, upon his return to the vice presidency, he frequently presided. He continued to play a large role in evaluating communications and he served on a variety of committees. When the society voted to have Peale paint a portrait of their presi-

[17] Pa. House Mins., 2d sess., 13th assem., 192–93; Pa. Gaz., Mar. 25, 1789; James T. Mitchell and Henry Flanders, comps., The Statutes at Large of Pennsylvania (Harrisburg, 1908), xiii, 289–92.
[18] Pa. Col. Recs., xvi, 56–57.

dent, Rittenhouse called on Franklin to make the arrangements.[19]

The *Transactions* concerned him especially, but the publication of a third volume continued to elude the society, which could manage only the reprinting of its first volume. Rittenhouse told Robert Aitken, who served as printer, that several members felt his 1775 oration ought to be added in the new edition. Aitken prepared figures on the additional cost of this insertion but was unable to obtain the authority he needed to go ahead with it. When the volume appeared, it contained no new papers and little change except for rearrangement. Rittenhouse took ten copies—a subscription exceeded only by Franklin's.[20]

Despite Rittenhouse's interest in the society, he offered no scientific contributions of any moment. Early in 1789, he submitted a paper on the regularity of heavenly bodies in the form of a letter to Robert Patterson, but it was not sufficiently significant to publish. The only astronomical work of this period that was ultimately published under his name was a very few lines on a lunar eclipse and a transit of Mercury, both of which occurred in November 1789. He gave data from his continuing observations of Uranus to Andrew Ellicott, who presented the figures in an almanac. His one prepared paper which finally got into the *Transactions* was a joint effort with Dr. John Jones, describing a Philadelphia house struck by lightning.[21]

He often worked in his observatory, but seemed unable to accomplish anything beyond the strictly routine. Perhaps the most significant thing he did was to begin, on September 24, 1788, a regular daily record of meteorological and astronomical observations taken at his observatory.[22] Continued almost with-

[19] APS Mins., 1787–93, 106.
[20] Aitken to Franklin, Mar. 11, 1789; Subscribers to Transactions, Apr. 18, 1788, APS.
[21] APS Mins., 1787–93, 79; APS, *Trans.*, III (1791), 153, 119–22; Barton, *Memoirs*, 328.
[22] DR, Notebook, 1785–92, n.p., APS.

out a break, even after his death, this journal provided an important reservoir of information. He was capable of such mechanical activities, but apparently not of anything creative.

Curiously, this period of scientific and political impotence saw the issuance of his only literary work. In May 1789, Charles Cist announced the publication of *Lucy Sampson*, "Translated from the German By a Citizen of Philadelphia." The translator was David Rittenhouse; the play was Lessing's drama, usually rendered as *Miss Sarah Sampson, or the Unhappy Heiress*.[23]

He had been working on the translation since at least 1784, having been set to the task by a friend he did not identify. That he brought it to completion in this period of depression is understandable only in terms of his expressed attitude toward poetry and belles lettres as a form of escape in a very different category from science. At the same time, he saw the play as a study of the delicate relationship between a father and his daughter; a problem that was now close to his heart as his own daughters approached and entered the marriage state.[24]

Rittenhouse had undoubtedly been directed to this play because Lessing was regarded as a product of rationalism and of English influence; an ideal author for a Newtonian scholar. Lessing had one direct tie with England's premier eighteenth-century poet of nature and of Newton through his translation into German of Cibber's *Life of James Thomson*—and Rittenhouse already admired Thomson as he was expected to. If, after he translated *Sarah Sampson*, Rittenhouse concurred in the view that Lessing's play had something in common with the Newtonian view, he was wise enough not to admit it. He stated his admiration for the stilted, tear-jerking tragedy in terms of its "lessons of morality" and its human interest.[25]

He presented the anonymous translation with his usual hu-

[23] *Pa. Gaz.*, May 20, 1789; according to Barton, *Memoirs*, 592-93, DR also translated a fragment of Gessner's *Idyls*, but there is little evidence of this.
[24] Boyd, ed., *Papers of Jefferson*, VIII, 117-18; Barton, *Memoirs*, 231.
[25] [DR], *Lucy Sampson* (Phila., 1789), [ii].

mility overlaid with a wry air of resignation. He announced that his version was not strictly literal but that he departed from the sense of the author in only a very few instances. If the reader was dissatisfied with the translation, Rittenhouse declared, "his disappointment will certainly be less than mine. Those who read for the purpose of discovering faults, will not be displeased if relieved from the trouble of creating them."

The translation was surprisingly good as an isolated literary endeavor, but it was not faultless. Rittenhouse was ready to change the name of the heroine—surely an improvement—but not to remove so obvious a gaucherie as the consistent dubbing of the father as "Sir Sampson." He softened several expressions as he announced—but some he strengthened. A modern critic has found unintentional errors as well as intended alterations, but, nevertheless, regards Rittenhouse's work as truer to the spirit of the original than the next English translation, which did not appear for another hundred years.[26]

Within the circle of his family and friends, Rittenhouse enjoyed a warmth which he continued to return in full measure. In May 1789, he recommended Ellicott to John Page, and the following September his boundary line companion was appointed geographer of the United States. In William Barton's favor, he wrote to the new President of the United States, George Washington, who responded by nominating his nephew to be one of the judges of the Northwest Territory—an appointment Barton resigned almost immediately. He wrote to Jefferson less than a year later and to Thomas Willing after another interval in behalf of his nephew. He similarly used his influence to assist William's brother, Benjamin Smith Barton, in his medical career.[27]

The most important event in his immediate household was

[26] *Ibid.;* Ernest Bell, ed., *The Dramatic Works of G. E. Lessing* (London, 1891), I, I; Heinrich Schneider, "Lessings *Miss Sara Sampson,*" *Publ. of the Modern Language Assn. of Amer.,* 54 (1939), 495.

[27] DR to Page, May 7, 1789, HSP; *N.Y. Jour.,* Sep. 3, 1789; Barton, *Memoirs,* 329–30; DR to Jefferson, Apr. 20, 1790, Jefferson Papers, LC; DR to Willing, n.d., Etting Coll., HSP; DR to McKean, Dec. 26, 1795, Provincial Delegates, HSP.

the marriage of his elder daughter, Elizabeth, to Jonathan Dickinson Sergeant in December 1788. At twenty-one, Betsy was just half the age of her husband, but her social accomplishments, attested to by all who knew her, were such that she was able to preside easily over a much larger domestic establishment than her father's. Sergeant was a graduate of the College of New Jersey, a lawyer, and former attorney general of the Commonwealth. He was a radical Constitutionalist with whom Rittenhouse had had many associations and who had often visited the Rittenhouse home.

The marriage took place in John Ewing's First Presbyterian Church rather than in the Second Presbyterian Church, which the bride's family attended. The reason for this was Ewing's closeness to both families but especially to the groom; the clergyman's wife was Sergeant's half-sister.[28]

Outside the family, Rittenhouse still received many tokens of public esteem. In September 1789, the College of New Jersey awarded him the LL.D. degree; and thenceforth, he was frequently addressed as "Dr. Rittenhouse." But even this pleasant accolade could not avert his thoughts for long from the political crisis which rose again that fall to menacing proportions.[29]

After a summer of agitation in which over ten thousand signatures were collected favoring a state constitutional convention, the Assembly was finally ready to act. The Constitutionalists denied that a majority of the people favored a new constitution, and everyone recognized that the proposed approach was illegal; regardless, the Assembly passed resolutions providing for the election of the proposed convention. Beside this "counter-revolution," the simultaneous legislative demand that Rittenhouse furnish the register general a monthly account of all receipts and of payments of interest was only a pinprick.[30]

The October Assembly elections were overshadowed by the

[28] Daniel K. Cassel, *The Family Record of David Rittenhouse* (Norristown, 1897), 5.

[29] Barton, *Memoirs*, 594-95.

[30] *Pa. House Mins.*, 3d sess., 13th assem., 247, 259-60; *Pa. Gaz.*, Mar. 4, Aug. 26, 1789; *Indep. Gaz.*, Sep. 9, 1789.

election of delegates to the convention, major leaders of both parties being sent to the latter body. Clearly, the old Constitution and the offices and institutions established under it were doomed, but for the moment they still functioned.

The new Assembly met in Philadelphia on November 2 when it organized and reelected Richard Peters speaker. On the 5th, Peters led a delegation of house members to call on Rittenhouse at his home. It had been Rittenhouse's custom to submit his letter requesting reappointment just a few days after the Assembly organized each year and he might have been expected to write it out very soon. The 5th was also the date of a transit of Mercury over the face of the sun, which Rittenhouse invited his callers to watch through his telescope. If Jacob Hiltzheimer realized what he saw, he did not record it; he noted only that he watched a "black spot" on the sun.[31]

Neither he nor the other participants reported the nature of their conversations but, on November 9, Rittenhouse sent to the legislature his resignation as treasurer of the Commonwealth. His valedictory was also the obituary of a passing political age that was little lamented. He presented it without rancor.

In a dignified and direct statement, Rittenhouse gave ill-health and interest in astronomy as his reasons for declining reappointment—reasons he had ever at his elbow. He repeatedly thanked the Assembly for the honor they had done him in returning him to office annually for thirteen years. The limited emoluments and embarrassments of office, he neatly turned into a compliment by declaring that the conditions had not been generally known and that he was therefore the more obliged. Characteristically, he asked that any deficiency in his service, "be imputed to want of ability, and not of integrity." [32]

In accepting the resignation, the Assembly was "sensible of the integrity and assiduity" of their late treasurer and ordered

---

[31] *Pa. House Mins.*, 1st sess., 14th assem., 14; Hiltzheimer, *Diary*, 156; DR, Notebook, 1785–92, n.p.
[32] Barton, *Memoirs*, 330–32.

that his letter be entered in the minutes.[33] That was all! No word of thanks. No comment on the length and importance of his service. No allusion to his role in the Revolution. No denial of his "want of ability." To a man grown used to perfervid eulogy, this was as much a slap in the face as the charge of financial peculation had been to Timothy Matlack.

Without pausing overlong, the house appointed Colonel Christian Febiger to succeed Rittenhouse. Febiger was already a minor political figure who had held the lucrative post of auctioneer of the Northern Liberties. A crisp and well-organized man, he found no difficulty in agreeing with John Donnaldson that the treasurer's office suffered from a variety of malpractices and evils, chief of which was the application of the revenues from one fund to whatever demand pressed hardest at the moment.[34]

For some time before Rittenhouse's accounts were settled and his business entirely wound up, he was called on for odd bits of information. His notes of this tenor to Nicholson remained as warm as such formal communications can, his letters to Donnaldson were cold and sharp, and there are no communications to Febiger. Perhaps, as Nicholson asserted, Rittenhouse felt degraded in the character of the man who had been chosen to succeed him.[35]

There was one more twist of the screw. Rittenhouse's resignation as treasurer contained no evidence that he intended to resign the post of Loan Office trustee as well. On April 1, 1790, the Assembly abolished the Loan Office and annexed the business formerly adhering to it to the office of the treasurer. Rittenhouse was given thirty days to turn over all records, books, and papers.[36]

The atmosphere behind him continued to darken. Now even

[33] Pa. House Mins., 1st sess., 14th assem., 22.
[34] Pa. Col. Recs., xvi, 68, 214; Pa. Gaz., Nov. 18, 1789; Pa. Arch., 1st ser., xi, 649-50.
[35] Hogan, Pa. State Trials, 71.
[36] Statutes at Large of Pa., xiii, 492.

the Supreme Executive Council was in Republican hands, and that body freely reversed some of his actions as treasurer. Nicholson, almost alone in the arena, swung lustily at both Donnaldson and Febiger, while the Assembly reprimanded him and the Council passed a unanimous resolution highly disapproving actions he had taken. Somehow, he survived a motion to dismiss him from the office of comptroller general; but he remained under conditions Rittenhouse would not have endured.[37]

Over a year after Rittenhouse resigned the Treasury, Donnaldson completed the review of his accounts and they were settled. Despite a few minor deductions, the sum owing to the former treasurer was enormous—£5,438..6 in specie.[38] The receipt of this small fortune made no amends for the personal affronts he had suffered.

[37] *Pa. House Mins.*, 2d sess., 15th assem., 164, 239, 233; *Pa. Col. Recs.*, XVI, 263, 329, 330.
[38] *Ibid.*, 544, 547; *Dunlap's Am. Daily Adver.*, Sep. 12, 1791; John Donnaldson, Statement of DR Acct., Dec. 17, 1790, Photocopy, HSP.

CHAPTER XIX

The Mantle of Franklin

1790–1792

ENJAMIN FRANKLIN died after a long and painful illness on April 17, 1790. His death aroused universal sadness in Philadelphia and was a new source of depression for Rittenhouse. The two men had been separated by a large gulf of years and a larger gulf in most of their characteristics: Franklin was easy and brilliant in the company of men while Rittenhouse was diffident. In science, Franklin was an intuitive, experimental genius without knowledge of mathematics while Rittenhouse was a fastidious observer, an inventive experimenter, and a master of the mathematics required for the pursuit of astronomy. Yet both had begun as mechanics, and both had remained true to their heritage which included the dream of a republic of virtue where the welfare of the people came first.

In science and in politics, Rittenhouse had followed in the footsteps of Franklin—his way made easier because he trod in the path of so great a predecessor. At one point, Rittenhouse felt somewhat submerged by the greater acclaim that accompanied Franklin, but he discarded that attitude and accepted the honor, frequently offered, when men linked their names. Franklin valued Rittenhouse for what he was and referred to him as his "Dear Friend." He memorialized their friendship in his will by giving the astronomer his reflecting telescope, "for the use of his observatory." [1]

The death of its greatest citizen moved the city as perhaps it has never since been moved. Black-bordered papers pro-

[1] Franklin to DR, June 25, 1784, Franklin Papers, VI, 1335, LC; Albert H. Smyth, ed., *The Writings of Benjamin Franklin* (N.Y., 1905-7), X, 509.

309

claimed the loss and announced the funeral to be held on the 21st, when some twenty thousand—nearly half the city—turned out to pay their respects. The Supreme Executive Council and the Congress went into a month of mourning, and, across the Atlantic, the National Assembly of France decreed three days of mourning.[2]

Rittenhouse was one of the six pall bearers. He walked alongside Thomas Mifflin, president of the Commonwealth; Thomas McKean, Pennsylvania's chief justice; Thomas Willing, president of the Bank of North America; Samual Powel, mayor of Philadelphia; and William Bingham, perhaps the city's most distinguished economic leader. No printer was sufficiently celebrated to walk in that select group, no college professor, and no mere scientist. Rittenhouse may have been included as vice president of "Franklin's" Philosophical Society, as trustee of "Franklin's" University, or as Franklin's Revolutionary colleague. More likely, it was a combination of these things and more—his inclusion was simply inescapable. No one in the city had equal claim to be regarded as Franklin's mystical successor.

Behind the pall walked a long train of quiet men. After the family and the officers of government, came a succession of groups claiming some relationship to the deceased. First were the printers, to whom the Philosophical Society and the others had appropriately yielded priority, but in the line also were the Cincinnati and the College of Physicians, to whom Franklin had only an elliptical relationship. Everyone with the smallest share of sensitivity was conscious of a personal loss and wished in this way to mark it. His body was interred in the Christ Church burying ground beside Deborah. The man, however, was not so easily removed from the scene.

The Philosophical Society held a special meeting two days later to select the man who would deliver the eulogy to their late president. Surprisingly, William Smith received as many votes as Rittenhouse, and the society was unable to decide between them. The two men were asked to resolve the problem,

[2] *Pa. Gaz.*, Apr. 21, 28, 1790; *Pa. Packet*, May 19, 1790.

but neither was willing to put himself ahead of the other. Not until ten months later did Smith agree to accept the charge and then only on the basis of Rittenhouse's willingness to supply notes upon Franklin's scientific attainments.[3]

Smith's role was an indication of the resurgence of his reputation in the community—paralleling the political swing away from the radicals and toward the conservatives and old Tories. His choice was not inappropriate in view of his early association with Franklin, who was responsible for bringing him to Philadelphia, but the bitterness and depth of the political conflict between the two men was more remembered. His daughter is said to have remarked that his heart was not in the praise he lavished on "old Ben Lightning-rod," and, indeed, his hyperbole-laden eulogy was curious in some respects. Although he showed insight in describing Franklin's science, Smith never quite approximated its spirit and, in sketching the political chronology, he somehow lost sight altogether of Franklin's role in forming and sustaining the Constitution of 1776. He remained of two minds about the man, but of only one when he thought of Rittenhouse, whom he continued to regard as his own great discovery.[4]

Years later, he put into verse the sentiment he thought he *ought* to have spoken shortly after Franklin's death when a dinner party at President Mifflin's was interrupted by a thunder storm.

> Cease, cease, Ye Clouds, your elemental Strife;
> Oh! rage not thus, as if to threaten life!
> Seek, seek no more to shake our Souls with Dread!
> What busy Mortal told You—FRANKLIN'S DEAD?
> What though he Yields to JOVE's imperious *Nodd?*
> With RITTENHOUSE, he left his MAGIC ROD! [5]

[3] APS Mins., 1787–93, 135–36, 166, 167, 171.
[4] William Smith, *Eulogium on Benjamin Franklin* (Phila., 1792); Horace W. Smith, *Life and Correspondence of the Rev. William Smith, D.D.* (Phila., 1879–90), II, 344.
[5] Butterfield, ed., *Letters of Rush*, II, 853n.

It was not so, even in the most alliterative sense, and yet, to many, Rittenhouse emerged as the first scientist of the republic. Long before he could sublimate his feelings about the political reverses he had suffered, he began to receive a series of commissions and appeals which forced him to look outward.

Most pressing and most important was a series of letters, the first of which reached him in June 1790, from Thomas Jefferson, now secretary of state under the new Constitution. Jefferson wrote from New York, where he was engaged in completing his monumental "Report on Weights and Measures," and where he could only lament his distance from effective library assistance. Virtually singlehandedly, he applied careful study to the construction of a coherent and interrelated decimal system of weights, measures, and coinage. He provided for two alternatives: his complete, newly-invented decimal system or a system which depended primarily upon existing units but which expressed them in terms of one another. In either case, the structure would rest upon one reasonably invariable measure—a pendulum beating out single seconds with each cycle and generally known as the second pendulum.[6]

Jefferson worked his way through to his third and final draft without accepting much help from anyone but James Madison. He then informed Hamilton of his ideas and confronted Rittenhouse with a series of specific inquiries. He looked to Rittenhouse for support of his conceptions and solutions and for the correction of any mathematical errors he might have made. He invited assistance in "every part of it," but still, it was the parts rather than the whole of the report he wanted criticized.[7]

Rittenhouse received the draft of the report and four separate letters before he could respond with even a preliminary

---

[6] *American State Papers* (Wash., 1832–61), *Miscellaneous*, I, 14–20; C. Doris Hellman, "Jefferson's Efforts Towards the Decimalization of United States Weights and Measures," *Isis*, xvi (1931), 266–314; Boyd, ed., *Papers of Jefferson*, xvi, 494.
[7] *Ibid.*, 484, 614.

acknowledgment. When the Philadelphian sat down to reply, only a week after the initial letter, he found himself at something of a loss. Despite Jefferson's industry in acquainting himself with the best British and French writings on weights and measures and despite the high level of his capacity, there was a certain naïveté in his approach. Jefferson wrote, as he had on the subject of mountain sea shells, more in the manner of an advocate presenting a case than a scientist seeking the truth.

Rittenhouse was afflicted by Jefferson's contrast of black with white as he argued in favor of the second pendulum. The scientist refused to accept the assertion that although matter was variable in length, the motion of the earth on its axis was "uniform and invariable." On the contrary, Rittenhouse insisted, there were good reasons for supposing that this motion was "not perfectly Equable." Further, he suggested that the true reason Jefferson sought to rely upon motion as a standard was "not because all matter is variable in its dimensions, for that is a difficulty we have to contend with after recourse is had to the motion of Pendulums." Rather, the problem was his doubt that a standard rod could be guaranteed permanence.[8]

Jefferson never penetrated Rittenhouse's basic position. He carefully adjusted the text to accord with his friend's surface comments by acknowledging that the earth's motion, "tho' not absolutely uniform and invariable, may be considered as such for every human purpose." He did not rethink his approach to the problem because he did not want to. Whitehurst, Miller, Talleyrand, and other European reformers all wrote in terms of the second pendulum. Jefferson was too involved in his own creation, built upon this foundation, to recognize the hint in Rittenhouse's guarded criticism that he regarded the standard rod as a simpler and more workable approach than the second pendulum. There can be little doubt that Rittenhouse preferred a linear standard such as the French finally adopted.[9]

[8] *Ibid.*, 546, 629.
[9] *Ibid.*, 650.

Rittenhouse certainly made it clear that the rod pendulum, adapted from a proposal of Robert Leslie, the Philadelphia clockmaker, did not have the obvious superiority Jefferson imagined it had over the usual bob pendulum or the double pendulum urged by John Whitehurst. Yet once again, Jefferson avoided seeing the deeper criticism and responded only to a surface error discovered. He altered his text to accept Rittenhouse's comment that the center of oscillation in a rod pendulum was two-thirds of its length—only when the diameter of the rod was so small that it disappeared as a significant factor and not in all cases as the draft stated.[10]

Rittenhouse filled much of his first letter and all of the two which followed with details and just the sort of commentary Jefferson sought. He answered specific questions and he checked calculations. Hesitatingly, he approved Talleyrand's proposal of $45°$ north latitude as the parallel to be used in standardizing the second pendulum—recognizing that this was a more satisfactory zone for France than for the United States. He met enthusiastically the proposed decimalization of the pound and he approved the rationalization of weights and measures. He balked a little at Jefferson's conversion factor for relating French and English linear measure, preferring Maskelyne's determinations while the secretary had used D'Alembert's. Jefferson held nevertheless to the Frenchman's figures.[11]

Rittenhouse did everything a friendship based upon reciprocal honesty permitted; he extended every aid short of praising directly a report which remained for him insufficiently perceptive. He offered to send books that might not be available in New York, and he sought out and read the books Jefferson mentioned. He abstracted and discussed one significant article from the *Philosophical Transactions*, which he feared his friend had not seen. He discussed the underlying causes of the different

[10] *Ibid.*, 485, 546, 651–52; John Whitehurst, *An Attempt towards Obtaining Invariable Measures of Length, Capacity, and Weight* (London, 1787).

[11] Boyd, ed., *Papers of Jefferson*, XVI, 546, 568–70, 607–8.

values for the length of the second pendulum obtained at various times and places on the surface of the earth. He stressed the impossibility of knowing whether the figure of the earth was uniform or whether it had the shape it was assumed to have. He gave the answers requested and he corrected specific errors. He pressed none of his doubts. He made it clear that he was available for a more penetrating examination of the scientific problems. Jefferson was not interested.[12]

When the report was put before Congress, Rittenhouse stood ready to support Jefferson's proposals. He told General Philip Schuyler that the second pendulum would provide a reliable standard. He denied that a special vault with invariable temperature would be "indispensibly necessary," although privately to Jefferson, he suggested that the subcellars of Philosophical Hall might be arranged to accommodate the second pendulum. To Ralph Izard, chairman of the Senate committee considering the report, he reiterated the feasibility of the second pendulum, assuring him that Jefferson's report contained no "Philosophical or Mathematical impropriety." [13]

Rittenhouse took pleasure in ripping apart an attack by the Britisher, George Skene Keith, upon Jefferson's proposal of a rod pendulum. Its absurdities, he declared, demonstrated both a lack of candor and lack of ability. At the same time, he could not refrain from pointing out that Keith barely hinted at the objection he regarded as most material and which he had urged from the beginning—the difficulty of producing a rod of uniform thickness.[14]

Jefferson's report was never put into effect, either as a complete decimal reform or in its minimal form. The secretary of state continued to press for its adoption, and Rittenhouse could never wholly escape it. Even in the last year of his life, Congress

[12] *Ibid.*, 545–47, 567–70, 594–96.
[13] DR to Schuyler, Feb. 26, 1791, APS; DR to Jefferson, Jan. 4, 1791, Jefferson Papers, LC; DR to Izard, Dec. 21, 1791, APS.
[14] George Skene Keith, *Tracts on Weights, Measures, and Coins* (London, 1791); DR to Jefferson, June 11, 1792, Jefferson Papers, LC.

considered and rejected a proposal to have the scientist determine the length of the second pendulum in Philadelphia.[15]

After the national government moved to Philadelphia in the summer of 1790, the Philadelphia circle became richer than ever and Rittenhouse enjoyed his friends and the respect they accorded him. When he donated an unusual clock with a single hand to the University and simultaneously submitted his resignation from the Board of Trustees, he was unanimously reelected, for even though he attended but little, his name was regarded as an asset. After the College and the University were united the following year, Rittenhouse continued to serve as trustee of the combined institution.[16]

Hetty, his second daughter, married a physician, Dr. Nicholas B. Waters, on October 22, 1790, in Dr. Ewing's church. Waters was a young man, not yet widely known in the city, whom Rittenhouse introduced to membership in the Philosophical Society and to a variety of acquaintances. The couple moved into the Rittenhouse mansion, Waters not yet being able to establish a separate house such as the Sergeants maintained a few doors down on Mulberry Street.[17]

At this point, Rittenhouse vigorously tried to free himself from an obligation contracted during his tenure as treasurer. He addressed an urgent request to President Mifflin on November 10, 1790, outlining the story of the sloop *Active* and his inability to withdraw from the case which was still in suit. The admiralty court continued to hold Rittenhouse's personal bond for £22,000, which he had given in 1779, while he continued to hold the state's share of the prize. With ample justification, he demanded, "I must request the Hon'ble Council to take such measures as will extricate me from this difficulty, in which the State only is interested." [18]

[15] Boyd, ed., *Papers of Jefferson*, xvi, 617.
[16] Trustees Mins., iv, 67, Univ. of Pa.; *Pa. Arch.*, 9th ser., i, 272–73.
[17] *Pa. Packet*, Nov. 1, 1790; Clement Biddle, *The Philadelphia Directory* (Phila., 1791), 108, 137.
[18] *Pa. Arch.*, 1st ser., xi, 743.

Unfortunately, the Council did not act nor did the new government under the constitution Pennsylvania adopted in 1790. Rittenhouse had no alternative but to retain the securities and the obligations and to pass the entire problem to his heirs when he died. Years later, in 1809, his daughters were unnecessarily involved in a crisis which erupted over the controversy and which provided one of the classic tests of federal versus state authority.

The American Philosophical Society chose Rittenhouse as its president on January 7, 1791, in an election which had symbolic significance for the community and real importance for Rittenhouse. He dearly valued the honor which he had anticipated. Although ill-health had permitted him to attend scarcely at all during 1790, he did turn out for the two meetings just preceding the election and for the election meeting itself. He responded with open sincerity, "I am extreamly sensible of the Honour the members of the Philosophical Society have done me by electing me their President, in the room of that very worthy patron of the Society, the late Doctor Franklin." [19]

He attended more frequently after his election, and the society increasingly reflected something of its president. A circle of his greatest admirers constituted the nucleus that held the organization together from one meeting to another. Most conspicuous were his nephews, William and Benjamin Smith Barton, Andrew Ellicott, William Smith, James Hutchinson, Charles Willson Peale, and, with surprising frequency, Thomas Jefferson. Francis Hopkinson was prevented by illness from taking his place at the very center of this group. In addition, although they did not bear exactly the same relationship to Rittenhouse, John Ewing and Robert Patterson were regular attendants. Before the unification of November 1791, Smith served as provost of the College and Ewing as provost of the University, posts in which they could not avoid competing.

[19] APS Mins., 1787-93, 160; DR to Robert Patterson, Jan. 21, 1790 [91], APS.

317

They continued their pre-Revolutionary competition in the Philosophical Society also, where each now served as a vice president; there they squabbled even over the matter of priority in signing membership certificates.[20]

The political complexion of the society, too, came to resemble Rittenhouse's more than ever. Less frequently than Jefferson, but occasionally, James Madison and John Page attended the meetings. William Findley, elected earlier, was joined in January by an odd half-dozen, minor, western Pennsylvania politicians with little qualification other than their congenial politics to associate them with this scientific society— John Smilie and Albert Gallatin, most prominent among them. The simultaneous election of Alexander Hamilton did nothing to alter the complexion of the slate. In July, the addition of John Nicholson, Alexander James Dallas, Peter Stephen Duponceau, and John Beckley further deepened the color of the dye.[21]

Rittenhouse's concept of the role of the president of the society was made clear later in the year. In his election acknowledgment, he had made a strange reference to Franklin as a "patron" rather than as a scientist, a philosopher, or any of a number of other words that seem more appropriate. It was no ineptness of phrase; in underwriting the building of Philosophical Hall, Franklin had been, in fact, the society's greatest single benefactor. Rittenhouse's stress on this function was made clear with the death of his good friend, Francis Hopkinson, on May 11. He made a striking announcement a few days after the funeral which, at Rittenhouse's request, the society attended in a body. He reported that he had paid in full the debt still owed Hopkinson's heirs for the society's purchase of his lot in 1784. This sum of $300 plus $8 interest was a large donation for a man in Rittenhouse's circumstances but one which established the relationship he sought and also honored his friend.[22]

[20] Smith to Jonathan Williams, Feb. 5, 1792, APS; APS Mins., *passim.*
[21] *Ibid.*, 1787–93, 164–65, 190–91.
[22] *Ibid.*, 186, 203, 217; DR to APS, [Dec. 16, 1791], APS.

The society was surprised and genuinely grateful. It went on to make partially successful efforts to reduce remaining debts, as Rittenhouse urged. In a more personal vein, the members commissioned Peale to paint a portrait of their president to be placed in Philosophical Hall. Once again, Peale painted in his own esteem and affection, and he added a significant touch— he presented Rittenhouse in the same blue brocade dressing gown in which he had rendered Franklin as president of the society in 1789.[23]

Identified from this time on as president of the society, Rittenhouse was conspicuous in a succession of practical projects, the most far-ranging of which was a program for improving roads and rivers and for building a canal network. The impulse toward internal improvements had risen sharply toward the end of the colonial period and it resumed again with the end of the war. In Pennsylvania, it reached a hitherto unattained peak in the early nineties.

Rittenhouse was called in to aid at almost every stage of these developments. He had surveyed several of the rivers which formed Pennsylvania's natural highways, and he had served on commissions charged with improving their navigation. He had been engaged in 1772 and in 1784 in surveys of canal routes between the Delaware–Schuylkill River system and the Susquehanna. Now he was called to service again with men of a variety of interests. Some were land speculators and some were motivated by the wish to promote the public welfare—more often than not, both motives were combined in the same individual as in the cases of John Nicholson and William Smith. Business leaders of Philadelphia sought their own profit in seeking prosperity for the city; such were Robert Morris, William Bingham, and Samuel Powel. All of them shared the vision of opening the West and holding it to the Pennsylvania commercial system.

Since 1789, the Society for Promoting the Improvement of Roads and Inland Navigation had been at work on plans for

[23] APS Mins., 1787-93, 207, 209; *PMHB*, LX, 8-9.

improving internal transportation. It met when the legislature was in session because the proponents began with the assumption that government action was necessary to accomplish their ends. They hoped that the government established under the 1790 Constitution was capable of and prepared to support a vigorous effort. Early in 1791, the society called its activities to the attention of the public and presented the legislature with a well-digested program.[24]

Over the signatures of Robert Morris, president, and Timothy Matlack, secretary of the society, the comprehensive memorial projected a long series of improvements, including roads, rivers, and canals. Routes were sketched and expenses estimated on the basis of inadequate information, but such information as was available owed much to work performed by Rittenhouse. The most striking conclusion was the great saving in cost that would result from providing water carriage between the Delaware and the Susquehanna.

Enthusiasm within and without the legislature rose rapidly. In response to a joint resolution of the senate and house, Mifflin, now governor under the new constitution, enthusiastically invited proposals for digging a lock canal from the tributaries of the Schuylkill to the tributaries of the Susquehanna, for clearing the Susquehanna from Wrightstown south to the border, and for running a turnpike from Philadelphia through Lancaster to the Susquehanna. The society pushed its own efforts to stimulate the submission of proposals.

On May 10, under an act to improve several western roads and navigable waters, Mifflin appointed Rittenhouse, William Smith, and William Findley, "Agents of Information." They were authorized to explore the roads and rivers in the Susquehanna region and specifically directed to examine the Juniata and certain other tributaries. Sometime after July 18, they left

[24] Ibid., LXV, 446; [William Smith], An Historical Account of the Rise, Progress and Present State of Canal Navigation in Pennsylvania (Phila., 1795), XVI; Dunlap's Am. Daily Adver., Jan. 10, 1792.

to execute this commission, and their recommendations led to the decision to build a canal around the treacherous Conewago Falls of the Susquehanna. Nearly a year afterward, on July 3, 1792, the state executed an agreement with a group of seventeen men, of whom Rittenhouse was one, to build the relatively short Conewago Canal.[25]

So much state interest in transportation and in canals generated private action as well. Thomas Leiper hired James Brindley to work out plans for a canal connecting his mill with the Delaware River. When his neighbors objected that it would take away water needed for their own mills, Leiper engaged Rittenhouse and Ewing to examine the ground through which the canal would pass and to review Brindley's calculations. They did so and offered an enthusiastic endorsement of the project; they even predicted that the heads of water at the neighboring mills would be raised rather than lowered. Although James Brindley carried a great family name in English canal building, Rittenhouse's and Ewing's had more meaning in Pennsylvania and Leiper happily printed their statement.[26]

On September 29, 1791, the legislature authorized the governor to incorporate a company to build a lock canal between the Susquehanna and Schuylkill Rivers. This would follow the same general route Rittenhouse had surveyed with Hutchins in 1784, and soon after its establishment, the Susquehanna and Schuylkill Canal Company called Rittenhouse into service.

But even before that company opened its subscription for stock, he received another official commission. On October 10 at the direction of the legislature, Mifflin appointed Rittenhouse, Ewing, and John Nancarrow commissioners "to view and Mark out a Road" from Philadelphia to Lancaster. The commissioners only directed the survey; they did not do much of the field work. John Hall, a competent surveyor, took the courses, dis-

[25] *Pa. Arch.*, 9th ser., I, 85, 107, 160, 161, 201, 421; *Pa. Gaz.*, Apr. 27, 1791; [Smith], *Historical Account*, 44, 67.
[26] DR and Ewing, Endorsement of Brindley Calculation, Sep. 15, 1791, Patterson Papers, APS; *Dunlap's Am. Daily Adver.*, Jan. 10, 1792.

tances, and levels during thirty-three days in November and December, and the commissioners' report rested heavily upon his figures, which in turn rested upon earlier measurements made by Rittenhouse. Hall followed Rittenhouse's notes, which had been placed at his disposal, and, when challenged on the height he assigned to a hill along the route, his answer was that his value did not differ by more than two feet from Rittenhouse's. "When I have therefore ascertained the height of this hill so nearly the same with that which had been previously determined by Dr. Rittenhouse, whose accuracy and abilities are so well known, both in Europe and America, I need be under no apprehensions." [27]

The legislature followed through on April 9 with an act enabling the governor to incorporate a turnpike company to construct a superior road along the route of the survey. The company was speedily formed and the $300,000 subscription met with great popular enthusiasm; in Philadelphia, 2,276 people sought at least one of the 600 shares allotted to the city. When the subscribers met to organize, they named William Bingham president, and Rittenhouse first among the twelve managers.[28]

Almost simultaneously, Rittenhouse was involved, still more heavily, in the Delaware and Schuylkill Navigation Company, which the legislature authorized on April 10 to build a canal across the northern end of the city from the Delaware to the Schuylkill above the falls. This canal would combine with the Susquehanna and Schuylkill Canal by providing the eastern link of the water carriage route to the West. Among subordinate objectives, it would improve the city's water supply.

Rittenhouse was appointed one of five commissioners to receive subscriptions. Again the subscription was easily met, and again he was first named on the board of managers, which included a great many of the same men who constituted the

[27] *Pa. Arch.*, 9th ser., I, 229, 240, 301, 421; *Pa. Gaz.*, Feb. 29, 1792.
[28] *Ibid.*, Apr. 25, May 2, Aug. 1, 22, 1792; *Statutes at Large of Pa.*, xiv, 279–94.

boards of the Susquehanna and Schuylkill Canal Company, the Lancaster Turnpike Company, and the Conewago Canal Company. They were all parts of a great interlocking enterprise designed to provide the needed transportation to the West. This effort also included river and road improvements, such as the road over Vanderen's Hill in Roxbury Township, which followed the route Rittenhouse and Hutchins surveyed in 1783.[29]

Rittenhouse was recognized as the leading technical expert by each of the companies; they expected him to apply his scientific knowledge to their problems of routing and construction. He was associated in the direction of three of the four companies, and scarcely less relied upon by the board of the Susquehanna and Schuylkill, which invited him to inspect the ground with the rest of the managers late in May.[30]

Digging and construction began almost immediately on all of the projects. This preceded the engagement of an experienced canal engineer, to which the companies agreed, following advice Rittenhouse had been offering ever since 1773. In the interim, Rittenhouse played a large role in planning and directing, although he superintended none of the projects, which were divided among several local men. John Bull took responsibility for the Susquehanna and Schuylkill, Jonathan Robeson for the Delaware and Schuylkill, and James Brindley for the Conewago Canal, while the turnpike was constructed under several section superintendents.[31]

William Weston, a British engineer, was engaged in November 1792 to direct the two major canals, although his advice was sought on the other projects as well. When he arrived in America, in January 1793, he found 600 men at work on the canals: 200 at Norristown and 400 between Lebanon and Myerstown.

[29] [Smith], *Historical Account*, 33; *Pa. Gaz.*, Apr. 18, 25, July 4, 1792; *Dunlap's Am. Daily Adver.*, June 30, 1792; General Rules, Delaware and Schuylkill Canal, July 2, 1792, Union Canal Co. Papers, Berks County Hist. Soc.; *Pa. Arch.*, 9th ser., I, 367.
[30] *Dunlap's Am. Daily Adver.*, June 13, 1792.
[31] [Smith], *Historical Account*, 68.

He professed himself well satisfied with the work in progress, although in terms of the obstacles and the inexperience of the workmen, he estimated the projects to be overly expensive by European standards. Rittenhouse's surveys he specifically commended as "uncommonly correct, the variation not greater than would happen to the most carefull man and with the best instrument in repeated trials." He found the plan, "in general . . . perfectly just," preferring, however, an aqueduct at one point to the longer ground level route Rittenhouse had followed. Weston demonstrated an attitude increasingly shown toward the Philadelphian; he wrote as if all earlier surveys and direction had been exclusively Rittenhouse's. Like Franklin, Rittenhouse found that whatever he touched was frequently credited to him alone.[32]

Unfortunately, homage was not enough; nor was Weston's skill. The great projects were only partially completed. The turnpike, after several bad beginnings—especially in poorly conceived construction and surfacing—was carried through to resounding success and became one of the great highways of history. The Conewago Canal did not meet its contractual deadline of January 1, 1796, but it was completed in the following year. The two major canal companies ran out of money long before they were able to finish their construction—the design had to wait for another era before it could be completed.[33]

Rittenhouse gave much to the canal and road projects—not least of all his name. Everywhere, his name gave credit to scientific or technological ideas which he was ready to approve. In consequence, men brought increasing numbers of projects to him from a child's book on science—which he was willing to endorse—to much more important problems.[34]

[32] William Weston, Report, Apr. 2, 1792, Union Canal Co. Papers, Berks County Hist. Soc.; Richard S. Kirby, "William Weston," *Newcomen Soc. Trans.*, XVI (1935–36), 111, 114.
[33] *Ibid.*, 117; *Pa. Arch.*, 9th ser., II, 979, 982, 1021, 1088; [James T. Callender], *The American Annual Register . . . 1796* (Phila., 1797), 37.
[34] Charles C. Reiche, *Fifteen Discourses* (Phila., 1791), second p. 1.

Jefferson, now in Philadelphia, gained Rittenhouse's participation in a series of experiments designed to test Jacob Isaacs'
claim to have discovered a new and easier method of dis-
tilling sea water. With Dr. Caspar Wistar, professor of chemistry in the College, and Dr. James Hutchinson, professor of
chemistry in the University, Jefferson and Rittenhouse spent
almost a week during March 1791 in these investigations. The
results failed to confirm the advantage of Isaacs' secret powder,
which he added to water before running it through a familiar
still. Jefferson recommended that no patent be granted but
urged that ordinary distillation methods be called to the attention of sea captains.[35]

Sometime in these years, Jefferson also brought to Rittenhouse his plan for a "mould-board of least resistance," in which
he sought to design a more efficient plow. Jefferson had begun
to consider this problem as early as 1788, and he finally published his solution in 1799. He reported that Rittenhouse supported his principles before he went on to test them in practice,
where they were further confirmed.[36]

Rittenhouse's usual bench for hearing proposals remained
the Philosophical Society. Most of the communications to the
society passed through his hands, but many of them, he transmitted without comment. Papers referred to him, he confronted
squarely. He described a paper on gauging as competent but,
characteristically, remarked that only experiments with the proposed instrument could determine its utility. He subjected the
conclusions of another paper, on the expansion of steel springs,
to a series of his own tests in which he duplicated the experiments described. "The Result was directly Contrary to the
assertions" of the author, who had maintained that springs did

---

[35] Jefferson, Notes on Distillation, Nov. 21, 1791, Jefferson Papers, LC;
Dunlap's Am. Daily Adver., Feb. 26, 1791; Samuel L. Mitchill to Caspar
Wistar, Feb. 14, 1792 [91], Wistar Papers, APS; A. G. Lipscomb and A. A.
Bergh, eds., *The Writings of Thomas Jefferson* (Washington, 1903-4),
III, 1–8; VIII, 151.
[36] *Ibid.*, X, 15–16; XVII, 278.

not lose "strength" when heated and gain it when cold as commonly believed.[37]

In a similar manner, he tested the proposal Robert Patterson made in a paper he submitted for the Magellanic Premium; Patterson urged that lightning rods be protected by tipping them with "black lead," or graphite. This idea immediately interested Rittenhouse because he had previously observed through his telescope that the tips of many Philadelphia lightning rods showed indications of melting. His tests confirmed the high melting point of graphite and its other valuable characteristics. As a result, a premium was awarded to Patterson.[38]

Rittenhouse always gave his attention to anything pertaining to lightning—one of the areas in which he duplicated Franklin's interests. He was more concerned with the practical side of the problem, however, and less with theory than Franklin had been. Just before Hopkinson died, Rittenhouse and he wrote a paper on the effects of lightning upon a Philadelphia house in which they concluded that deep grounding of lightning rods was an essential sometimes neglected. Rittenhouse even suggested to Peale that a water well offered a good grounding opportunity because the ground must be led to earth that remained moist. Inevitably, Rittenhouse chaired the committee charged with placing lightning rods on Philosophical Hall.[39]

The Philosophical Society might have become a kind of testing laboratory if other members had followed Rittenhouse's lead in subjecting proposals to experimental proof, but he remained unique. The community, indeed, increasingly regarded Rittenhouse as a unique individual and placed him in a series of honorary posts. There is no indication that he ever attended the infrequent meetings of the Society of Visitors of

---

[37] DR, Endorsement of paper on gauging, MS Comm., Mechanics, 13, APS; APS Mins., 1787–93, 225.

[38] Ibid., 150, 154, 167, 211, 258–59; Dunlap's Am. Daily Adver., Mar. 28, 1791.

[39] APS, Trans., III (1793), 122–25; APS Mins., 1787–93, 184, 198–99; Charles W. Peale, Diary, July 14, 1799, Fordham Univ.

Peale's newly established museum, but his name alone aided the enterprise. By appointment of Washington, he served, beside his old acquaintances and political opponents, Thomas Willing and Lambert Cadwalader, as a commissioner to receive subscriptions to the newly chartered Bank of the United States.[40]

In politics, his old friends continued to imagine that his name would strengthen their tickets. He was put forward as a candidate for the Pennsylvania House of Representatives in 1791 and as a presidential elector in 1792; in both cases he was unsuccessful. The political currents still ran heavily against the old Constitutionalists—now increasingly referred to as Republicans—and as much as voters might admire Rittenhouse the man, too few admired his politics.[41]

He remained close to Jefferson, Madison, and the leadership of the slowly evolving opposition to the Washington-Hamilton administration. His correspondence with Jefferson, however, did not relate to politics but to opposums and natural history. Jefferson invited his friend to accompany Madison and him on the famous "botanizing trip" through New York and Connecticut in May 1791—a trip that has been much misinterpreted. Many historians have seen in it the foundation of the Jeffersonian Republican party and the formulation of the New York–Virginia alliance, but the record is totally lacking in evidence of such activity. It was unquestionably conceived primarily as a vacation of amateur naturalists. Rittenhouse did not go along, Jefferson reporting, "He says he cannot find a good horse." [42]

His health remained precarious, but his spirits were good. Except for the mounting demands for his services in the internal

[40] Peale Museum Mins., Mar. 8, 1792, APS; Sellers, *Peale*, II, 45; *Dunlap's Am. Daily Adver.*, May 5, 31, July 8, 1791, Mar. 16, 1792.
[41] *Ibid.*, Oct. 8, 10, 11, 13, 1791; *Pa. Gaz.*, Sep. 5, 26, Oct. 3, Nov. 7, 1792.
[42] Philip M. Marsh, "The Jefferson-Madison Vacation," *PMHB*, LXXI (1947), 71.

improvement program and in other practical matters, he was favorably situated to pursue his own scientific interests. Much of his time, he devoted to astronomical observation.

With great constancy, he maintained a careful routine in his observatory. He recorded meteorological conditions every day without fail, regardless of the state of his health, and he arranged to have the record kept by others whenever he was absent from the city. He worked over his instruments continuingly, checking them and improving their adjustment and performance. He missed few of the significant events within the solar system. From the end of 1789 through 1792, he observed six solar or lunar eclipses, including one annular eclipse, and he observed one transit of Mercury. In most instances, he recorded sparely the times of the beginning and end of the phenomenon with just a few other measurements, such as the sun's diameter. On one occasion, he was able to compare predicted times from Mayer's tables with Charles Mason's new tables—slightly to the advantage of Mason. He was more descriptive of the unusual annular eclipse of April 4, 1791. All of this activity he entered in his notebook, publishing only a few of the items. Occasionally, he recorded information on sunspots but made no long series of observations. During one period, he became interested in a variable star, although, despite his anticipations of profit from the study of fixed stars, he confined most of his investigation to the solar system.[43]

Throughout the world, Rittenhouse was now recognized by other astronomers as a competent colleague. In the 1792 edition of his *Astronomie*, Lalande commented that Rittenhouse's was the only American observatory of which he had any knowledge. Lalande was especially pleased when he received the Philadelphian's report of his observations of the 1791 annular eclipse, to which he responded in a personal letter, and he made use of these figures in print. In 1792 also, Franz von Zach, Thuringian astronomer, incorporated into his new *Tabulae Motuum Solis* Rittenhouse's method of calculating the sun's

[43] DR, Notebook, 1785–92, n.p., APS; APS, *Trans.*, III (1793), 154–55.

meridian time, described in the Philosophical Society's first volume of *Transactions*.[44]

Rittenhouse wrote the first of his mathematical papers in May 1792. Stimulated by a practical investigation in which he sought to determine the period of a pendulum, he encountered what he regarded as "an elegant theorem." Although he never described it, he presented the end product of some of the mathematics he used in applying it. In his words, he found "the sums of the several powers of the sines," or in more familiar terminology, he developed solutions to the definite integral,

$$\int_0^{\frac{\pi}{2}} \sin^n x \, dx.$$

However, he gave no indication of using calculus in his work.[45]

He prefaced this paper with the suggestion that he had not read widely in the literature of mathematics and that he did not imagine he was contributing to the advance of knowledge in this field. "I cannot suppose," he commented, "that it has escaped the notice of mathematicians." He was perfectly correct, for John Wallis had done all the essential work on the problem over a century before in his *Arithmetica Infinitorum*. Rittenhouse, nevertheless, was amply rewarded by the pure beauty of the exercise, the "pleasing regularity" he discovered.

Moreover, when his abstracted conclusions were published in the Philosophical Society's *Transactions*, they had a surprising effect. For the American audience, the paper represented a new level of mathematical thought and stimulated some of the best minds for years afterward. In 1803, Nathaniel Bowditch produced his own demonstration of Rittenhouse's solution. In 1808, Eugenius Nulty went behind the published presentation to reconstruct the theorem Rittenhouse had discovered but never described.[46]

[44] Jérome le François Lalande, *Astronomie* (Paris, 1792), I, li; Zach, *Tabulae Motuum Solis*, I, 155; Barton, *Memoirs*, 432–33, 433n.–50n. [-34n.].
[45] APS, *Trans.*, III (1793), 155–56.
[46] *Ibid.*, VI, pt. 2 (1809), 395–400; APS Mins., (1799–1805), 138; W. Carl Rufus, "David Rittenhouse as a Mathematical Disciple of Newton," *Scripta Mathematica*, VIII (1941), 228–31.

By this time, Rittenhouse had fulfilled in a remarkable way the anticipations his admirers held of him. He was successful, beyond reason, in confronting and contributing constructively to a number of practical problems. It is idle to attempt to separate "basic" and "applied" science in his approach; his mathematical paper revealed the manner in which practical clock construction, physics, and mathematics were related in his life. He remained a mechanic to whom practice was the only consideration in certain projects. At the same time, he enjoyed the beauty of scientific truth isolated sometimes from any application.

CHAPTER XX

Liberty Cap Pennies

1792–1795

PRESIDENT WASHINGTON appointed David Rittenhouse director of the mint of the United States on April 14, 1792, less than two weeks after the act establishing it became law. This step was the culmination of long continued efforts. As early as 1782, Robert Morris, then superintendent of finance, had called Rittenhouse in to advise on the machinery for the mint he was urging Congress to authorize. After the adoption of the United States Constitution, Hamilton wrote a report favoring a national mint, but Jefferson became its most impassioned advocate. As secretary of state, he was responsible for killing efforts to contract abroad for the purchase of American coins.

The only official coinage of this entire period was the "Fugio" or "Franklin cent" of 1787, produced by domestic contract immediately following the adoption of the decimal system of coinage. These coins bore an unusual legend, which had appeared also on the pattern "Continental" dollars of 1776; the obverse showed, in addition to a sundial under a meridian sun and the date, the words "Fugio" and "Mind Your Business." A haunting coincidence unites this penny with a clock Rittenhouse made for the Bartons in 1756; on its face, it bore the familiar motto "Tempus fugit," coupled with the less familiar, "Go about your business!" [1]

The choice of Rittenhouse as director seemed peculiarly appropriate to men who differed on other subjects. Regarded in

---

[1] *Dunlap's Am. Daily Adver.*, Apr. 18, 1792; *Am. State Papers, Finance*, I, 44–45; "Notes . . . from Robert Morris's Diary," *Historical Magazine*, I [1867], 30–32; Barton, *Memoirs*, 467n.

all quarters as the leading Newtonian philosopher in America, he was popularly most honored as a practical scientist—a mechanic-scientist. What could be a more fitting capstone to his career or a more fortunate result for the nation than that Rittenhouse, like Newton, should become "Master of the Mint."

Yet Rittenhouse hesitated. His health was poor. Since his retirement from office, he had maintained a regular schedule only in his observatory; he attended hardly any of the meetings of the Philosophical Society, the trustees of the University, or the other organizations to which he belonged. He could meet the demands of the canal and road companies because they were so occasional and so irregular.

Moreover, like the Pennsylvania Treasury, the Mint was a public institution which rested on the shifting sands of politics. Rittenhouse had demonstrated that he could absorb political opposition and assault, but his expulsion from the Treasury left ineradicable marks upon him. Should a sixty-year-old man, now in a position to contribute both to the improvement of American society and to the enrichment of American thought, voluntarily jump again into the pit of conflict? The technical difficulties in an area unfamiliar to Rittenhouse were a sufficient deterrent without having to endure the political aggravations that were certain to accrue.

Rittenhouse hesitated until July 1, when he took the oath of office; he sent Washington his formal acceptance on July 9 with reluctance and only "for the present." He was seriously concerned that sickness might prevent him from giving continuous attention to the post. He recorded his deep and sincere appreciation of the honor and then devoted most of his letter to the business surrounding the establishment of the institution.[2]

In fact, long before he committed himself, Rittenhouse worked over the design and plans of the Mint and even took steps to obtain the needed men, materials, and buildings. In this

[2] DR to Washington, July 9, 1792, Nat. Arch.

period of indecision, he seems to have been testing himself to see whether his health would permit him to undertake the post. In addition, he did not want to delay the work which the administration was anxious to press forward.

Under the director, three technical officers were required in addition to the treasurer, who was merely an exalted bookkeeper and relatively easy to find. Tristram Dalton, social and political leader of Newburyport, was quickly appointed to the latter post. The chief coiner, the assayer, and the engraver had to be men of an experience and competence not likely to be found on this side of the Atlantic. There was no dearth of applicants, but early efforts were made to find Europeans with suitable mint experience. Jefferson hoped to attract to America the celebrated Swiss die-sinker, Jean Pierre Droz, who had worked at the Boulton mint near Birmingham and had contested one of his inventions with Matthew Boulton, but he proved impossible to move from Paris. Both Thomas Pinckney in London and Gouverneur Morris in Paris were pressed into service to locate competent men. Washington insisted that none but those better qualified than available Americans be considered.[3]

The sole yield of these efforts was Albion Cox, whom Pinckney finally engaged on March 8, 1793, to serve as assayer. Cox was exceptionally skilled in all minting operations and certainly qualified to serve as assayer. Strikingly, he had already had experience in coining money for America, having been one of the contractors for the New Jersey cents of 1787. He was well-connected in England, but his American ventures had turned out poorly and his finances were in bad shape. He arrived in Philadelphia early in May with chests full of glassware, scales, and weights.[4]

[3] *Pa. Gaz.*, June 6, 1792; Joseph Priestley to Matthew Boulton, Nov. 10, 1790, Birmingham Assay Office; Frank H. Stewart, *History of the First United States Mint* (n.p., 1924), 199; Fitzpatrick, ed., *Writings of Washington*, xxxii, 57.

[4] Agreement, Albion Cox and Thomas Pinckney, Mar. 8, 1793, Mint Rec., Nat. Arch.; William Cox, Certificate, Feb. 25, 1793, *ibid.*; Stewart, *First Mint*, 89.

Long before this, Rittenhouse found a man who bore the major responsibility for building the mint machinery and setting it in motion. Henry Voight, the German-born clockmaker who had worked for Rittenhouse on his orreries and had worked with Fitch on his steamboat, had had experience in a mint before he came to America. Still more important, he was a facile and inventive workman, truly an ingenious mechanic. Rittenhouse hired him as temporary chief coiner and engraver, assuming that a better qualified European would be found before long. None ever was.[5]

The location and plan of the Mint depended upon the form of power to be employed. Water power was not available in the city, although the completion of the Delaware and Schuylkill Canal would bring it within reach of some locations. In the meantime, the alternatives were steam or horse power, neither of which depended on location. According to Voight, Rittenhouse planned to use steam from the beginning, but to save expenses relied on horse mills at the outset; they were perfectly adequate for rolling copper and might be replaced by steam when dollar coinage was begun. The coining presses were hand powered, as was usual.[6]

Under these circumstances, an available location on Seventh Street between Mulberry and Market was very attractive. In addition to its proximity to Rittenhouse's own home, it already contained a brick house, several outhouses, and a horse-mill, and it could be obtained at a reasonable price. After receiving Washington's approbation, Rittenhouse bought the property, tore down the distillery that had stood on the lot, and, on July 31, laid the foundation stone of the new Mint. By October, after three coining presses had been received from abroad, parts of the Mint could be set in motion.[7]

[5] John Fitch, History, III, 220–21, LCP.
[6] Am. State Papers, Finance, I, 354; James L. Whithead, "Survey of Federal Archives in Philadelphia," PMHB, LXII (1938), 167.
[7] DR to Jefferson, June 16, 1792, Photocopy, HSP; Fitzpatrick, ed., Writings of Washington, XXXII, 84, 86; Barton, Memoirs, 387.

It took many more months and much frustration before the whole complex was operating. Ultimately, it consisted of two rolling mills, one for hot and one for cold metal; a drawing machine for equalizing strips; three cutting presses for planchets or coin blanks; a milling machine; four coining presses, three of which were newly equipped with machinery for supplying and discharging themselves; two turning lathes; a boring machine; three annealing furnaces; one boiling furnace; two forges; and three furnaces for assaying and melting.

Much of it was put together by the "hunt and try" process, without sufficient knowledge of the best practices in the best mints. Many of the tools required to build the machinery had to be conceived and built first. Often the related technology of the country was inadequate to the demands put upon it; it was especially difficult to get steel that could sustain the punishment to which the dies were subjected, and far too often they broke. When one component failed and was redesigned, often the whole machine had to be rebuilt. Because the power was limited, metal for some coins had to be heated before rolling, which shortened the life of the rollers—thus one difficulty provoked another. On top of it all, competent workmen remained extremely difficult to find.[8]

Yet, one by one, the Mint was able to assume its functions. The assay of foreign coins, directed by Congress on November 29, was begun before the end of the year and observed at one point by the President. David Ott carried out this work under the supervision of Rittenhouse before Albion Cox arrived. The year 1792 saw also the production of several pattern pieces: half-dimes struck in silver and mentioned by Washington in his annual address; dimes; half-eagles in base metals; and at least two varieties of cents. The history of these coins is not clear, but Voight engraved the dies for some of them and was entirely responsible for the most unusual one—the silver center cent. This was a copper coin with a small plug of silver in its

[8] *Am. State Papers, Finance*, I, 353, 356.

center which brought its value up to the nominal value of the cent without increasing its size to unmanageable proportions. Rittenhouse also sought to achieve this objective by alloying copper with silver, but in the end, the cents produced were token coins—with a value well below their nominal value—as, in fact, the legislation provided.[9]

Throughout these efforts, Washington remained very much interested and wholly cooperative. He did everything he could to provide the metal required for coinage, especially by expediting the foreign purchase of copper for coins of the smallest denominations. Washington insisted that the Mint be a responsibility of the State Department, rather than the Treasury Department. In this relationship, Rittenhouse used Jefferson as something of a buffer, declining through him on one occasion a dinner invitation from the president. Not depending upon his health as a crutch this time, he wrote a little too starkly, "My Engagements for this day are such as will make it inconvenient for me to Dine with the President, You will please to make my Apology to his Excellency." [10]

The Mint drew Rittenhouse and Jefferson closer together than ever. When, in January 1793, Jefferson packed up for his periodic return to Monticello, he presented to the Philadelphian the bust Houdon had done of him in Paris. Protesting its "uselessness," he accompanied the gift with his own "sincere affection." [11]

Deeply touched, Rittenhouse responded in one of the warmest letters he ever wrote. "To me," he declared, "it is more acceptable than any other thing of its kind in existence." He went on to lament Jefferson's departure and to tell him how

[9] DR to Tobias Lear, Dec. 27, 1792, Jefferson to Washington, Dec. 18, 1792, Nat. Arch.; DR to Jefferson, Jan. 7, 1793, Jefferson Papers, LC; Fitzpatrick, ed., *Writings of Washington*, XXXII, 210; Edward Ingersoll, ed., *An Abridgement of the Acts of Congress* (Phila., 1825), 421–22.

[10] Fitzpatrick, ed., *Writings of Washington*, XXXII, 187; DR to Jefferson, June 16, 1792, Photocopy, HSP.

[11] Jefferson to DR, Jan. 7, 1793, Jefferson Papers, LC.

336

much his friendship meant to a man who, outside his immediate family, had never enjoyed but a handful of friends.[12]

He turned his telescope to the stars on that very evening and made an exciting discovery; in the constellation of Cepheus, he found a new comet. Night after night, he traced its course through Cassiopea, Andromeda, the Triangle, and Aries. He recorded its geocentric position at each point, and he set to work on the elements of its orbit. A little south of the Whale, he saw it on February 8 for the last time. To an astronomer, such a discovery was exciting and satisfying, but as the year 1793 unfolded, it brought to mind the ancient view of comets as portents of disaster.[13]

A year of violence followed: European war and atrocity; political discord and confusion throughout the nation; and, in the city, the unleased pestilence of nature. For Rittenhouse, the year began with a New Year's Day assault against John Nicholson in the form of specific charges of malfeasance by Christian Febiger, still treasurer of the Commonwealth.[14] This bitter denunciation was followed by a year-long struggle which was more significant for the forces marshaled in attack and defense than for the facts in dispute.

Philadelphia saw also the full drama of rising partisanship within the Federal government and the coalescing of more permanent political parties as Jefferson, in the Cabinet, and Madison, in the Congress, grew increasingly disenchanted with the administration program. Madison, who served initially as floor leader for administration proposals, had become a nucleus of opposition. Jefferson vented his antagonism to the Hamiltonian program by plotting assaults against the Treasury Department, the excise, the impost, and the bank. The Mint also became a political target, attacked, however, by the partisans of

[12] DR to Jefferson, Jan. 11, 1793, *ibid.*
[13] APS, *Trans.*, III (1793), 261.
[14] [Hogan], *Pa. State Trials,* I, 67.

the administration. Madison's friends stood ready to defend it on the floors of Congress while Jefferson was its great shield in the Cabinet.

International crises widened the splits and solidified the factions which were fundamentally domestic in origin. When the French Revolution first broke out, most Americans hailed it as an extension of their own. By 1793, the storming of the Tuilleries and the "September massacres" revealed some of the viciousness of which the French were capable. In January, the king was executed, and in February, the Convention, already at war with Austria and Prussia, declared war on Britain, Spain, and the Netherlands.

For several months, Americans could permit themselves the luxury of seeing whichever side of the French coin they preferred. Federalists saw the violence, the perfidy, the breakdown of civil law, the misery of individuals, and the probability of worse to come. The men with whom Rittenhouse was associated, more and more frequently called Republicans, saw the other side. They hailed the new France as a sister republic, they hailed each new reform, and they looked beyond momentary disorder and abuse to the attainment of a stable system under which liberty, equality, and fraternity would, in fact, prevail. Enthusiasts addressed each other as "citizen," waved liberty poles, and wore red Phrygian liberty caps.

While the Cabinet and the nation divided on the issue of neutrality in the French wars of aggression, a minor international problem was unobtrusively dropped into the lap of the Philosophical Society. André Michaux, a French botanist who had been in this country several years, accepted a private project which had great appeal to the secretary of state and which he communicated to Rittenhouse. Michaux sought support for an expedition he wanted to undertake across the Mississippi, up the Missouri, and over the Rockies to the Pacific Ocean. This was an object Jefferson had had in mind since at least as early as 1783, but he had so far been unable to ac-

338

complish it. Michaux had already undertaken explorations in Florida, the Carolinas, and the Bahamas, and he had conducted two botanical gardens in the United States from which he returned to the government of Louis XVI specimens he thought promised utility in France. Now, with his relationship to the succession government in France uncertain, he asked for voluntary American support in a much greater expedition.

Rittenhouse was favorably inclined but uncertain whether to leave the enterprise as a subscription of individuals or to lay it before the Philosophical Society. On Jefferson's advice, he presented the project to the society, which voted, with Jefferson attending on April 19, to assume sponsorship. It formed three committees: one to solicit subscriptions, a second to collect the pledged money and turn it over to Rittenhouse for disbursement, and a third to draw up instructions.[15]

The committee on instructions, under Rittenhouse's chairmanship and including Jefferson, Smith, Ewing, Rush, and Wistar, wrote out directions in which the national objective was as prominent as it had been in Jefferson's earlier efforts to promote a continental exploration. Michaux was informed that his primary purpose would be to identify the shortest and best route from the United States to the Pacific. The society would arrange to have Indians then in the city guide him to Kaskaskia, a few miles south of the mouth of the Missouri River, where he would begin his exploration. He was directed to locate the best river running into the Pacific, which the committee expected to be the Columbia. Michaux was to take notes on the topography, inhabitants, animal, vegetable, and mineral productions —and to look especially for the mammoth and the Peruvian llama. He was forewarned not to lose his notes and to bring back other proofs of his trip. The society would pay him one-quarter of the subscription as soon as he was ready to set out, and the balance on his return—provided he reached the Pacific.

[15] DR to Jefferson, Rec'd Apr. 10, 1793, Jefferson Papers, LC; Jefferson to DR, Apr. 11, 1793, APS; APS Mins., 1787–93, 13.

If he got only to the continental divide, he would receive a lesser portion.[16]

The care with which the committee hedged in Michaux by these instructions owed something to the political tensions of the day, but the Philadelphians had no fear that he posed a threat to the national security. The possibility that Michaux might turn the expedition to political purposes did not arise until the arrival of the new minister of the French Republic, Edmond Charles Genêt.

He arrived in Charleston, South Carolina, on April 8, 1793, to begin a remarkable ministry. His lack of tact and perception compounded the evil of his instructions, which directed him to turn public opinion against officers of the American government whenever necessary. In Charleston, he outfitted privateers and commissioned American volunteers to operate them. He found some coldness on his trip north to the capital, but much more enthusiasm, warmly expressed. On May 16, he was met at Gray's Ferry by a cheering throng and escorted into Philadelphia, about three miles away.

Charles Biddle presided at a general meeting held that evening in the State House, propelled into the chair by the portly Dr. James Hutchinson, Jonathan Dickinson Sergeant, and others who sponsored the meeting. Biddle, a respected former sea captain and merchant, later reported that he had consented in the hope that he might prevent the ardent advocates of Genêt from adopting violent measures. In fact, the meeting did little more than appoint a committee to prepare an address to Genêt. Included on the drafting committee were Biddle, Hutchinson, Sergeant, Alexander James Dallas, and Peter Stephen Duponceau; the chairman was David Rittenhouse. The committee met the following morning at Biddle's house, where they worked their different versions into a single essay.[17]

The meeting of that afternoon, grown so large it had to be

[16] APS Instructions to Michaud, n.d., Wistar Papers, APS.
[17] *General Adver.*, May 17, 1793; Biddle, *Autobiography*, 251.

adjourned out-of-doors to the State House yard, unanimously adopted the committee's draft and appointed a greatly expanded committee to deliver it. With the members of the original drafting committee at the head of the column and the citizens at the tail, the entire assemblage then walked, three abreast, to the City Tavern in Second Street, where Genêt had taken lodgings. The committee went inside to read the address to the minister—a thoroughly unexceptionable performance which never strayed for a moment from the path of stringent patriotism. It stressed the fraternal attachment of Americans to France and the value they set upon "republican principles." In complete harmony with Washington's neutrality proclamation, it accepted unequivocally the fact that the United States was not a party to the present war, but suggested, "she may be able, in a state of peace, to demonstrate the sincerity of her friendship, by affording very useful assistance to the Citizens of her sister republic." [18]

Shouts, salutations, and applause followed. Genêt responded within the room and then from a window to the crowd in the streets. He answered in writing the following day—but he never understood. When the administration received him with limited cordiality, Genêt behaved rudely to the President, threatened to go above him to the Congress, and above the Congress, if necessary, to the people. Even Jefferson became outraged, although for a time he hoped he might be able to counsel the misguided Frenchman to a saner course.

The secretary of state met Genêt's new plans for Michaux with firmness. He refused the minister's request that Michaux be appointed French consul in Kentucky, on the grounds that consuls were permitted only at American ports. When Genêt openly declared that Michaux was to be the French agent to raise American recruits for an assault on Spanish Louisiana, Jefferson grew irate. If the French minister enticed officers and soldiers from Kentucky to go against Spain, he would put a

[18] *Pa. Gaz.*, May 22, 1793.

halter around their necks, for "they would assuredly be hung." At Genêt's request, Jefferson supplied a letter to Governor Isaac Shelby, presenting Michaux as a botanist. When the French minister demurred, insisting that he wanted more official recognition of his agent, Jefferson was willing to add only that Michaux enjoyed Genêt's esteem.[19]

This development killed all chances of a transcontinental expedition; the mission Michaux did carry out for the French minister had no relationship to Jefferson's great dream or to the Philosophical Society's plans. Not all of the money pledged by subscribers came in, but Rittenhouse was left with $128.25 which he did not know how to handle. He continued to hold it, hoping that some way might be found to apply it to the original purposes.[20]

Meanwhile, Philadelphians favorable to France launched another project designed to express their kinship with the newborn republic across the sea. They founded the Democratic Society of Pennsylvania, not the first of the pro-French democratic clubs established in America, but the most influential. Its first recorded meeting was held on June 20, and on July 3 officers were elected. Hutchinson, Sergeant, Dallas, and Duponceau, the prime movers of the group, were given places on the slate, but the presidency was handed to David Rittenhouse and the vice presidency to Charles Biddle. Rittenhouse and Biddle were the most generally respected men who had participated in the welcome to Genêt, and the leaders of the society were anxious to associate them with the enterprise; Biddle laid this strategy to Hutchinson.[21]

Both Biddle and William Barton reported that Rittenhouse never attended a meeting of the club, and there is no contradictory evidence. Even so, his name remained at its masthead for another half-year for he neither declined nor resigned. As

[19] Jefferson, Notes on Conference with Genêt, July 5, 1793, Jefferson Papers, LC.
[20] John Vaughan to Samuel H. Smith, Mar. 18, 1799, APS.
[21] Democratic Society of Pennsylvania Minutes, 1793–94, HSP; Eugene P. Link, *Democratic-Republican Societies, 1790–1800* (N.Y., 1942), 10, 80.

similar societies were formed throughout the country, men thought of David Rittenhouse as president of the Democratic Society of Pennsylvania.[22]

The initial addresses of the society expressed attachment to French friendship and to republican principles. Opponents, however, saw violence in their assertion that revolutions in the two countries had taught them "to erect the temple of *Liberty* on the ruins of *Palaces* and *Thrones*." William Cobbett, scourge of the Republicans, saw still more. He charged that the society, which he tagged a Jacobin club, was the result of Genêt's distribution of over 20,000 Louis d'or in Philadelphia and, specifically, that Rittenhouse was among those bribed.[23]

He was right to the extent of regarding the society as a political action unit rather than a mere Franco-American friendship club. It became a strong political force; through its participation in a network of committees of correspondence, its efforts were related to those of democratic societies in other parts of the country. Discounting altogether the French factor, Jefferson asserted that the sole purpose of the Pennsylvania society was the election of a Republican governor.[24]

Political clubs and scientific societies as well as governments and governmental institutions were disordered by the plague of yellow fever which struck Philadelphia in the summer of 1793. First decisively recognized on August 19, it spread with alarming speed, killed quickly, and terrorized everyone. The preferred medical treatment only hastened death, and no preventive action was worthwhile except flight. Some 17,000 streamed out of a city of 55,000; of those who remained, 4,000 died.[25]

Often Rittenhouse had left the city during the summer for

[22] Biddle, *Autobiography*, 252; Barton, *Memoirs*, 463n.
[23] *Pa. Gaz.*, July 17, 1793; [William Cobbett], *History of the American Jacobins* (Phila., 1796), 16, 21, 27; [William Cobbett], *Porcupine's Works* [Phila., 1797], 69.
[24] Paul L. Ford, ed., *Writings of Thomas Jefferson* (N.Y., 1892–99), I, 253.
[25] Matthew Carey, *A Short Account of the Malignant Fever* (Phila., 1794), [118–20]; *Pa. Gaz.*, Nov. 20, 1793; J. H. Powell, *Bring Out Your Dead* (Phila., 1949).

his Norriton farm, a refuge in earlier years from heat, humidity, and the frustrations of politics. In 1793, perhaps because of the Mint, he seems to have stayed in the city through most of the summer; he was still there on September 6 but planning soon to leave. His son-in-law, Jonathan Dickinson Sergeant, remained through the crisis and served faithfully as a member of the mayor's committee which met daily to provide all the government and order that remained to the stricken city. On October 8, he fell dead of the fever, leaving Betsy with two children and a third within a few weeks of delivery. Hannah stayed beside her step-daughter in the city, but by October 22, Rittenhouse was out at the Norriton farm, where he had taken Hetty and her children. He wrote Hannah as if he maintained no restricted exile but occasionally rode in to Norristown or Germantown, and he announced that he would be back in the city again by the 26th.[26]

Toward the end of October, the plague faded away, and Rittenhouse had the same trouble picking up the pieces at the Mint that everyone else encountered. Several of the workmen were dead and others scattered; dead too was Joseph Wright, who had been engaged as engraver and had cut the dies for the truly promising production of cents and half-cents. The Mint was unable to proceed in the planned coinage of silver and gold because the bonds for the coiner and assayer had been set higher than either could meet. The supply of copper was still uncertain and inadequate.[27]

Jefferson made an urgent effort to solve each of these problems—but he had little time. To Rittenhouse's great dismay, he planned to resign from the State Department at the end of the year. Jefferson felt a bafflement with politics that was not new to him and a sense of relief at the thought of removing

[26] Jefferson to DR, Sep. 6, 1793, Photocopy, HSP; DR to Hannah Rittenhouse, Oct. 22, 1793, Photocopy, HSP.
[27] Jefferson to DR, Nov. 6, 1793, Photocopy, HSP; Jefferson to Washington, Aug. 15, 1793, Nat. Arch.; Fitzpatrick, ed., *Writings of Washington*, xxxiii, 118.

himself from an increasingly unpleasant position. To Rittenhouse in the Mint, this could only signal a new disaster of the
sort he had suffered in the Pennsylvania Treasury.

Yet despite the plague, the new troubles, and the old ones,
there were encouraging aspects to the performance of the Mint.
When the year was up, the reported output of coin was 255,900
pieces, entirely of copper cents and half-cents. In this period
too, the design of American coins went through a brief evolu-
tion and reached the general pattern it would maintain for many
years. Congress, reflecting pervasive equalitarian and anti-
monarchical feelings, required that instead of an individual's
face, the coins should carry a figure "emblematic of liberty."
This resulted in a female head representing liberty as the
central item on the obverse of all coins. In the first cent minted,
she was presented with flowing hair, the word "Liberty" above
her and "1793" below. The reverse bore the legend "United
States of America" surrounding a chain of fifteen links, which
in turn surrounded the words "One Cent" and "$\frac{1}{100}$." Although the chain was copied from the Continental dollar of
1776 and the Fugio cent of 1787, it carried the wrong overtones
for a nation dedicated to liberty! It was soon replaced by a
wreath.[28]

The design that finally became standard for both the cent
and the half-cent contained only one significant addition—a
liberty cap! Suspended on a liberty pole, behind and slightly
above the figure, was an unmistakable Phrygian liberty cap.
This, of course, was a republican symbol, a symbol of liberty,
but it was a French symbol which in the United States was primarily associated with the Republicans who advocated French
friendship. It was a taunt to the other party, although after
Robert Scot became engraver, it was a beautiful taunt. His
"Liberty" emerged as a lovely young woman in place of the
Medusa-locked female who had first appeared. So long as Rit-

[28] *Debates and Proceedings in the Congress of the U.S. . . . Second
Congress* (Washington, 1849), 483–89.

tenhouse remained director of the Mint, the liberty cap remained. When Federalist Elias Boudinot succeeded to the office, he lost little time in dropping the cap from the cent; a year later, he discontinued coinage of the half-cent—cap and all.

Rittenhouse never hesitated to affirm his political beliefs or to use his name and office to promote his faith, but he retained a strong sense of propriety. As a matter of course, he was reelected president of the Democratic Society on January 2, 1794 —just as he was reelected president of the Philosophical Society on the day following. In the case of the Democratic Society, the question now arose whether the group opposed Federal measures so directly that an officer of the Federal government ought not to lend the society his name. Already Charles Biddle had withdrawn from the organization, declining to stand again for the office he had been given, unsought. A series of resolutions the society adopted on January 9 underlined the problem. This time the society not only praised France but referred to her as an ally and attacked Britain for failing to fulfill her treaty obligations.[29]

The next day, Rittenhouse submitted his resignation—on the grounds that a president who did not attend was not a satisfactory officer. He further requested that his name not be affixed to the resolutions because he had not been present when they were adopted—although he asserted that they had his "most cordial approbation." [30]

This withdrawal removed Rittenhouse from participation in politics just before violence erupted. In May, the Democratic Society adopted still more inflammatory resolutions, this time against the United States excise tax. In consequence, the Whiskey Rebellion, which followed, was laid to the charge of the democratic societies, not only by Federalist journalists but by Washington himself, whose single pronouncement of disap-

[29] Democratic Soc. Mins., 1793–94, 30–38, HSP.
[30] DR to Benjamin Franklin Bache, Jan. 10, 1794, Franklin Papers, HSP.

probation was credited with destroying the societies as a political force.[31]

With Jefferson out of office, Sergeant and Hutchinson dead, and Rittenhouse's friends in state and national government under assault, the political clouds again turned black. The impeachment trial of John Nicholson by the Pennsylvania Senate was particularly unpleasant because it recalled his own experiences. Ably defended by William Bradford and supported by Albert Gallatin and other Republicans, the comptroller general's long and grueling defense succeeded. Nicholson's career in government was none the less ended; he resigned as soon as the sentence of acquittal was delivered, and his place was quickly filled by John Donnaldson. More time and more violence were required to bring Nicholson down, but the final result was no different from Rittenhouse's expulsion from the Treasury.[32]

The outward course of Rittenhouse's life shifted little in response to the unfavorable political outlook; the Mint, the canals, and the turnpike were more than sufficient to absorb his whole time, but he also maintained his attention to the Philosophical Society. He took great pleasure in seeing the third volume of *Transactions* issue from the press at the end of 1793, and he subscribed for five copies, the maximum bought by any of the members. His written contributions were limited to the comet he discovered, some odd astronomical observations, and the two papers on lightning, but this time he did not express unhappiness at the extent of his work represented. Inside the society and outside, his scientific stature was more secure than it had ever been.[33]

The society, however, had difficulty in recovering from the interruption of the yellow fever plague. A committee appointed

[31] *General Adver.*, May 11, 1794; William Miller, "First Fruits of the Republican Organization," *PMHB*, LXIII (1939), 138.
[32] Hiltzheimer, *Diary*, 202, 204; [Hogan], *Pa. State Trials*, 767-76.
[33] Subscription List for Transactions, June 25, 1793, APS; *Gaz. of the U.S.*, Dec. 20, 1793; APS, *Trans.*, III (1793), 261, 119-25.

to revive it met little success, and no paper worthy of the Magellanic Premium was submitted in 1794. Most of the papers and donations to the society continued to pass through the president's hands, including officially communicated reports on the French reform of weights and measures. Through the society, Rittenhouse was brought into contact with Joseph Priestley, the English chemist who emigrated to Pennsylvania in the middle of 1794, and he chaired the committee which drew up an official welcome. Priestley's scientific accomplishments as well as his political views made him congenial to most of the members and especially to Rittenhouse. The Philadelphians were unable to keep him in the city with either a chair in the University or a Unitarian pulpit, but he often visited from Northumberland County, where he made his home. On these occasions, he sometimes stayed with Rittenhouse and he always asked for the astronomer when he wrote to his Philadelphia friends.[34]

In the community, Rittenhouse remained the great scientific arbiter. Samuel Hopkins had received the first patent ever granted by the United States, for his method of producing pot and pearl ash; but he had trouble converting it into money. He found it preferable to highlight in his newspaper advertising a few endorsements by men who checked his process in 1793—including especially Rittenhouse. Again, when Matthew Carey brought out the first American edition of William Guthrie's *New System of Modern Geography* in February 1794, he prominently announced, "THE ASTRONOMICAL PARTS CORRECTED BY DR. RITTENHOUSE." The data on Uranus was certainly Rittenhouse's, but his most valuable contribution, once again, was his name.[35]

Aside from his continuing attention to the observatory, Rittenhouse's only independent research in this period related to

[34] APS Mins., 1793-98, 20-21, 27, 43, 45-47; Priestley to B. S. Barton, June 16, 1796, APS.
[35] Samuel Hopkins Patent, July 31, 1790, Chicago Hist. Soc. (through the courtesy of Mr. Evans Kahn); *Pa. Gaz.*, July 3, 1793, Apr. 8, 1794; Guthrie, *New System*, 32.

clockmaking and the astronomer's need for a more accurate clock. He turned his thoughts to the "last and least" of the factors causing pendulum irregularity; to the effect of the changing density of the air. He recognized that greater air density, or higher barometric pressure, increased the buoyant force acting on the bob and effectively retarded its descent. At the same time, of course, this change advanced its ascent, but not in exactly the same measure. He constructed a pendulum with the point of suspension at the center of a rod, the ends of which carried bodies of equivalent shape and volume—but the bottom body was heavy and served as the bob while its counterpart at the top was hollow and as light as possible. The buoyant force acting on each would be equal, so that the component opposing rotation on one body would always be exactly balanced by the component of the equivalent buoyant force aiding rotation on the other body.[36]

Rittenhouse made a few experiments comparing the behavior of the pendulum in water with its behavior in air, the results of which seemed to confirm his ideas. However, the error for which he sought to compensate was much less than even he imagined, and it was also less than the "barometric error," or the change in resistance to pendulum motion caused by each change in the density of the air. This error would have been doubled by his pendulum. He did not carry his investigations to the point of practical application, however. He left them as the demonstration of an idea about the effects of buoyant force on pendulum motion.[37]

His attention was directed to so many different objects that he had even less time than usual to pursue such ideas, but he did not curb the friendliness he always extended to congenial souls. To the visiting Italian sculptor, Giuseppe Ceracchi, for example, he was conspicuously kind. He entertained him and took him along on one of his canal inspection trips to point out

[36] APS, *Trans.,* iv (1799), 26–28.
[37] See George L. Overton, *Clocks and Watches* (London, 1922), 37–39.

the kinds of stone, especially marble, native to that part of the country. In return, Cerrachi, who was disappointed in his hope of doing a great monument celebrating the American Revolution, carved a bust of his host and presented it to the Philosophical Society in 1795 before he left the country.[38]

On the other hand, William De Peyster reported to Peale that when he was introduced to Rittenhouse, the astronomer lost all interest in conversation as soon as De Peyster confessed that he had no knowledge of natural philosophy. The testimony of all who knew Rittenhouse well suggests that this was a matter of diffidence and lack of small talk rather than the overweening rudeness De Peyster read into his behavior.[39]

With John Nicholson, Rittenhouse was indulgent but not unguarded. In an early partnership, Nicholson had contracted to do some of the work on the Delaware and Schuylkill Canal, but after he left the comptroller general's office he applied his major energy to a vast speculative empire in western lands which soon became an object of wonder. Associated in part with Robert Morris, he approached Rittenhouse more than once to solicit investment in his properties and companies. Rittenhouse responded to a point; most of the small sum he invested in land went through Nicholson, but thereafter he refused further participation even though Nicholson pledged his own word to save him from any loss. He was well-advised, for Nicholson descended, in company with Morris, more rapidly than he had arisen—a bankrupt by millions of dollars.[40]

The summer of 1794 brought a return of yellow fever, but the plague was not as extensive and it did not dislocate things as much as before. In the Rittenhouse family, the season, but not the fever, claimed another life. Nicholas Waters, Hetty's

[38] APS Mins., 1793–98, 62.

[39] De Peyster to Peale, May 4, 1796, Peale-Sellers Letters, v, 20, APS.

[40] A. Donaldson and J. Nicholson Contract, Apr. 24, 1793, Union Canal Co. Papers, Berks County Hist. Soc.; DR to Nicholson, Nov. 29, 1794, Gilbert Coll., iii, 395, College of Physicians, Phila.; Anthony, *Report on Liens*, 4–6.

husband, died on August 20 of a respiratory infection. Now both girls were widows and all the grandchildren, fatherless. Both daughters and their families spent the balance of the summer at Norriton, but Rittenhouse and Hannah remained, at least for a large part of the summer, in the city.[41]

Before and after the plague season, the successes of the Mint were less obvious than its problems and the criticism that began to rise against it. Over a million copper pieces were coined in 1794—a total not substantially exceeded until 1800—and a beginning was made in silver coinage. Half-dimes, half-dollars, and dollars were issued, all to a fineness that differed markedly from the specifications laid down by Congress. The act of April 2, 1792, required a fineness of 892.4, distinctly more base than the better issues of the Spanish dollar and equivalent coins. Since the weight was also specified this fineness would have left American coins deficient in value. Rittenhouse's assays uncovered the error, and he decided to conform the silver coins to the intention of the law rather than to its letter.[42]

He encountered no end of internal problems. Some were minor: the city refused him permission to erect a small building and furnace on one of the public squares. Some were temporary: deficits in Mint operations he covered out of his own pocket. He always recovered this money when additional warrants were issued, but he could not escape the rising pressure to cut costs. Nicholas Way, who succeeded Tristram Dalton as treasurer, reported that Rittenhouse paid for work done at the Mint out of his own salary whenever he felt the charge was more than the government should bear. William Barton documented this assertion with the case of a fine scale which his uncle refused to charge against the Mint. Such petty economies did not reduce the pressure, however, which was sufficient to

[41] Barton, *Memoirs*, 50n.; Hannah Rittenhouse to Elizabeth Sergeant, Sep. 22, 29, [1794], Photocopy, HSP.
[42] DR to Jefferson, Jan. 7, 1793, Jefferson Papers, LC; Ingersoll, *Abridgement of Acts of Congress*, 416-21; David K. Watson, *History of American Coinage* (N.Y., 1899), 251-53.

prevent badly needed expenditures. Most strikingly, it prevented the installation of a steam engine, which would unquestionably have been costly in that stage of its development but which was badly needed to roll the silver used in dollar coinage.[43]

The supply of metals was never wholly satisfactory. War interfered with the importation of copper, and, when copper was available, Rittenhouse worried about large purchases pushing up the market price. Matthew Boulton continued his readiness to supply from Birmingham copper strips, planchets, finished coins, or even a complete mint such as the Russians purchased from him. Rittenhouse was not responsive to such solutions because to him a national mint transcended the story that could be read in the ledgers; it was an attribute of sovereignty.[44]

Silver presented a different series of problems. At the beginning of this coinage, more silver in bar or ingot form was offered to the Mint than was needed, but it usually required refining to bring it to the designated standard of fineness. In European mints, the supplier was responsible for refining his silver before offering it, but, in the United States, the Mint had to assume this function, which placed an additional charge on its operations. Yet, the pressure for economy prevented authorization of a refiner until March 1795, and even then Rittenhouse hesitated to hire one.[45]

By the end of the year, external criticism rose to serious proportions. On December 9, Joshua Coit of Connecticut introduced in the House of Representatives a resolution calling for an investigation of the Mint. Elias Boudinot, following his dramatization of the shortcomings of the Mint, was appointed

[43] Phila. Common Council Mins., Apr. 1, 3, 1793, City Hall Annex; Rush, *Eulogium*, 40; Barton, *Memoirs*, 389n.; DR to Jefferson, July 19, 1794, Nat. Arch.

[44] Ralph Mather to Matthew Boulton, Nov. 19, 1792, Birmingham Assay Office; Mint Day Book, 1795–98, 62, *ibid.*

[45] Ingersoll, *Abridgement of Acts of Congress*, 423–24.

chairman of the investigating committee. He told a story of going to the Bank of the United States, where he was informed that there were no cents to be had because they could not be obtained from the Mint. At the Mint, he was told that cents were not coined faster because the mint officers did not know where to get them vented. He reported that the establishment cost $24,000 a year to maintain, which meant that each cent cost several cents to produce; he added that New Jersey had bought copper cents on private contract at a fraction of this cost. Other congressmen filled in the picture with charges that the shortage of copper coin in distant parts of the country was almost total; the Mint benefited only the Philadelphia region, and that very slightly.[46]

Soon the Mint was swarming with questioners and investigators. Rittenhouse and all of the principal officers of the Mint wrote out responses to specific inquiries. Nicholas Way stood by Rittenhouse with traditional adulation, but the views of Henry Voight and Albion Cox reflected a significant conflict. Voight staunchly and unyieldingly defended the Mint and Rittenhouse; Cox, with reluctance that was probably sincere, lodged serious charges.[47]

Albion Cox's position is not as simple and obvious as that of Voight, who had built the Mint and felt personally affronted by any criticism of it. Cox knew the Boulton mint, which Voight had never seen, and he knew that the Philadelphia Mint fell short of it in many respects. He told Boudinot that, if the defects of the Mint were not remedied, it must very shortly be destroyed. He referred him for practical information on how coinage should be managed to John Harper, with whom Cox had been associated in the New Jersey cent contract and who had earlier sold some of his coining machinery to the Mint. Soon, however, the motivation behind Cox's antagonism to the

[46] *Debates and Proc., Third Congress,* 971–72; Callender, *Am. Annual Register,* 70–75.
[47] Nicholas Way, Answers, Dec. 20, 1794, Nat. Arch.; Whithead, "Survey," 167; Albion Cox to Boudinot, Jan. 8, 1795, Nat. Arch.

Mint was subjected to question by charges laid against him. He was said to have engaged in "forming private works with others," incompatible with his association with the Mint. More serious still, a shortage of $974.75 in silver was charged to Cox, of which only $428.47 could be recovered.[48]

An independent opinion was offered by James Davy, an Englishman also familiar with the Boulton mint, in which he confirmed and spelled out the defects Cox reported. His analysis should have been very useful. He emphasized the familiar problems, the irregular supply of metal and the inadequate power source, but he pointed to several detailed improvements that might be made. He showed ways in which the machinery could be bettered and he urged further division of labor. When, however, he suggested the use of child labor, he entered an area in which economy was not the sole consideration.[49]

The defects Davy referred to were real enough, and Voight's disdain for "a prejudiced Englishman" did not eliminate them.[50] Neither his defense nor that of Page and Madison on the floors of Congress pointed to the real difficulty, however, which lay in unreasonable expectations. The legislation provided that gold and silver coins would contain their nominal value in metal and that the public would assume the costs of coinage. To make money, then, would inevitably cost money. Since the overhead charge against coining an eagle, or ten-dollar gold piece, would not differ much from the charge for coining a half-cent, the rising coinage of silver and the coming coinage of gold would greatly reduce the percentage cost of the dollar output of coins. Furthermore, the entire investment in land, machinery, and labor could not reasonably be written off against the initial output of coppers.

In the end, Boudinot's report recognized the real problems and exonerated Rittenhouse. It stated categorically that the

[48] Ibid.; Am. State Papers, Finance, I, 357; Stewart, First Mint, 90.
[49] James Davy to Edmund Randolph, Dec. 27, 1794, Nat. Arch.
[50] Whithead, "Survey," 167.

complaints of heavy expenses were without foundation. It urged improved business methods, wider distribution of coin, and legislation to specify a finer standard for silver and a smaller weight of copper in the cents and half-cents. Its more fundamental recommendations could only have increased immediate costs: more power, either steam or water, and the engagement of a refiner—needs long obvious to the director.[51]

Rittenhouse waited only until the report was in before submitting his resignation, to become effective June 30, 1795. He had been dissuaded several times from resigning, but now he was finished. His health and his attitude had, before this, restricted him more than ever to his home. He did not visit the Mint every day, although when he did not, he received reports in his home. He had stopped attending the sessions of the Philosophical Society almost entirely.[52]

In the sequel, Henry William de Saussure spent four unhappy months as Rittenhouse's successor, and left office praising all the works of the first director. Elias Boudinot came in as the third director and ran a much tauter ship, but, for several years, he was unable to raise production levels significantly although he did increase running expenses. He bypassed problems of rolling by buying planchets from Boulton, as Rittenhouse— on principle—had refused to do. Years later, in Jefferson's presidency, the liberty caps Boudinot removed from the coins were restored, placed squarely on the head of "Liberty." [53]

[51] *Am. State Papers, Finance,* I, 355.
[52] Edmund Randolph to DR, Apr. 22, 1795, Nat. Arch.; APS Mins., *passim.*
[53] The liberty cap appeared in 1807 on the half-dollar and half-eagle.

CHAPTER XXI

The Final Occultation
1795–1796

WITH Rittenhouse's retirement on June 30, 1795, he was freer from obligations than he had ever been. He retained the presidency of the Philosophical Society but no longer attended except for the annual election meetings. He continued as a trustee of the University of Pennsylvania and a manager of the Delaware and Schuylkill Canal but contributed regularly to neither. Most of his other connections fell by default. The bulk of his time he spent in his observatory, in his garden, and at home with his family. In this period of quiet retreat, his stature as an elder statesman of science and of public service was secure; some of his finest honors reached him at this time.

The year 1795 brought recognition from both Britain and France. The Earl of Buchan sent over a curious memorial, a writing box with a representation of Copernicus on its lid and one of Napier inside. It was dedicated to Rittenhouse's use during his lifetime and to the use of his successors in the presidency of the Philosophical Society, thereafter. From France, Lalande saluted him with praise for his astronomical observations reported in the third volume of the *Transactions*. He invited correspondence.[1]

Phineas Bond, the British consul in Philadelphia, informally reported the highest award in June 1795, and it was confirmed a few months later. Rittenhouse was elected, on the foreign list, to the Royal Society of London—long the premier scientific accolade in the English-speaking world. The significance of

[1] Barton, *Memoirs*, 423–27, 432–[34].

this was heightened by the coolness which still marked the attitude of Britain toward America. Rittenhouse was one of only two Americans elected between the Revolution and 1800. Among those who supported his election were Henry Cavendish, Nevil Maskelyne, and Jesse Ramsden, the instrument maker.[2]

Rittenhouse pushed himself less now than he had during most of his life. Benjamin Smith Barton reported that his uncle "was not a laborious student" in his declining years. His reading ranged widely but was desultory; he looked into many books but worked on few. Rush asserted that no man ever found him unemployed; but he also observed that in these months Rittenhouse sometimes spent whole evenings with his enlarged family.[3]

With the death of his two sons-in-law, his home indeed assumed an altogether different character. Betsy, Hetty, and the four grandchildren transformed the big house on Seventh and Mulberry. In 1795, Betsy's daughters were six and two, and her son, less than a month older than Hetty's son, was four. Incredibly, both boys were named David Rittenhouse! Two little "Davys" running around the house could not but have reduced the quiet of an old man's retirement.[4]

Rittenhouse undertook no large projects of public character, but he did respond to a couple of appointments. In May 1795, he accepted chairmanship of a committee to plan a lottery just authorized by the Pennsylvania legislature in an effort to bail out both the Susquehanna and Schuylkill and the Delaware and Schuylkill Canal Companies. If the projected $400,000 could be raised in this fashion, canal construction might continue. Rittenhouse's committee exercised general supervision, col-

[2] *Ibid.*, 430-31; Raymond P. Stearns, "Colonial Fellows of the Royal Society," *William and Mary Quar.*, 3d ser., III (1946), 268n.; the other American was James Bowdoin.

[3] Barton, *Memoirs*, 604; Rush, *Eulogium*, 38, 40.

[4] DR, Notebook, 1785-92, APS, under date Aug. 4, 1791 records "Rittenhouse born," which appears to establish the birth date of David Rittenhouse Waters.

lected the $10 paid for each ticket, and deposited the receipts in the Bank of the United States. The drawing was scheduled for September 1, but was deferred until the 28th, and even then the subscription was nowhere nearly filled. The drawing began, nevertheless, and was continued from day to day at the same time that strenuous efforts were made to sell more tickets. Into 1796, broadsides and newspaper advertisements sought to stimulate interest; announcements of the "state of the wheel"— the prizes yet to be drawn—were regularly made. In the end, the results were too poor to encourage a renewal of hope, and before long the companies' stocks were listed at zero value.[5]

More successful was Rittenhouse's service as one of three state commissioners to provide for the inspection of gunpowder. He helped to develop plans for a building to house the activities of an inspector of gunpowder which the governor approved and proceeded to carry out along with other recommendations of the commissioners.[6]

Rittenhouse did not show any disposition to finish tedious tasks he had passed over in earlier years when too heavily employed. This was notably true of his failure to complete repairs on the Princeton orrery, portions of which had been in his hands for that purpose for several years. In the summer or early fall of 1795, the Reverend Dr. Ashbel Green called on Rittenhouse in the name of the Board of Trustees of the College of New Jersey to request that he complete the repairs as soon as possible. He promised to comply, "health permitting," but he never did; he never even made a good beginning.[7]

Green called willingly, because Rittenhouse was a member of the congregation of his Second Presbyterian Church. From 1779 or 1780, he shared the rent of a gallery pew, most of this

[5] *Aurora*, July 5, 1795, Jan. 19, 1796; *Claypoole's Am. Daily Adver.*, Feb. 3, 1796; Broadside: Canal Lottery, No. Two, Apr. 20, 1796, HSP; *Pa. Arch.*, 9th ser., II, 978–83, 1021.
[6] *Ibid.*, 997.
[7] Rice, *Rittenhouse Orrery*, 54–55; *Dunlap's Am. Daily Adver.*, Jan. 12, 1793.

time with Azariah Horton, a Philadelphian who served for a time as treasurer of the Society for Promoting the Improvement of Roads and Inland Navigation. Founded by the "new lights," the Second Presbyterian had been the church of George Bryan, John Nicholson, and other of Rittenhouse's political associates. He attended so infrequently, however, that even William Barton did not realize he maintained a pew there.[8]

The clergy never ceased to worry about Rittenhouse's religious views. Green once quoted the Reverend Mr. James Sproat, his predecessor, to the effect that Rittenhouse had asserted his belief in everything contained in the Bible, and Rush asserted that he accepted the most essential doctrines of Christianity. But no direct statement in which he approved Christianity or accepted it has been preserved. Rittenhouse was a deeply religious man in the true sense of the word, but he undoubtedly remained more a deist than a Christian.[9]

Hannah, who probably knew best the direction of his thoughts, would not commit herself concerning them. She commented that he was in the habit of thinking much more than he chose to say and that he did not "consider it necessary to proclaim to the world" his religious opinions. She provided an almost decisive clue in reporting, "Dr. Price's Opinions Respecting Christianity Were More in Unison with His Own than Almost any other of the Divines." Richard Price, of course, was a very liberal dissenter, who usually dealt with the moral rather than the doctrinal and in many sermons anchored his thoughts on observations of nature as the works of God. These sermons, according to Hannah, most appealed to Rittenhouse.[10]

Rittenhouse's science took an odd turn. Whether because his interests moved in that direction, or because he felt he should demonstrate proficiency in mathematics, he produced one ex-

[8] Second Presbyterian Church, Pew Rent Books, 1779, 1781, 1783–89, 1793; Mins. of the Corporation, II, 223–24, Presbyterian Hist. Soc., Phila.
[9] Rush to William Barton, draft, May 20, 1812, Rush Papers, LCP.
[10] Hannah to Rush, Aug. 20, 1797, *ibid.*; Richard Price, *Sermons on the Security and Happiness of a Virtuous Course* (Phila., 1788).

perimental and two mathematical papers—and none in observational astronomy. His experimental interests had been constant, but he had not written his first mathematical paper until 1794.

The experimental study was a continuation of an old problem and largely a repetition of work he had done several years before but never published. He carried through a fine series of tests of the linear expansion of wood with heat, directed to the problem of controlling the rate of going of a clock. He sought to test the assertion, sometimes made, that wood did not expand with heat, like metal, and hence would not be liable to the error produced by expansion and contraction in a metal pendulum rod.

Carefully, he provided for measurement and control. He used a microscope equipped with a micrometer to measure the change in length of a thirty-nine-inch hickory rod which he placed, under tension, inside a pyrometer. He discovered an irregularity in expansion and contraction which decreased once the rod was thoroughly dry and which he consequently attributed to the effects of moisture. His trials were so carefully conducted that both the data he obtained in 1789 and the figures he gave the Philosophical Society in 1795 yield values close to current estimates of the coefficient of thermal expansion. But Rittenhouse's most important result was the discovery that expansion varied with both temperature and moisture content in a manner that made control of an exposed pendulum very difficult. The expansion, however, was less than that for "any of the metals or even glass." [11]

One of the mathematical papers was brief and limited in significance. In it, he offered a method that depended only on arithmetical operations for finding logarithms good to the ninth place. He used little but division, extractions of roots, and com-

[11] DR, Notebook, 1785–92, Feb. 2, 1789, *passim*, APS; APS, *Trans.*, IV (1799), 29–31; his figures yield a coefficient of .00000208 inches per inch per degree centigrade, which compares well with established coefficients for similar woods. See *Timber Design and Construction Handbook* (N.Y., 1956), 8.

pound fractions, but, after going through lengthy operations, he attained good results.[12]

The second mathematical paper was more ambitious. Here, he offered an original solution for finding the place of a planet in its orbit—a classic problem represented by Kepler's equation, $M = E - e \sin E$. Kepler had given the first approximate answer for a special case, and Newton worked out a general approach based on the cycloid, which provided an approximate geometrical solution for special applications. Rittenhouse's work suggests that he studied the geometrical methods of Newton and followed them. Beginning with the mean anomaly (the angular distance of the planet from its perihelion) and the eccentricity, he made use of converging series to provide separate approaches for the required distance in the upper half and the lower half of the orbit. His solution freed the denominators of the terms in his series from powers involving the eccentricity, facilitating computation and increasing accuracy, especially when the eccentricity is large. The paper showed again the enjoyment he derived from mathematics, but it is not at a level with his best experimental work.[13]

Indeed, in terms of his former successes, Rittenhouse was inactive. He continued in the presidency of the Philosophical Society, and, in January 1796, he returned to the presidency of the Democratic Society. Despite the cloud which hung over the latter society following the Whiskey Rebellion and the Genêt affair, he did not hesitate to place himself at its head—now that he was free of Federal office. He did not attend the sessions of either group or venture abroad for many occasions. Once he met with the trustees of the University, and, in March 1796, he attended a special dinner given for Priestley, who was in the city for a series of lectures that spring.[14]

In April 1796, Rittenhouse agreed to run as a presidential elector for Thomas Jefferson; again his reputation was expected

[12] APS, *Trans.*, IV (1799), 29-31.
[13] *Ibid.*, 21-26; Rufus, "Rittenhouse," 230-31.
[14] *Claypoole's Am. Daily Adver.*, Jan. 13, 1796; Trustees Mins., V, 148, Univ. of Pa.

to strengthen the ticket. In June, he visited his nephew, Benjamin Smith Barton to observe studies he was making of the opossum—a subject to which Jefferson had earlier called his attention. In fact, the Virginian had sent Rittenhouse the speculations of his own nephew, Thomas Mann Randolph, on the unusual animal.[15]

Frequently but not seriously ill, Rittenhouse several times expressed the feeling during that spring that his career was at an end. He remained much with his family, read Rousseau and Pascal but pursued no serious study, and was more than usually depressed.

Then, on June 22, he suffered an attack so severe that Barton was summoned to attend him. The doctor diagnosed the disease as cholera, although the body temperature was higher than usual in that complaint and was accompanied by a great increase of pain and oppression in the region of the stomach or duodenum, where Rittenhouse had always experienced intermittent trouble. When the symptoms grew worse on the following day, Dr. Adam Kuhn was called in to consult. Rittenhouse then permitted his nephew to draw some blood, despite his lifelong opposition to the practice. He reported "relief" following the operation but remained convinced that he was not going to recover.[16]

On the same day, his lawyer, Peter Thompson, was called in to write up the will. This proved a difficult and unpleasant task—perhaps the reason it had been delayed so long. The problem followed from Hannah's not being the mother of his two daughters. All three women would soon be widows and he was anxious to provide for each as well as possible; beyond that, he wanted the residue of his estate to pass through his daughters to his grandchildren.

The beginning was easy; he left the house, the "Rittenhouse mansion," to Hannah during her lifetime, to pass to the two

[15] Tinkcom, *Republicans and Federalists,* 304.
[16] Barton, *Memoirs,* 441–45.

girls at her death. Then he separated from his personal property a $1,500 bond which he gave to Betsy—because he had sometime earlier given an equivalent amount to Hetty. The balance, he began to divide equally between the two girls, except for the Norriton farm, which he gave for the balance of her life to his sister, Eleanor, who was then occupying it. He stopped at one troublesome item. He thought first of assigning his household goods and five shares of the Bank of North America to Hannah for her lifetime use, but he dismissed Thompson without deciding finally upon it. Two days later he willed to Hannah outright, the furnishings, the bank stock, and ten additional shares of the Bank of the United States. This proved to be an almost exact three-way division of his personal property.[17]

Even if the arithmetic was still easy for him, the thoughts surrounding it were painful. Barton reported that throughout the illness he preserved "a most happy temperament of mind," and Hannah wrote nothing directly contradictory, but in the final days Rittenhouse found fault with everything she did. When she reminded him of his intention of establishing a family burial ground in the observatory, he asked her to say no more about it. When she reported that she had turned friends away from the door because he was too weak to talk, he reproved her with the comment that he could at least have squeezed their hands. On his last day, he reminded her that she had forgotten to finish Price's sermon on "The Goodness of God," which she had been reading him.[18]

His shortness of temper was in part a result of pain, and in part it reflected the peculiar outlook of a dying man; but there was more. At this confrontation with death, he could not think of his family without recalling Eleanor, half-myth though she had become. No one whom his life had touched ever meant

[17] DR, Will, June 23, 1796, Photocopy, HSP; [Peter Thompson], Notes on Rittenhouse's Will, June 23, 1796, Gratz Coll., HSP.
[18] Barton, *Memoirs*, 444; Hannah to Rush, Aug. 20, 1797, Rush Papers, LCP.

half so much or burned half so deeply. In 1793, when Betsy lost her husband, he expressed the wish that she might learn to set a "proper value" on life—and "no more." This he knew he had conspicuously failed to do with Eleanor; on his own life, he imagined that he set no very high value.[19]

During the evening of the 25th, the pain became severe, and a poultice of meal and laudanum was applied externally. Less than two hours later, Barton called to ask whether he did not feel more comfortable. "Yes," Rittenhouse replied calmly, in a manner cherished by those generations which looked on dying words as windows to a world beyond, "you have made the way to God easier." [20]

About midnight, Rittenhouse became mildly delerious and Hannah left the room, unable to contend with her feelings. Only Barton and Hetty were at his side at ten minutes before two in the morning, when he at last found the way to peace.

[19] DR to Hannah, Oct. 22, 1793, Photocopy, HSP.
[20] Barton, *Memoirs*, 444.

CHAPTER XXII

The Afterglow

ALTHOUGH the man was dead, the image of David Rittenhouse persisted. He had become a part of the substance of men's thoughts and even of their way of thinking. David Rittenhouse was a synonym for precise knowledge, for integrity, and for science in the service of man. He was the American mechanic rising to greatness. Because of him, men looked forward confidently to American achievement in science and to the beneficent effect of science upon the lives and morals of mankind.

It did not matter that few comprehended the significance of his observations and his experimental studies or that men misinterpreted his orrery, his compass, and his Mint. They knew correctly that his craftsmanship was exquisite, his wartime services critical, his politics lofty, his contributions to the economy numerous, and his science always competent and sometimes creative. Yet all who had heard the name of David Rittenhouse realized that there was something more—throughout his life he had lived an ideal which now became a part of the American heritage.

His funeral was quiet. The newspapers burst forth with poetic praise but there was no public procession, no church service. His family, a few friends, members of the American Philosophical Society, and members of the Democratic Society of Pennsylvania gathered at his home and in his garden. There, at six o'clock on the evening of June 27, the Reverend Dr. Ashbel Green offered a very short address. He attempted no eulogy but his reflections recalled the faith Rittenhouse had proclaimed back in 1775 when he looked forward to a paradise in which his understanding of nature and his capacity for virtue would be vastly expanded. That state of bliss, Green knew, he had now attained. With accurate understanding of the meaning of David Rittenhouse, he exhorted the mourners: "Go from this tomb, and resolve to aim at the high destiny of our nature. Rightly aiming at this, we shall fill up life with usefulness and duty." [1]

Few who recorded their attendance at the funeral failed to remark the unusual place of burial. Rittenhouse's body was laid beneath the floor of his observatory at a spot soon afterward marked by a marble slab upon which was inscribed only his name, the date of his death, and his age. The symbolism particularly struck Moreau de St. Méry, who wrote excitedly, "How philosophically significant, this union of his perishable ashes with a building dedicated to the observation of the more sublime wonders of nature! What a contrast between man's nothingness and his genius!" [2]

Through his monument, through his works, and through his reputation, the faith of David Rittenhouse reached many. His hard and quiet faith rested on man: on man's ability to make some sense of his world and on man's duty to build as well as his knowledge permitted. This was the heritage he left and despite its strength, his death left also a void. His place as a man of science was not soon filled. For many years, Americans looked back over the heads of men of lesser eminence and lamented that they could find none to compare. They were at least fortunate that the slowly receding image was of such a man.

[1] *Gazette of the U.S.*, June 27, 1796; *Aurora*, June 27, 1796; *New-York Magazine*, n.s., 1 (1796), 378–80; *Phila. Gaz.*, June 28, 1796.

[2] Hiltzheimer, *Diary*, 229; Samuel Emlen, Jr., to William Dillwyn, July 15, 1796, LCP; Moreau de St. Méry, *Journey*, 218.

Bibliographical Note

D AVID RITTENHOUSE left behind him few writings of any sort. His personal correspondence was limited because most of his acquaintances were neighbors, and his published scientific papers were small in bulk. Yet, the offices and commissions he accepted in government, in private institutions, and in service organizations were recorded officially and noted in newspapers and in private correspondence. His craftsmanship and engineering left behind numerous three-dimensional records. Many of his contemporaries reflected his deep influence. When the widely scattered documents and artifacts are squeezed, they yield an impressive quantity of information.

The Minutes, Archives, and Miscellaneous Manuscripts of the American Philosophical Society are rich sources because most of Rittenhouse's scientific life revolved about this institution. The Franklin Papers and Bache Papers are useful and the three manuscript notebooks kept by Rittenhouse even more valuable. In addition, the society holds Rittenhouse's transit telescope, his astronomical clock, a surveyor's compass he may have made, Ceracchi's bust of him, and Peale's portrait of 1792.

The Historical Society of Pennsylvania has Rittenhouse letters, receipts, and orders widely scattered through its extensive collections. The most significant materials are found in the William Henry Papers, the Benjamin Smith Barton Papers, the Jacobs Papers, the Penn Papers, and the Brinton Collection of William Smith Papers. The minutes of the Democratic Society of Pennsylvania, the Pennsylvania Society for the Encouragement of Manufactures and the Useful Arts, and the Society for Promoting the Improvement of Roads and Inland Navigation are important. The Rittenhouse Bicentennial Celebration of 1932 provided the opportunity for the Historical Society to

367

acquire photostatic copies of Rittenhouse materials, of which most of the originals remain in private hands. At the same time, photographs of Rittenhouse clocks and instruments were collected. The society owns one clock.

The University of Pennsylvania possesses good minutes of its Board of Trustees throughout the period Rittenhouse was associated with the institution, as well as other related manuscript materials. It has placed its Rittenhouse orrery in a deservedly conspicuous place in its new library, it owns an unusual Rittenhouse clock with one hand, and the Peale portrait of 1772.

Also in the city, the Library Company of Philadelphia has important materials in its Benjamin Rush Papers, in the Minutes of its Board of Directors, and in its John Fitch volumes. It also owns a striking watercolor of the Rittenhouse mansion. The Presbyterian Historical Society has records documenting his relationship with the Second Presbyterian Church, and the Department of Records of the Philadelphia Yearly Meeting of the Society of Friends has more personal material relating to Eleanor. The Drexel Institute of Technology displays his most elaborate clock, and the Pennsylvania Hospital has one only slightly less remarkable. His will is filed in the City Hall, and references to him are found in the Common and Select Council Minutes preserved in the City Hall Annex. His birthplace still stands just off the Wissahickon Creek.

In Harrisburg, the Pennsylvania Historical and Museum Commission has custody of the ledgers, journals, waste books, and other materials that constituted the records of the Pennsylvania Treasury during the period Rittenhouse presided over it. The commission also holds the great bulk of the state archives throughout the time Rittenhouse served with the Committee and Council of Safety as well as with the Treasury. However, these have been published in the several series of *Pennsylvania Archives*—although sometimes inaccurately. The remaining manuscript records constitute only a portion of the published

Archives, many items of which have disappeared, some to reappear in other collections. The published *Archives* have been used in this study except for a couple of items found only in manuscript form.

Princeton University made excellent use of the reconstruction of its Rittenhouse orrery in 1953 to collect photographic copies of Rittenhouse material in the Minutes of its Board of Trustees and of materials and artifacts held elsewhere. It, too, has placed its orrery prominently in its new library.

In Washington, the Library of Congress has numbers of Rittenhouse items, the most numerous in the Thomas Jefferson Papers and among the Andrew Ellicott Letters. The National Archives preserves extensive records related to the United States Mint while Rittenhouse served as director. The Smithsonian Institution has two zenith sectors and at least one compass constructed by Rittenhouse.

Elsewhere in this country, Rittenhouse materials are widely scattered in institutional and private hands. The Roberts Collection at Haverford College has Rittenhouse items. The Berks County Historical Society holds the Union Canal Company Papers, including items from the period of Rittenhouse's canal activities. The Germantown Historical Society and the Montgomery County Historical Society have Rittenhouse instruments. Manuscripts important to the Rittenhouse story are held by the New York Public Library and by the New-York Historical Society, and New York University owns a Rittenhouse clock. Vernier compasses made by Rittenhouse are held by the New York State Library and the Gurley Museum.

Abroad, the most important manuscripts are the Matthew Boulton Papers in the Assay Office, Birmingham, England. Rittenhouse's skill as an instrument maker is best evaluated by comparing his work with the collections of the Science Museum in South Kensington, the Whipple Museum at Cambridge, the Museum of the History of Science at Oxford, and the National Maritime Museum at Greenwich. Across the Channel, revealing comparisons can be made with the collections of the National Museum for the History of Science at Leiden, the instruments of Jean Dominique, Comte de Cassini, in the Musée Astronomique of the Observatoire in Paris, and the instruments of Christian Meyer in the Heidelberg Sternwarte.

Rittenhouse published most of his scientific papers in the American Philosophical Society, *Transactions*, vols. 1–4 (1771–99). His papers in the second volume were reprinted in *Philosophical Papers* (London, 1787) and others were reprinted in various volumes of the *American Museum*. His papers on natural history appeared in the *Columbian Magazine*, vol. 1 (1786–87), and his report of experiments with the electric eel came out after his death in the *Philadelphia Medical and Physical Journal*, vol. 1 (1805). He published letters on science in the *Pennsylvania Gazette* (October 8, 1767) and in the *Pennsylvania Magazine*, vol. 1 (1776). He dealt with the history of astronomy in *An Oration, Delivered February 24, 1775, Before the American Philosophical Society* (Phila., 1775). His only literary publication was his translation of the Lessing play, which he called *Lucy Sampson, or the Unhappy Heiress, a Tragedy, in Five Acts* (Phila., 1789).

Some guidance to his usually undocumented contributions to several series of almanacs is provided in the text. He offered endorsements in several books which were sometimes printed in the newspapers as well as in the work itself. As vice president of the Council of Safety he signed a number of notices which appeared as broadsides and often as newspaper announcements also. Indeed, the newspapers were peppered with his letters, notices, and advertisements during his tenure in the Council of Safety, the Treasury, and the Loan Office. All of them reflected his impact, but the most responsive were the *Pennsylvania Chronicle* and the *Freeman's Journal*. His Treasury accounts are available in great detail in a series of booklets of somewhat varying title beginning with *A Brief View of the Accounts of the Treasury of Pennsylvania, From the time of the commencement of the Revolution to the First of October, 1781* (Phila., 1784). Other occasional publications of the comptroller general contain aspects of the financial record. Some of Rittenhouse's letters and reports on the Mint are contained in *American State Papers*, vol. 5, *Finances*, vol. 1 (Washington, 1832).

William Barton, *Memoirs of the Life of David Rittenhouse* (Phila., 1813), offers an indispensable and frustrating collection of Rittenhouse materials, the originals of which have largely disappeared. Excerpts are preserved here from Rittenhouse letters and from letters to and about him. Comparison with those original manuscripts which can be located gives confidence that Barton did not consciously alter or distort, although he did select only the portions he liked and he deleted words and phrases.

The papers of Rittenhouse's correspondents are invaluable, especially those of Thomas Jefferson, which can be best used in Julian P. Boyd (ed.), *The Papers of Thomas Jefferson* (16 vols., Princeton, 1950—). For the period after 1790, manuscripts or earlier editions of Jefferson papers must be used. For Franklin correspondence, the most reliable collection for Rittenhouse's period is Albert Henry Smyth (ed.), *The Writings of Benjamin Franklin* (10 vols., N.Y., 1905–7), but it too must be supplemented by earlier editions. Even John C. Fitzpatrick (ed.), *The Writings of George Washington* (39 vols., Washington, 1931–44), is insufficiently complete. Also useful are L. H. Butterfield (ed.), *Letters of Benjamin Rush* (2 vols., Princeton, 1951), Catharine Van C. Mathews, *Andrew Ellicott, His Life and Letters* (N.Y., 1908), Philip S. Foner (ed.), *Complete Writings of Thomas Paine* (2 vols., N.Y., 1945), and Lester J. Cappon (ed.), *The Adams-Jefferson Letters* (2 vols., Chapel Hill, 1959). The most pertinent diaries are: Christopher Marshall, *Extracts from the Diary* (Albany, 1877), Charles Biddle, *Autobiography* (Phila., 1883), and Jacob Hiltzheimer, *Extracts from the Diary* (Phila., 1893). The *Pennsylvania Maga-*

zine of History and Biography (87 vols., 1877—) is a mine of letters, journals, and articles.

Rittenhouse's role in government left a clear trail. For Pennsylvania, this begins with the *Colonial Records* (16 vols., Phila., 1852–53) and the *Pennsylvania Archives* (9 ser., 138 vols., Phila. and Harrisburg, 1852–1949). Imperative too, are the *Journals of the House of Representatives of the Commonwealth of Pennsylvania* (Phila., 1782), the *Minutes of the General Assembly of the Commonwealth of Pennsylvania* (Phila., 1781–92), and Thomas Lloyd, *Proceedings and Debates of the General Assembly* (4 vols., Phila., 1787–88). There are several collections of laws; Alexander J. Dallas (comp.) *Laws of the Commonwealth of Pennsylvania* (4 vols., Phila. and Lancaster, 1793–1801) is convenient. Pertinent cases are documented in Richard Peters, Jun., *The Whole Proceedings in the Case of Olmsted and Others versus Rittenhouse's Executrices* (Phila., 1809) and [Edmund Hogan], *The Pennsylvania State Trials* (Phila., 1794). Among the collections dealing with the boundary settlements are *Report of the Secretary of Internal Affairs of the Commonwealth of Pennsylvania, containing Reports of the Surveys and Resurveys of the Boundary Lines of the Commonwealth, accompanied with Maps of the Same* (Harrisburg, 1887) and *Report of the Regents of the University on the Boundaries of the State of New York* (Albany, 1874).

For the United States government, the legislative journals are useful: Worthington C. Ford (ed.), *Journals of the Continental Congress* (34 vols., Washington, 1904–37) and the *Debates and Proceedings in the Congress of the U.S.* (42 vols., Washington, 1834–56).

Biographical notices of Rittenhouse began to appear in his own day and a large number have since been written. The most ambitious and lengthy was William Barton's, which, as a biography, is unbalanced, uncritical, and poorly organized; yet, it is the beginning point in biography just as it is in the assembling of Rittenhouse documents. James Renwick, in 1839, wrote a "Life of David Rittenhouse," *The Library of American Biography*, edited by Jared Sparks (N.Y., 1839), vol. 7, pp. 295–398, which is largely a condensation of Barton. Edward Ford's *David Rittenhouse, Astronomer-Patriot, 1732–1796* (Phila., 1946), is a surprisingly full chronicle of the external facts. Of the shorter accounts, the best is Maurice J. Babb, "David Rittenhouse," *Pennsylvania Magazine of History and Biography*, 56 (1932), 193–224. Daniel K. Cassel's genealogical writings, especially *A Genea-Biographical History of the Rittenhouse Family* (Phila., 1893), contain glaring errors but, if used carefully and in conjunction with other genealogical studies, they are very helpful.

Studies of various aspects of Rittenhouse's work are important primarily for their assistance in evaluation. Howard C. Rice, Jr., *The Rittenhouse Orrery, Princeton's Eighteenth-Century Planetarium, 1767–1954, A Commentary on an Exhibition held in the Princeton University Library* (Princeton, 1954), offers an excellent discussion based both upon historical research and upon an analysis of the Princeton orrery itself, made possible by its restoration in 1952–1953. Thomas D. Cope, "The Rittenhouse Diffraction Grating," *Journal of the Franklin Institute*, 214 (1932), 99–104, is a careful appraisal by a physicist. Simon Newcomb, "Discussion of Observations of the Transits of Venus in 1761 and 1769," *Astronomical Papers Prepared for the Use of the American Ephemeris and Nautical Almanac* (Washington, 1891), II, 259–405, is an appraisal of an astronomical episode. Brooke and Helen M. Hindle, "David Rittenhouse and the Illusion of Reversible Relief," *Isis*, 50 (1959), 135–40, and the forthcoming Brooke Hindle, "David Rittenhouse's Theory of Magnetic Dipoles" (in the Acts of the Tenth International Congress of the History of Science, pp. 663–66) present evaluations of the achievement against the historical background. W. Carl Rufus, "David Rittenhouse as a Mathematical Disciple of Newton," *Scripta Mathematica*, 8 (1941), 228–31, although a mathematician's study, is too laudatory. A detailed literary analysis is presented in Heinrich Schneider, "Lessings *Miss Sara Sampson:* die erste Englische Uebersetzung," *Publications of the Modern Language Association of America,* 54 (1939), 483–95.

The American background of Rittenhouse's science is outlined in Brooke Hindle, *The Pursuit of Science in Revolutionary America* (Chapel Hill, 1956). The Philadelphia setting is described in Carl and Jessica Bridenbaugh, *Rebels and Gentlemen* (Phila., 1943). The early canal story is best told in [William Smith], *An Historical Account of the Rise, Progress and Present State of Canal Navigation in Pennsylvania* (Phila., 1795). The story of the Mint is offered in Frank H. Stewart, *History of the First United States Mint* (n.p., 1924). The setting for Rittenhouse's clockmaking is presented in George H. Eckhardt, *Pennsylvania Clocks and Clockmakers* (N.Y., 1955) and the setting for his instrument making in Charles E. Smart, *The Makers of Surveying Instruments in America since 1700* (Troy, 1962).

Rittenhouse's career in government and politics is neatly spanned by a series of surveys: Theodore Thayer, *Pennsylvania Politics and the Growth of Democracy, 1740–1760* (Harrisburg, 1953); Charles H. Lincoln, *The Revolutionary Movement in Pennsylvania, 1760–1776* (Phila., 1901); David Hawke, *In the Midst of a Revolution* (Phila., 1961); J. Paul Selsam, *The Pennsylvania Constitution of 1776* (Phila., 1936); Robert L. Brunhouse, *The Counter-Revolution in Pennsylvania, 1776–1790* (Harrisburg, 1942); and Harry M. Tinkcom, *Republicans and Federalists in Pennsylvania, 1790–1801* (Harrisburg, 1950). Suggestive too, is Elisha P. Douglass, *Rebels and Democrats* (Chapel Hill, 1955). Anne Bezanson, *et al., Prices and Inflation during the American Revolution, Pennsylvania 1770–1790* (Phila., 1951), is essential.

Of the many biographies, two must be used; the first excellent and the other very poor. Charles Coleman Sellers, *Charles Willson Peale* (2 vols., Phila., 1947), offers insights and new materials. Francis Jordan, *The Life of William Henry of Lancaster, 1729–1786* (Lancaster, 1910) offers a few excerpts from lost letters.

Among briefer studies of specific episodes involving Rittenhouse are: Brooke Hindle, "The March of the Paxton Boys," *William and Mary Quarterly*, 3d ser., 3 (1946), 461–86; Hampton L. Carson, "The Case of the Sloop 'Active,'" *Pennsylvania Magazine of History and Biography*, 16 (1892), 385–98; and Hubertis Cummings, "Robert Morris and the Episode of the Polacre 'Victorius,'" *Pennsylvania Magazine of History and Biography*, 70 (1946), 239–57. C. Doris Hellman, "Jefferson's efforts towards the Decimalization of United States Weights and Measures," *Isis*, 49 (1931), 266–314 must be used in conjunction with the editorial analysis presented in Boyd, *Papers of Jefferson*, XVI, 602–75.

Index

INDEX

INDEX

INDEX

Mannheim, Germany, 214
manufactures, 71, 85, 88, 125, 126–27, 128, 135, 136, 161–62, 290–91. *See also*, cannon, clocks
Marcus Hook, 125
Marshall, Christopher, 172
Marshall, Humphrey, 97
Martin, Benjamin, 28, 29, 34, 73, 228
Maryland, 216, 283
Maryland Flying Camp, 172
Maskelyne, Nevil, transit of Venus, 42, 47, 65–66, 69, 77, 80; projected Philadelphia observatory, 107, 108, 110; science, 110–11, 288, 314; Royal Society, 357
Mason, Charles, 21, 328
Mason and Dixon, 8, 66, 77, 282
Mason-Dixon line, 216, 217, 252, 253, 256, 263
Mason, George, 153
Massachusetts, 42, 68
mathematics, 14, 15, 34, 89, 221, 329, 359–61
mathematical instruments, *see* instruments
Matlack, Timothy, and Constitution of 1776, 146, 148, 151, 158–59, 165; Pennsylvania politics, 147, 166, 168, 170, 205, 209; resignation, 238, 239, 307; institutional activities, 221, 245–46, 320; and DR, 122, 201, 226
May Day, 1773, 123
Mayer, Christian, 214, 225
Mayer, Tobias, tables, 328
Mechanical Society, 272
Mechanics Association, 123–24
Mennonites, 12, 13, 14, 19
Mercury, 33, 116. *See also* transits of Mercury
meridian time, 328
Messier, Charles, 75–76
meteorology, 219, 243, 260, 284, 302–3, 328
meteors, 219, 225, 278
Michaux, André, 338–40, 341–42
microscopes, 243, 360
Mifflin, Thomas, 170, 290, 299, 301, 310, 311, 316–17, 320, 321
Miles, Samuel, 182, 239
Milky Way, 116–17, 118

Miller, Sir John Riggs, 313
milling machine, 335
militia, 132, 162, 163, 169, 170–71, 172–73, 223, 232. *See also* associators
Milton, John, 267
Mint, 331–36, 344–46, 351–55
Mississippi River, 46, 338
Missouri River, 338, 339
Mitchell, John, 228
moderate Whigs, 143, 165, 167
Mohawk language, 282
molecular magnetism, 226–29
monarchy, 120
Monoshoe Creek, 12
Montgomery, John, 133
Monthly Review, 229
Monticello, 5, 201
Montresor, John, 66–67
Moody, Baltis, 126–27
moon, 30, 32, 102, 116
Moore, Samuel Preston, 184, 222
Moore, William, 233
Moravians, 143, 167
Moreau de St. Méry, Médéric Louis Élie, 366
Morgan, John, 100
Morris County jail, 163
Morris, Gouverneur, 333
Morris, Robert, Pennsylvania politics, 165, 166, 181, 205–7; finances, 232, 235, 331; and John Nicholson, 236, 239, 350; internal improvements, 319, 320
Morris, Samuel, Jr., 129, 166
Muhlenberg, Henry Melchior, 156
Muhlenberg, Peter, 299
munitions, 136, 161, 162, 168, 192. *See also* cannon, gunpowder, saltpeter
Murgatroyd, John, 88
Myerstown, 323

Nairne, Edward, 16, 48
Nancarrow, John, 321
Napier, John, 356
natural history, 83, 264, 267–68, 284–86, 327, 338–39, 362
natural philosophy, 86, 221
Nautical Almanac, 61, 65
Navy Board, 178, 181
Nesbitt, John Maxwell, 181

INDEX

Paine, Thomas, 146, 179, 188–89, 193–94, 205, 210, 248
Pallas, Peter Simon, 285
paper supply, 128
Parker, Joseph, 135, 138, 166
Parry, Caleb, 133, 190
Pascal, Blaise, 362
patents, 325, 348
Patterson, Robert, 5, 9, 279, 302, 317, 326
Paxton Boys, 21–23
Paxton massacres, 195
Peale, Charles Willson, portraits and drawings, 90, 281, 284, 301–2, 319; and the War, 127, 128, 195; politics, 179, 189; inventions, 247, 326; American Philosophical Society, 317; and DR, 5, 350
Peale's Museum, 326–27
pendulum irregularity, 349
pendulums, 49–50, 287, 312, 313, 315, 316, 329, 360
Penn, John, boundaries and surveys, 93, 94, 105–7, 125, 131–32; and Revolution, 123; and DR, 71, 75, 133
Penn, Thomas, orrery, 37, 38; transit of Venus, 47–48, 50, 63, 65, 69; boundary dispute, 105
Penn, William, 12, 216
Penns, the, 209
Pennsylvania Assembly (colonial), transit of Venus, 45–47, 78–79; orrery, 72, 85, 87; grants, 46–47, 85, 87, 88, 98; Loan Office project, 70–71; projected public observatory, 108–10; canals, 94–96; War, 124, 126–27, 128, 132, 134, 138; Revolutionary politics, 130–32, 133, 135, 136; independence, 136–37, 138, 139, 146
Pennsylvania Assembly (state), in Constitution of 1776, 157, 158; early vicissitudes, 167, 170–71, 175, 176, 177–78, 182, 186; Lancaster exile, 192, 197, 198, 200; politics, 204; finances, 168, 183–85, 202, 222–23, 232–33, 236–37, 273; charters, 214, 235; boundaries and surveys, 217, 245, 251; grants and projected grants, 226,

242, 248–49; ends Constitutionalist power, 297, 299, 300–301, 305, 306, 307, 308
Pennsylvania Assembly (under 1790 Constitution), 3–4
Pennsylvania Chronicle, 39–40, 62
Pennsylvania-Connecticut dispute, 105, 131–32, 135
Pennsylvania Constitutionalists, *see* Constitutionalists
Pennsylvania elections, 1776, 136, 166–67; 1777, 177–78, 198, 203; 1778, 203; 1779, 209; 1780, 223; 1781, 234; 1782, 238; 1784, 257; 1785, 272; 1786, 293; 1787, 293, 299; 1788, 295, 299; 1789, 305–6; 1791, 327
Pennsylvania Gazette, 35, 39, 40, 62, 63
Pennsylvania Hospital, 134
Pennsylvania Journal, 112–13
Pennsylvania judiciary, 157
Pennsylvania Line of the Continental army, 174, 231, 234
Pennsylvania Magazine, 138–39
Pennsylvania-Maryland boundary, 20–21, 66, 216. *See also* Mason and Dixon, Mason-Dixon line
Pennsylvania, motto, 131
Pennsylvania-New York boundary, 105–7, 261–62, 279–83
Pennsylvania Republicans, *see* Republicans, Pennsylvania
Pennsylvania rifle, 126
Pennsylvania row galleys, 124, 137–38, 160
Pennsylvania Senate, 4
Pennsylvania Society for the Encouragement of Manufactures and the Useful Arts, 290–91
Pennsylvania Supreme Executive Council, in Constitution of 1776, 157, 158; early vicissitudes, 166, 167, 175, 177–78, 179–80, 183; finances, 184–85, 202, 203, 210, 222, 233–34, 238; boundary disputes, 251, 260, 261; actions, 186, 189, 191; Lancaster exile, 192, 197, 198, 200; politics, 299, 300, 301; captured by Republicans, 307–8, 317; Franklin's death, 310

387

INDEX

Red Bank, 130
Reed, Joseph, 182, 203, 213, 217, 222, 223, 231-32
refiner, 352, 355
Regiomontanus, 114
register general post established, 301-2
religion, 89, 117, 155-56, 194
religion and science, 117-19
Republican Society, 178-79
Republican ultimatum, 181-82, 185
Republicans, Jeffersonian, 9, 327, 337, 338, 343, 345, 347
Republicans, Pennsylvania, 186, 204, 234, 238, 239, 258, 272, 293, 299-301
reversible relief, illusion of, 101-4, 276
Rhoads, Samuel, 95, 213
Rhode Island, 68
Rittenhouse, Benjamin, DR's brother, 12, 14, 24, 168-69
Rittenhouse, David, *personal:* ancestry, 11-14; birth, 13, 13n; education, 7, 8, 10, 11, 14-15, 16, 280; reading, 89, 267, 362; language facility, 7, 13, 225, 303-4; literary publications, 303-4, 303n; music, 259; religious views, 9-10, 14, 117-19, 121, 156, 194, 358-59
supports family, 23-24, 304; and Eleanor Coulston Rittenhouse, 24, 82, 85, 87, 90; Elizabeth Rittenhouse Sergeant, 24-25, 304; Esther Rittenhouse Waters, 17, 316; and Hannah Jacobs Rittenhouse, 96, 194, 195, 258; residences, 23, 82, 83, 192, 193-94, 200, 272-73, 275, 357; income, 258, 272, 306, 308, 350; circles of friends, 4-6, 17, 194, 196-97, 247, 272-73, 274, 317-18, 336-37, 349-50
appearance, 18; personality, 18-19, 56, 249, 309, 350; early health, 17-19, 52-53, 56, 72, 82, 94; depression, 85, 89, 90, 96; health in the Treasury, 199, 201, 235, 261, 266, 274, 292, 306; frustration and complaints, 138-39, 231, 266-67, 273, 283; later health, 327-28, 332,

355, 362; final illness, 362-64, 365-66
clock and instrument making: enters clockmaking trade, 12, 14, 15-16, 20; unusual clocks, 25-26, 316; clockmaking, 31, 33, 35, 83, 124, 201, 331; astronomical clocks, 49-50, 52, 253, 265; clock maintenance, 124; clock innovations and studies, 136, 286-87, 329, 349
instruments, 15-16, 20, 25, 47, 83, 84-85, 124, 246-47, 252, 255; orrery plans, 26, 29, 30, 31, 32-33, 38, 39-40; the orreries, 72-75, 82-83, 85, 86-87, 88, 91, 244-45; telescopes, 48-49, 50-52, 262, 278, 309
science: scientific resources, 34-35, 225, 248, 259, 271-72; attitudes toward science, 114, 121, 225, 309, 330; experimental science, 276-79, 325, 360-61
general astronomy, 20, 200, 265, 278, 280, 328, 347; transit of Venus plans, 40, 43-44; transit of Venus observations, 51-53, 54-59, 60-62; transit of Venus results, 61-62, 64, 65-66, 72, 77, 78, 79-80, 121-22; transits of Mercury, 67-69, 244, 306, 328; comets, 75-77, 116, 244, 337; meteors, 219, 225; ideas on astronomy, 116, 187-88, 214-15, 302, 328; observatory, 226, 243, 260, 348-49
mathematics, 14, 15, 21, 89, 329, 359-61; optics, 19, 20, 115; on compressibility of water, 34; Archimedes' maxim, 35, 36; electric eel, 98-100; reversible relief, 101-4; Witherspoon paper, 138-39; magnetism, 226-30; combustion experiments, 248; lightning, 302, 326, 347; pendulum studies, 329, 349, 360
natural history, 83, 264, 267-68, 284, 327, 362; eruption of water, 218-19, 225; meteorology, 219, 243, 260, 284, 302, 328; fossils, 263, 281, 284, 285-86; geology, 268-69, 284-85; scientific papers published, 291

389

INDEX

Sergeant, Frances Rittenhouse, DR's granddaughter, 357
Sergeant, Jonathan Dickinson, 258, 304–5, 316, 340, 342, 344, 347
Seven Years' War, 19
Seventh Day Baptists, 19
Shaffer, Christian, 203
Shakespeare, William, 89
Shelby, Isaac, 342
Shippen, Joseph, 44
Shippen, William, 74–75, 213
Short, James, 16, 66, 79
Shriner, Jacob, 166
Shubert, Michael, 166
silver center cent, 335–36
silver supply, 352
Simitière, Pierre Eugene du, 191, 248
Sisson, Jonathan, 50
Six, James, 76
slavery, 120, 209
Smilie, John, 318
Smith, James, 165
Smith, Jonathan Bayard, 166, 205
Smith, Rebecca, daughter of William Smith, see Rebecca Smith Blodget
Smith, Robert, 104
Smith, Thomas, 148, 150
Smith, William, 36; and American Philosophical Society, 38, 39, 112, 212–13, 317; transit of Venus preparations, 42–43, 44, 47, 48; transit of Venus observations, 53, 54–55, 60; transit of Venus report, 61, 63–65; transit of Venus aftermath, 66, 77–78, 79–81, 188; transit of Mercury, 68–69; aids DR, 69–70, 71–72, 82, 86, 87, 107–10, 311; and orrery, 72, 73–75, 85, 86, 88; and the College, 221, 245; and Revolution, 133–34, 156, 190–91, 195; science, 187, 200, 219, 339; surveys and internal improvements, 93–94, 319, 320; personal relationships, 9, 310–11 discovery of DR, 5, 21, 36–37
Society for Promoting the Improvement of Roads and Inland Navigation, 319–20, 359
Society for the Propagation of the Gospel in Foreign Parts, 19

solar parallax, 41–42, 45, 65–66, 76–77, 78, 79–81
Sollekoff, Mr., 206–7
Sons of Liberty, 123
Sons of St. Tammany, 123
South Amboy, 180
South Carolina, 98
South Mountain, 262
Spain, 120, 341
Spanish dollars, 351
spider web cross hair, 278
spring block, 287
Sproat, James, 359
Stamp Act, 123, 166
State House, 147, 340
State House Square (State House yard), 77, 124, 135, 137, 170, 258, 341
Staten Island, 143, 160, 163
steamboat, 288–89, 334
steam engine, 98, 334, 352
steam power, 355
steel, 335
Stiegel, William Henry, 88, 98
Stiles, Ezra, 241, 243
Stone, Edmund, 29
Stuck, Henry, 203
sulphur, 128
Sulphur Springs, 19
sunspots, 97, 116, 328
Surinam, 98
surveying, 20, 92
surveying instruments, 20, 84, 246–47
surveying methods, 282
Susquehanna Company, 105
Susquehanna River, 94, 95, 194, 280, 281, 283, 284, 320
Susquehanna and Schuylkill canal, 250, 319, 320, 321, 323, 324, 357–58
Swanwick, John, 235
Swatara Creek, 250

Talleyrand-Perigord, Charles Maurice de, 313, 314
tax collection, 183, 203, 210, 222–23, 240, 273, 296, 298
tax embezzlement and robbery, 234
Tea Act, 166
Tea Party, 123
telescopes, manufacture, 20, 84, 225;

INDEX